W9-BRU-986

Statistics in Action

UNDERSTANDING A WORLD OF DATA

Ann E. Watkins
Richard L. Scheaffer
George W. Cobb

Key Curriculum Press
Innovators in Mathematics Education

Consulting Editor	Cindy Clements
Editors	Anna Werner, Mary Jo Cittadino
Project Administrator	Kristin Burke
Editorial Assistants	Heather Dever, Michael Hyett
Teacher Consultant	Jim Bohan, Manheim Township School District, Lancaster, Pennsylvania
Mathematics Reviewer	Mary Parker, Austin Community College, Austin, Texas
AP Instructor Reviewers	Angelo DeMattia, Columbia High School, Maplewood, New Jersey
	Beth Fox-McManus, formerly of Alan C. Pope High School, Marietta, Georgia
	Dan Johnson, Silver Creek High School, San Jose, California
Accuracy Checkers	Monica Johnston
Editorial Production Manager	Deborah Cogan
Production Editor	Jacqueline Gamble
Production Director	Diana Jean Parks
Production Coordinator	Charice Silverman
Text Designer	Monotype Composition
Compositor	The Cowans
Art Editor	Laura Murray
Technical Artist	Matt Perry
Technical Art Consultant	Brett Garrett
Art and Design Coordinator	Kavitha Becker
Cover Designer	Greg Dundis
Cover Photo Credit	*top:* Strauss-Curtis/Corbis; *center left:* Hulton Deutsch Collection/Corbis; *center right:* Tom Nebbia/Corbis; *bottom:* Bettman/Corbis
Prepress and Printer	Data Reproductions
Executive Editor	Casey FitzSimons
Textbook Product Manager	Fred Duncan
Publisher	Steven Rasmussen

Key Curriculum Press
1150 65th Street
Emeryville, CA 94608
510-595-7000
editorial@keypress.com
http://www.keypress.com

Printed in the United States of America
10 9 8 7 6 5 4 3 2 1   07 06 05 04 03   ISBN: 1-55953-335-8

Acknowledgments

Statistics in Action: Understanding a World of Data is designed for an introductory statistics course—either an introductory college course or its high school equivalent, Advanced Placement Statistics—and includes all of the standard topics for that course. The authors have field-tested the ideas and activities of *Statistics in Action* in their own college courses since 1997 and have utilized this material since it developed into a workable manuscript.

Many statisticians and teachers have been actively involved in helping the introductory statistics course evolve into one that emphasizes activity-based learning of statistical concepts, while reflecting modern statistical practice. *Statistics in Action* is a product of what the authors have learned from these statisticians and teachers. This book is written in the spirit of the recommendations from the Mathematical Association of America's STATS project and Focus Group on Statistics, the American Statistical Association's Quantitative Literacy projects, the College Board's AP Statistics course, and these AP Statistics field testers:

Jim Bohan, Manheim Township School District, Lancaster, Pennsylvania

Monica Brogan, Gloucester High School, Gloucester, Virginia

Gretchen Davis, Santa Monica High School, Santa Monica, California

Sheila Davis, Alan C. Pope High School, Marietta, Georgia

Angelo DeMattia, Columbia High School, Maplewood, New Jersey

Beth Fox-McManus, formerly of Alan C. Pope High School, Marietta, Georgia

Katherine France, Niles North High School, Skokie, Illinois

Will Frazer, Buchholz High School, Gainesville, Florida

Richard Fulton, Deerfield Beach High School, Deerfield Beach, Florida

Alaine Gorfinkle, Ramaz Upper School, New York, New York

Michelle Greene, Lamar High School, Lamar, South Carolina

Jeanette Hart, Melbourne High School, Melbourne, Florida

Philip Hogarth, The Webb Schools, Claremont, California

Dan Johnson, Silver Creek High School, San Jose, California

Pat Johnson, New Trier High School, Winnetka, Illinois

Allan King, Andrew Hill High School, San Jose, California

Sia Lux, Coachella Valley High School, Thermal, California

Padma Maui, Andrew Hill High School, San Jose, California

Mark Mavis, Pleasant Valley High School, Chico, California

Leona Mirza, North Park University, Chicago, Illinois

Valerie Muller, Eastside High School, Taylors, South Carolina

Lauren Nobles, Conway High School, Conway, South Carolina

Jennifer North Morris, West Hills High School, Santee, California

Robert Palma, Columbia High School, Maplewood, New Jersey

Diane Pors, East Side Union High School, San Jose, California

Karen Riggs, Lake Region High School, Eagle Lake, Florida

Murray Siegel, J. L. Mann High School, Greenville, South Carolina

Frank Steinhart, North Park University, Chicago, Illinois

William Stevens, Summerville High School, Summerville, South Carolina

Kathleen Strange, West Hills High School, Santee, California

Josh Tabor, Wilson High School, Hacienda Heights, California

David Thiel, Green Valley High School, Henderson, Nevada

Chris Tsuji, Santa Teresa High School, San Jose, California

Mark Vosskamp, North Cross School, Roanoke, Virginia

Susan Wallis, Terry Parker High School, Jacksonville, Florida

Jack Welc, Mt. Pleasant High School, San Jose, California

Joy Williams, Riverside High School, Greer, South Carolina

Hyman Yip, Independence High School, San Jose, California

Contents

Teaching with *Statistics in Action*

Producing and analyzing data require action on the part of the statistician. *Statistics in Action: Understanding a World of Data* helps you, the teacher, bring that action into the classroom so that your students can learn the concepts and tools of statistics in much the same way that it is practiced in the field. *Statistics in Action* will help you turn your classroom into a statistics laboratory where students will "learn by doing." Together you will work to discover the fundamental logic of statistics and why it is essential to the quantitative thinking required in the modern world. As a by-product, your students will be well prepared if they are taking the Advanced Placement Statistics examination.

We've designed *Statistics in Action: Understanding a World of Data* to help you accomplish two objectives. Your students will

- learn the fundamental logic and tools of statistics
- learn about the actual practice of statistics in real-world situations

Statistics in Action is built around activities, discussion questions, practice problems, and exercises. Simply reading the textbook will not be sufficient. Most activities are to be done in class or in a lab period so that students will have the opportunity to think critically about how data is collected and analyzed, and to articulate issues about basic statistical concepts. Discussion questions foster further debate over important issues among the whole class. Your close guidance is indispensable—you'll help your students stay on track, add emphasis to their discoveries, and clarify, focus, and connect the ideas they accumulate.

You may find that you'll follow the textbook quite closely. We have designed *Statistics in Action* much like a protocol for analysis, if not exactly as a script for teaching class sessions. If you guide your class through the material sequentially, doing the activities and addressing discussion questions in order, you'll find that your students will learn the important concepts in ways that foster understanding. They will adopt a healthy skepticism concerning data analysis (much the way that professionals do), and cultivate an interest and self-motivation for further study. In short, they will get caught up in the action!

Here's how you might proceed through a section of *Statistics in Action*.

Preparation

This *Statistics in Action Instructor's Guide* consists of two volumes. Volume 1 includes Chapters 1 through 5; Chapters 6 through 12 appear in Volume 2. Each chapter of this *Instructor's Guide* opens with an overview that highlights the goals and content to be mastered. The overview is followed by suggested time schedules, a list of materials needed, and suggested classwork and homework assignments. At the beginning of each section more specific objectives are listed, along with a list of the important terms and concepts introduced in that section. The suggested class time for the section, materials needed (if any), and suggested assignments for the section follow. In addition, in each section you will find extensive teacher's notes giving you additional information about the topics presented in the student text. For example, in Chapter 2 you will find extensive notes on why we typically use the standard deviation as the measure of spread.

Introduction and Activity

After you introduce the lesson, typically you will begin each section with an activity in which students work with partners or in small groups. (A few activities can be assigned as individual homework with class discussion in the following class session.) Students work through the activity while you circulate around the room and elicit answers to all the questions it poses. As work on the activity concludes, you'll be checking with each group to make sure that the students have answered the questions correctly or sensibly. Finally, you might pose a general question to the whole class that elicits the concept the activity was designed to introduce.

Notes for the activities in this *Instructor's Guide* offer practical step-by-step guidelines for moving through the activity, and present clear and realistic answers supported by plots and computer-generated data. As with all the notes in this *Instructor's Guide,* the activity notes are designed to provide a unique, in-depth focus on the statistical language being explored and the complexities behind the vocabulary of the lesson. Doing the activities aligns both the AP Statistics course and the college course with the goal of active engagement of the students in their learning, and helps students develop a powerful quantitative perspective.

Text

The activity leads to expository material that you usually will present to the class, describing the concepts and techniques and working through examples. Occasionally, you'll assign students to read the material on their own—and we've made every effort to make it lively reading—but you'll want to be sure that they understand when a rule must be used, what its exceptions are, and how to tell when a computation or a logical step has likely gone wrong.

Increasingly, students have had to read in their mathematics and statistics classes. Because of this greater emphasis on independent reading and research, we have tried to engage the student with clear text and attractive graphics. Still, there is a great reliance on you, the instructor, to present, explain, and emphasize; in this *Instructor's Guide,* you will find many lesson notes to aid your own understanding of the subject matter.

However you decide to implement the expository material, you'll always want to structure your time so your students have the opportunity to work on all of the essential and recommended discussion and practice questions.

Discussion Questions

Discussion questions occur periodically after text material. Because they often are open-ended, with no clear-cut "best" answer, they are meant for whole-class discussion. Many questions probe quite deeply into the concepts underlying the topic being discussed. Your guidance will be necessary. It is in these group discussions that students develop their instincts, support their reasoning, field challenges, and offer creative ideas. Sometimes you can precede a whole-class discussion by small-group discussions that go on while you circulate among the groups, giving hints or posing stepwise queries to be sure all groups are on track.

You won't usually want students to write out the answers to discussion questions: That would become tedious for both you and your students, and it might impede the dynamic exchange of views and easy reevaluation of an individual's position on an issue. However, most students will want to take notes because the answers to discussion questions do not appear in the back of the student book. Occasionally, you can have students write out a summary of the discussion to be sure that they understand the idea discussed.

This *Instructor's Guide,* Volume 1, includes a full solution for each discussion question in Chapters 1 through 5.

Practice Problems

Practice problems occur at intervals in the text for you to check that each student understands the preceding material. Students typically should work the assigned practice questions independently, either as an assignment or in class, as they encounter them while reading. We have designed the questions to solidify student skills and boost student confidence. These questions do not introduce new material or rely on complex scenarios, but we consider them important nonetheless: They are an opportunity for students to "digest" what they have done or read, and to make sure they are ready before going on.

Brief answers to practice questions (but not full solutions or graphics) are in the back of the student book; complete solutions—including graphics—for all practice questions in Chapters 1 through 5 are provided in this *Instructor's Guide,* Volume 1.

Exercises

A set of exercises appears at the end of each section. Typically, exercises are done at home as individual assignments, although you can assign some of the more difficult questions as collaborative work. Brief answers to most odd exercises are in the back of the student book, while fully detailed solutions to exercises in Chapters 1 through 5 are provided in this *Instructor's Guide,* Volume 1.

Technology

Students should, at a minimum, have access to a graphing calculator with statistics capabilities in order to carry out routine computations, create graphical displays, and perform some analyses. Your students should also learn to read a standard computer printout. To help students acquire this ability, a variety of program printouts—including Fathom, Minitab, Data Desk, and JMP-IN—are explained in greater detail in the student book and detailed in this *Instructor's Guide.* However, be sure that students can set up and conduct small-scale simulations without the use of a calculator or computer.

Reviewing for Exams

The *Statistics in Action* student book includes many features to aid students in self-guided review. Important vocabulary is indicated in boldface type and important concepts and theorems appear in boxes. We have also given special attention to the appearance of examples, so that they are visually easy to follow, and conceptual steps are clearly linked. Margin notes direct students to key ideas for review, as well as help to retain their attention during a first reading. Summaries are comprehensive; every summary uses important terms in full sentences, linking them to prior learning and to concepts under development.

There are more review problems in the student book than you will want to assign. You can use the remaining ones as a review for the course final examination or for the AP Statistics exam. In this *Instructor's Guide* you will find a chart at the end of each section which suggests essential, recommended, and optional review exercises for students to use as practice before exams.

The Joy of Teaching Statistics

We hope that you enjoy teaching statistics as much as we do. You will never have to ask yourself, "Do my students really need to know this?" Much of the progress of the last century, both in basic scientific research and in applied fields like agriculture, medicine, and industry, was progress guided and propelled by statistical thinking. Your students will come to realize this as the course progresses. As one of our own students said, "After taking your statistics class, I will never see the world in quite the same way again. Now everywhere I look, I see chance and variation."

Ann E. Watkins
Richard L. Scheaffer
George W. Cobb

A CASE STUDY OF STATISTICS IN ACTION

Overview

Goals

Although statistics is a mathematical science, it is not a branch of mathematics the way probability is. Statistical thinking differs from mathematical thinking in important ways. The goal of this chapter is to involve students from the start in two important differences present throughout the book: the role of context and the logic of statistical inference. We will begin with examples illustrating these differences in order to give students the longest possible time to work with them.

Role of Context

"Although mathematicians often rely on applied context both for motivation and as a source of problems for research, the ultimate focus in mathematical thinking is on abstract patterns: the context is part of the irrelevant detail that must be boiled off over the flame of abstraction in order to reveal the previously hidden crystal of pure structure. *In mathematics, context obscures structure.* Like mathematicians, data analysts also look for patterns, but ultimately, in data analysis, whether the patterns have meaning, and whether they have any value, depends on how the threads of those patterns interweave with the complementary threads of the story line. *In data analysis, context provides meaning.*" [George W. Cobb and David S. Moore, "Mathematics, Statistics and Teaching," *American Mathematical Monthly,* vol. 104, 1997, pp. 801–824.]

Some students may be tempted to dismiss the story line (and the questions related to it) as something to plow through in a hurry to get to "the real stuff," like formulas or computing algorithms. In statistics, unlike pure mathematics, it is important to encourage students to think carefully about the context for its own sake—not just to ask what a result means in the context of a particular application but also to let the context suggest questions to be answered, even if the method *du jour* does not and cannot provide an answer. To learn to think like a statistician, the student needs to be aware of the questions that a method cannot answer, as well as those that can be answered.

Logic of Statistical Inference

A second important difference between mathematics and statistics has to do with the logic of statistical inference, which many students of statistics (at all levels!) experience as the most difficult part of the subject. The difficulties arise for a number of legitimate reasons. One is the "what if" nature of the reasoning, which is typically expressed using a conditional subjunctive: If this particular hypothesis were in fact true, how likely would it be to get data like ours? You can simplify the grammar (we do that in the text), but there is a warp built into the logic that you can't avoid if you want to do it right. It is verboten to ask the question we really want answered: Given our data, how likely is it that this particular hypothesis is true? No wonder students find inference difficult!

In this first chapter, we try to steer a middle course between the rock of ignoring the essential parts of the logic and the hard place of too much detail. We want students to get an honest look at what's hard in order for students to appreciate what is unique about statistical logic. But we don't want to swamp them with premature rigor. (Rigor can demand a preoccupation with details that fog up an otherwise clear explanation.)

Because some of the concepts and logic of inference are so hard, it is particularly important to do Activity 1.1, which is designed to give students hands-on experience with a concrete and comparatively simple version of the thinking they will be expected to learn and use in later chapters of the book.

Time Required

Traditional Schedule			Block	4 x 4 Block
Section 1.1				
1–2 days	Day 1	Overview, graphical displays	1 day	2 short days or 1 long day
	Day 2	Exploring data, summary, exercises		
Section 1.2				
2–3 days	Day 1	Activity 1.1, simulation	2 days	3 short days or 1 long and 1 short day
	Day 2	Logic of statistical inference		
	Day 3	Summary and exercises		
Review				
1–2 days			1 day	2 short days or 1 long day

Materials

Section 1.1: None

Section 1.2: D13 requires one coin per student. Activity 1.1 requires ten 3×5 cards (or small pieces of paper) per group.

Suggested Assignments

Classwork			
Section	**Essential**	**Recommended**	**Optional**
1.1	D2, D3, D6, D7, D8 P1, P2	D1, D4, D5	
1.2	Activity 1.1 D9, D10, D11 P3	D13 P4	D12

Homework			
Section	**Essential**	**Recommended**	**Optional**
1.1	E1, E2	E4, E5	E3
1.2	E6, E7	E9, E10	E8
Review	E11, E13	E14, E15	E12

1.1 Discrimination in the Workplace: Data Exploration

Objectives

- to explore a set of data related to an actual court case involving alleged age discrimination and practice relating patterns in data to possible meanings in the applied context
- to learn the basic structure of a data table, with cases as rows and variables as columns
- to learn by example what a distribution is and use dot plots to represent a distribution
- to organize categorical data in a two-way table

Important Terms and Concepts

- exploration versus inference
- cases and variables
- variability
- distribution
- dot plot

Lesson Planning

Class Time

One to two days

Materials

None

Suggested Assignments

Classwork		
Essential	**Recommended**	**Optional**
D2, D3, D6, D7, D8 P1, P2	D1, D4, D5	

Homework		
Essential	**Recommended**	**Optional**
E1, E2	E4, E5	E3

Lesson Notes: Exploring Data

Westvaco is pronounced with a long *a*, as in Waco, Texas.

This first lesson is a good place to explain the three types of questions used in the text: Discussion Questions, Practice Problems, and Exercises.

Throughout the text, students will be asked to justify their answers to a question. This includes stating assumptions, giving appropriate graphs and computations, and writing a conclusion in context.

Graphical displays are essential in the investigation of data because sometimes patterns in data are not at all obvious without a plot. You can model the importance of plotting data to find patterns by making graphical displays as often as possible.

In all problems, encourage students to relate their statistical work to its real-world context. In mathematics, what each example has in common with others in the same section is often emphasized. Although such patterns of shared structure are important, in statistics it is also essential to think about what makes one example different from another. For example, in the *Martin* case, it is reasonable to ask how other contextual matters, such as years of service at Westvaco, years of education and specialized training, etc. relate to the questions asked.

The answers to many discussion questions may vary depending on students' individual insights. Learning to think like a statistician becomes easier if students can learn to carry on a dialogue between their intuition and their formal learning. Intuition is a notoriously untrustworthy guide in probability problems, but students do better if they come to regard their intuition as a legitimate voice, albeit one that often needs to be educated by a second voice. The alternative—to leave the voice of intuition unattended—invites trouble.

Discussion

D1. Reasonable suggestions from students at this stage include

- compare the average age of those laid off and the average age of those retained;

- compare the proportion of those over, say, age 50 who were laid off with the proportion of those under age 50 who were laid off;

- make a graph that shows both the ages of those laid off and those not laid off.

(If students suggest this option, you might take the opportunity to show them how to make a back-to-back stem-and-leaf plot.)

Students may do a lot or a little with this question. In some classes, students may only offer very general ideas. On the other hand, students who have learned to "take charge" in their mathematics classes may want to thoroughly explore the data tables, bar graphs, and averages before continuing with the discussion. At any rate, all students should see the need for some method of summarizing and displaying the data in Display 1.1.

D2. This dot plot shows a possible case of age discrimination. The pattern shows that those laid off were, on balance, older than those who kept their jobs. Of the six workers under age 50, half kept their jobs. Of the eight workers over age 50, only one kept his or her job. This pattern provides some support for Martin's claim. (Without such a pattern, there would be no statistical evidence of discrimination, although there might be other evidence.)

Here are two important points that might be raised, which you can either discuss now or wait until D7 and D8.

- Is there enough evidence? Some students may think there are too few employees involved to make the pattern worth taking seriously. This is a key issue, one that will be addressed in D7 in a preliminary way and more fully in Section 1.2.

- The pattern of the ages says nothing about the reason for the pattern, which may or may not be age bias. (For example, suppose that Westvaco had decided to retain employees with better computer skills and that younger employees tended to have more experience with computers.) This is the focus of D8.

D3. Display 1.4 provides stronger support for Martin's case than Display 1.3. The pattern in the dot plots in Display 1.4 shows that of those laid off, older workers were selected in earlier rounds, younger workers in later rounds. Martin's argument used the fact that older workers were laid off earlier as evidence of age bias: If Westvaco had been able to stop the layoffs after the first two rounds, for example, the difference in ages (between those fired and those kept) would have been even more extreme than it actually was. Westvaco argued that this pattern was irrelevant because, regardless of how the preliminary planning was done, the actual layoffs occurred all at once.

D4. Both groups, hourly and salaried, show similar patterns: older workers were more likely than younger ones to lose their jobs. From the dot plots alone, it is hard to decide which group, hourly or salaried, provides stronger evidence of age bias. The salaried workers are a larger group, although the difference in ages between laid off and retained may be more pronounced for the hourly workers. On balance, though, variability makes it hard to judge the strength of the evidence from the dot plots. Useful as graphs are, they have limitations, and there are times when numerical summaries are helpful. Most of the time, a good analysis involves both graphical displays and appropriate numerical summaries.

D5. Overall, the pattern in Display 1.6 is strikingly similar to its counterpart in Display 1.4. The graphs show that older workers were especially likely to be targeted for layoff in the earlier rounds and that younger workers were more likely to be targeted in Rounds 4 and 5. Both displays also show that most of the layoffs were planned in the first two rounds.

D6. **a.** Yes. Older workers were slightly more likely than younger workers (52% vs. 44%) to lose their jobs. This pattern is consistent with age bias, but the two issues raised in the answer to D2 (and the focus of D7 and D8) are relevant here.

b.

		Laid Off	Retained	Total	% Laid Off
Under 50?	Yes	6	10	16	37.5%
	No	12	8	20	60.0%
	Total	18	18	36	50.0%

With "older" redefined as "50 or older," the evidence here is stronger than in part a. Here older workers were much more

likely than younger ones to lose their jobs (60% vs. 38%).

c. The pattern in the two tables taken together shows that workers 40 or older were more likely than those under 40 to lose their jobs, and those 50 or older were substantially more likely than those under 50 to lose their jobs. Thus, the two tables taken together provide stronger evidence in favor of Martin.

Note that the fact that age 40 and over is a protected class does not mean that we must divide the employees using that age only. The work force in Westvaco's Engineering Department was older than many groups of employees, as you can see from the various dot plots. Only 25% were under 40; 44% were under 50. Using 50 as the cutoff age to define "older" gives age groups roughly the same size and is more informative (other things being equal). The message of possible age discrimination may be stronger for the table split at age 50 because Westvaco may not be discriminating against workers aged 40 through 50, but only against workers older than that.

D7. Statistical inference can provide an answer to this question, and Section 1.2 will sketch how this is done. For now, the purpose of the question is to involve students in thinking about what the question asks and why it is important.

Students may be worried that there are too few workers to make conclusions or that the differences are too small to make any conclusions. Try to get them to focus on the crucial question: Do the patterns look like the kind you would expect to occur just by chance? No calculations are to be done; have students only observe the pattern.

D8. Considerations that might explain how older workers might have been laid off disproportionately without their being victims of age discrimination include the following: Older workers tended to hold jobs that had become obsolete. Older workers tended not to have the up-to-date training needed to use Westvaco's computers or other technology.

Practice

P1. This plot is rather striking; the older hourly workers were far more likely to be laid off in Rounds 1 through 3 than were the younger workers.

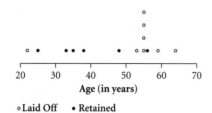

Age (in years)

○ Laid Off   • Retained

Students can construct this plot quickly and easily if they rely on the plots in Display 1.4.

This problem offers another opportunity to show students how to make a back-to-back stem-and-leaf plot.

P2. **a.** The two tables appear here. The second table, which uses 50 to define "older," shows stronger evidence of possible age bias.

		Laid Off	Retained	Total	% Laid Off
Under 40?	Yes	3	2	5	60.0%
	No	7	2	9	77.8%
	Total	10	4	14	71.4%

		Laid Off	Retained	Total	% Laid Off
Under 50?	Yes	3	3	6	50.0%
	No	7	1	8	87.5%
	Total	10	4	14	71.4%

b. The two patterns in the tables for hourly workers in part a are similar to those in the tables for the salaried workers. One pattern shows that older workers were more likely than younger ones to lose their jobs. The other pattern shows that the difference in the percentage laid off for the two age groups is much more pronounced when 50 rather than 40 is used to define "older."

Note that age discrimination could still be at work even if the *number* of younger workers laid off was larger than the number of older workers laid off. The next table illustrates this possibility for a hypothetical

company and the limitation of using counts as opposed to proportions.

		Laid Off	Retained	Total	% Laid Off
Under 40?	Yes	40	20	60	66.7%
	No	30	10	40	75.0%
	Total	70	30	100	70.0%

Here 30 older workers were laid off compared with 40 younger workers, yet a higher percentage of older workers (75%) were laid off than of younger workers (66.7%).

Exercises

E1.

		Laid Off	Retained	Total	% Laid Off
Pay Status	Hourly	10	4	14	71.4%
	Salaried	18	18	36	50.0%
	Total	28	22	50	56.0%

As the table makes clear, hourly workers were more likely than salaried workers to lose their jobs.

E2. **a.**

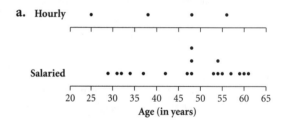

Only four hourly workers kept their jobs, making comparison difficult. However, the distribution of salaried workers who kept their jobs generally falls to the right of the distribution of hourly workers who kept their jobs. Indeed, the average age of the hourly workers laid off was 41.75, whereas it was 50.556 for the salaried workers.

b. We cannot conclude this from the dot plots in part a alone. We would have to take into consideration the age distributions for hourly and salaried workers *before* the layoffs began, as well as after. All we can say is that the salaried workers who kept their jobs tended to be older than the hourly workers who kept their jobs.

E3. a.

Round	Laid Off	40 or Older	Percentage
1	11	9	82%
2	9	8	89%
3	3	2.	67%
4	4	2	50%
5	1	0	0%

b. Most of the layoffs came early. Of the 28 who were chosen for layoff, 20 were identified in the first two rounds. Only 8 were chosen for layoff in the last three rounds altogether.

Early rounds hit the older workers harder; later rounds tended to have higher percentages of younger workers. In the first two rounds, the percentage was very high among those over 40 who were laid off, at 85% (17 of 20). In the later rounds, the percentage for those over 40 dropped to 67% in Round 3 (2 of 3), 50% in Round 4 (2 of 4), and 0% (0 of 1) in Round 5.

The pattern is consistent with what you would expect to see if the department head who planned the layoffs was trying to cut costs by laying off the older, more experienced, and thus possibly more expensive workers first.

E4. The work on this question can be as elaborate and involved as you have time for. One reasonable way to approach such an analysis is to follow the analysis of age, using year of hire as the variable. (This is equivalent to working with a new variable, *seniority*, defined as 1991 − *hire year*.) This dot plot compares the years of hire for those laid off and those retained.

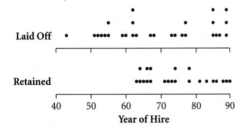

One striking feature is that all 12 of those hired in 1962 or earlier lost their jobs. Of those hired in 1985 or later, 8 of 13, or 62%, lost their jobs. Of those hired in the middle years, 1963–1984, only 8 of 25, or 32%, lost their jobs. The information seems to suggest that "last hired, first fired" was not the policy, except for the most recently hired (1985–1990).

Year of Hire	Laid Off	Retained	Total	% Laid Off
62 or before	12	0	12	100.0%
63–74	5	13	18	27.8%
75–83	3	4	7	42.9%
85–90	8	5	13	61.5%
Total	**28**	**22**	**50**	**56.0%**

E5. • *Major league baseball standings.* The cases are the teams. The variables include games won, games lost, winning percentage, and games behind the leader.

• *New York Stock Exchange.* The cases are the companies whose stock is listed on the NYSE. Variables include the opening price for the day, the low, the high, the close, and the net change from the previous day's close.

• *Nutritional summary.* The cases are the nutritional components, such as fat, carbohydrates, protein, cholesterol, and various vitamins and minerals. Variables might include amount per serving and percentage of the recommended daily allowance.

1.2 Discrimination in the Workplace: Inference

Objectives

- to learn how to use simulation to generate a sampling distribution and estimate a probability
- to use the concept of a sampling distribution and the logic of significance testing to make decisions about data

This section gives an "owner's manual" description of the "vehicle" that we call statistical inference. Students will learn how to drive this vehicle but will not fully understand how it works or know the technical names of all the parts. Chapters 8 through 12 will be more like a "service manual" description. Activity 1.1 is an excellent way to introduce statistical inference in a hands-on experience that is also fun.

Important Terms and Concepts

- summary statistic
- simulation
- chance model
- statistical inference

Lesson Planning

Class Time

Two to three days

Materials

D13 requires one coin per student. For Activity 1.1, each group of students will need ten 3×5 cards (or small pieces of paper).

Suggested Assignments

Classwork		
Essential	**Recommended**	**Optional**
Activity 1.1	D13	D12
D9, D10, D11	P4	
P3		

Homework		
Essential	**Recommended**	**Optional**
E6, E7	E9, E10	E8

Lesson Notes: Inference

Why the Hourly Workers?

Why does the text concentrate on the hourly workers when Bob Martin was salaried? First, Martin's case that Westvaco discriminated against older workers is strengthened by the analyses for hourly workers. Second, there were only 14 hourly workers and 36 salaried workers, so using the hourly workers makes the simulations a reasonable size.

Why It Is Important to Do Activity 1.1

Turning probability questions into simulations has a couple of advantages. Students can use probabilities without getting bogged down in the (often delightful but centrifugal) intricacies of particular computations, and it also reinforces the definition of probability as the proportion of "successes" in the long run. This activity gives students a sense of what the distribution should look like if layoffs were determined at random.

A Technical Summary

Because our introductory example deliberately avoids technical terms, we provide the following short summary that links the formal language of statistics to the example.

The *Martin* case example is typical of many examples of *statistical tests of hypotheses*. In this kind of test, we want to test whether an observed difference could reasonably be due just to chance. In the *Martin* case, the *null hypothesis* is that workers were chosen at random, without regard to age, for layoff. So in Activity 1.1, we set up a model that chooses three workers at random, with every worker given the same chance of being chosen. To test this hypothesis, we choose a *test statistic,* a summary number based on the data, such as the average age of those laid off. An extreme value of the test statistic (large average age) is evidence against the null hypothesis. We use *simulation* (or sometimes mathematical theory) to find the chance of getting a value for the test statistic as extreme as or more extreme than the one we actually observed if the null hypothesis is true. (This number is called the *P-value* or *significance level.*) If values as extreme as the test statistic are reasonably likely, we conclude that the observed effect could be due just to chance. If, on the other hand, a value that extreme is very unlikely, we *reject the null hypothesis*

and conclude that the observed effect is "real."

As students use statistical inference to make decisions, they can refine their mathematical thinking in a critical way. Most high school students develop their concepts of proof from the structured arena of Euclidean geometry. Decision making that involves considering uncertainty and variability is a very new and challenging task for students whose prior experience was limited to right answers and two-column proofs. In the case of inference, we build an argument based on the likelihood of a sample yielding results that are very different from the values expected under the null hypothesis. Such simulations do provide evidence of the results but do not prove or disprove the conjecture in the "pure" sense of proof.

E10 introduces systematic counting as an alternative to simulations for finding probabilities.

Discussion

D9. No, it is not likely. To get an average age of 58 or greater, you couldn't select any worker under age 55—and half the workers are under age 55.

D10. It favors Martin if it is unlikely to lay off, just by chance, workers as old as those laid off by Westvaco.

Activity 1.1: By Chance or by Design?

The activity should only take about 15 minutes and can be shortened or lengthened depending on the number of samples you have each group draw before you make a dot plot of the results.

1. Ideally, students should work in groups of two. Each group of students will need ten 3 × 5 cards or ten small identical pieces of paper. They can cut these themselves, or you might use a paper cutter ahead of time and provide each group with a handful of congruent rectangles. Students can draw either from a box or from a paper bag, but be sure to encourage them to mix the pieces thoroughly each time before they draw.

2–4. Sample results appear in the dot plot in Display 1.8 on page 13 of the student text. Using a dot plot when collecting the results from your class works well, giving students a sense of the distribution and where the average age of 58 would fall in that distribution.

If your class has had experience with stem-and-leaf plots, you may want to collect the data that way.

```
Average age
3 |
4 |
5 | 2 3
6 |

5 | 2 3 represents an average of 52.3 years.
```

5–6. To estimate the probability, divide the number of times the average age satisfies the condition (of being as extreme as or more extreme than 58) by the total number of samples collected in your class. The true probability of getting an average age of 58 or more is $6/120 = .05$ (Your class's estimate won't necessarily be close to .05, though). With $n = 50$ (5 groups of students doing 10 replications each), the margin of error is about 0.06. With $n = 200$ (20 groups doing 10 replications each), the margin of error is half that big. If your class's estimate is a lot larger than .05, talk informally about the relationship between the sample size and the precision of the estimate before going on to obtain a better estimate by increasing the number of repetitions.

Students will do this problem theoretically in E14, but it is still important that they learn to design and carry out a simulation and to understand a sampling distribution like that in Display 1.8.

Discussion

D11. The probability of getting any specified average age is quite small. For example, if Westvaco laid off the 35-, 38-, and 48-year-olds, the average age would be 40.3 and there certainly would have been no suspicion of age discrimination. However, if you look at Display 1.8, you see that the probability of getting an average age of exactly 40.3 is actually smaller than getting an average age of 58. Westvaco shouldn't be under suspicion because the average age of its laid-off workers was exactly 58, and getting exactly 58 just by chance is very unlikely; Westvaco should be under suspicion because the average age it got is in the extreme upper part of the distribution of all possibilities. That is, *it is the location of age 58 in the distribution that is important, not the probability of getting that exact number.*

D12. **a.** No, the probability is larger than .025.
b. If the *Martin* probability had been .01, it would have met this requirement. If it had been .10, it would not have.

Note about significance levels: Using any one choice of threshold for deciding statistical significance is somewhat arbitrary, even though fixed-level testing using a significance level of .05 is so common. There is no best value (except in a strict decision-theoretic setting where you know the costs of Type I and Type II errors), but there is an unambiguous ordering: the smaller the probability, the stronger the evidence against the null hypothesis. Though students may legitimately disagree about how low a value they personally would require in order to rule out the chance model, they should all come to recognize that a lower significance level means stronger evidence is required.

D13. **a.** If the coin were fair, it would be very unlikely to get 19 heads or more in 20 tosses. (The probability is $\approx .00002$.)
b. The chance model is that the coin is fair. Students should flip a fair (or assumed to be fair) coin 20 times and count the number of heads. The number of heads is the summary statistic. This process should be repeated as many times as you have time for in your class. You may display the distribution on a dot plot. A typical distribution for 500 repetitions is given here.

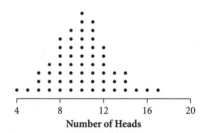

NOTE: When making this dot plot, Minitab prints "Each dot represents 10 points." However, there are 58 dots here for 500 sets of flips, so some dots represent fewer than 10 flips. Whenever the number of flips above a particular tick mark isn't a multiple of 10, Minitab uses a dot for the excess. For example, suppose the value 12 occurred 53 times. Then Minitab would use 7 dots above the 12. ∎

In this simulation of 500 repetitions, the largest number of heads ever to appear was 17. The probability of getting 19 or more heads is very close to 0. If the coin is fair, it is extremely unlikely to get 19 or 20 heads, so we conclude that the coin is not fair.

Summarizing, here's the logic: Assume the model is correct that your friend's coin is fair. Question: Is the actual data (19 heads in 20 tosses) easy to get from this model? Answer: No, it's almost impossible to get 19 heads in 20 tosses of a fair coin. Conclusion: Your friend's coin is not fair.

Emphasize to your students that you can estimate the chance of getting 19 or more heads from a fair coin, but you cannot estimate the chance that your friend's coin is fair. If you assume the model is correct (the coin is fair), you can estimate the probability you need by simulation. Notice, however, that it doesn't work to assume that outcome (19 heads) and then use simulation to estimate the chance of a fair coin.

Practice

P3. **a.** The average age is now 52.67. On the dot plot of Display 1.8, this is the column that is just a bit more than half-way between 50 and 55. That is, it is the tallest column in the group of seven columns of dots *between* 50 and 55. The number of repetitions out of 1000 that gave an average age of 52.67 or larger is 5(31) = 155. Thus, the estimated probability of getting an average age of 52.67 or larger is .155.

b. There is no evidence of age discrimination because an average age of 52.67 or larger is relatively easy to get just by chance.

P4. **a.** The average of 33 and 35 is 34.

b. The chance model is that two workers were selected at random for layoff in Round 3 from six workers with ages 25, 33, 35, 38, 48, and 56. Place those ages on six cards and draw two at random. Repeat many times, computing the average age each time. Make a dot plot showing the distribution of these average ages and compute the proportion of times you get an average age of 34 or larger.

Simulations will vary. For example, a student might first get the ages 25 and 38, for an average of 31.5.

c. Answers will vary according to the simulation, but the chance is quite large, well above 50%. In fact, it is equal to 12/15, or 80%.

No. If you look just at this one round, the average age of people laid off is about what you would expect by chance alone.

Exercises

E6. **a.** Simulations will vary. For example, a student might draw the following 10 ages: 22, 25, 33, 48, 53, 55, 55, 55, 56, and 59. The summary statistic would then be 7 because 7 of the 10 are age 40 or older.

Note that instead of writing the ages on slips of paper, for the purposes of this problem students could just write "40 or over" or "under 40" for each person. Also, note that you can save time by utilizing the complementary event—drawing 10 workers out of 14 who are laid off is equivalent to drawing only 4 out of 14 who are retained. Students can then analyze the remaining 10 slips of paper. Some students may not understand that this is legitimate.

Simulations will vary, but the number of workers in the protected class should center around 6.4, which is the average number of workers aged 40 or more that you would get when drawing 10 workers to lay off from the 14 hourly workers.

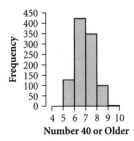

b. Student estimates will vary depending on their simulations. The theoretical probability of drawing 10 ages from the 14 and getting 7 or more who are aged 40 or older is 455/1001 ≈ .45.

c. It is quite likely to randomly draw 10 ages from the 14 and get 7 or more who are aged 40 or older. Thus, we reasonably can attribute the Westvaco result to chance. This test provides no evidence for Martin.

d. A general rule in statistics is that you should not throw away information that might be relevant. Only using whether the person is 40 or older throws away information—the person's exact age. For example, suppose Westvaco had laid off everyone over 60 and kept everyone under 60. That would be age discrimination but might not show up in an under/over age 40 analysis because all those aged 40–59 were kept.

Here is a specific example of that principle: In the *Martin* case, there were 10 hourly workers involved in the second round of lay-offs; 4 of these workers were under 40. Three were chosen to be laid off; all 3 were 40 or older. To see whether this result could reasonably be due just to chance, consider drawing 3 tickets at random from a box of 10 tickets, 4 of which say "Under 40" and 6 of which say "40 or older." A natural summary is the number of tickets out of 3 that say "40 or older." Simulating this process a large number of times shows that the chance that all 3 tickets say "40 or older" is about 1/6. (In fact, it is possible to count the possible outcomes. There are

$$\binom{10}{3} = 120$$

possible outcomes, of which

$$\binom{6}{3} = 20$$

have all 3 tickets saying "40 or older," so 1/6 is the exact probability.)

This probability is large enough that we cannot reasonably rule out the possibility that such data could arise by chance alone. Thus, this conclusion differs from the conclusion on the actual ages, which students analyzed in Activity 1.1. Because the analysis based on the actual ages uses more of the available information, it is more informative and trustworthy. The analysis based on the actual ages (the mean) uses more of the available information. On the other hand, it might be easier to convince a judge or jury by using 40 or over because that is the federal protected class.

E7.   **a.** A calculator can be used to do the simulation where 4 ages are drawn out of the 10 hourly workers. The ages of the workers can be numbered 1 through 10, and random drawings of four integers between 1 and 10 (that will correspond to the ages) generated

using the command RandInt(1,10,4). Students can then find the average age of the 4 workers whose ages correspond to the four random integers. As an alternative, write the ages of the 10 hourly workers on identical cards, mix the cards up, and draw four at random. Then find the average age of those 4 workers. This chance model reflects a situation where chance alone decides who is laid off. Repeat this process many times, displaying the average ages on a dot plot. Decide whether it is reasonably likely to get an average age of 57.25 or greater.

b. Simulations will vary. For example, a student might draw the four ages 33, 35, 56, and 64. The average age would then be 47. The distributions should center around 46.5.

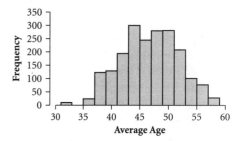

Conclusions may vary with the simulation, but students should realize that it is unlikely to get an average age as large as 57.25 just by chance. The theoretical probability of getting an average age of 57.25 or more is only 4/210 ≈ .019. That is, getting an average age this high would happen less than 2 times out of every 100, if selections were done randomly. This is strong evidence in Martin's favor.

E8.   **a.** The first two: sum of the ages, difference of the average ages. These are equivalent to the mean because you will get the same probability of a value as extreme as or even more extreme than the sum of the ages and the difference of the average ages as you do for the mean. To see this, if you have the sum of the ages, divide by 3 to get the average age. If you have the difference of the averages, D, it is an algebraic challenge to get the average age of those laid off: multiply D by the number of workers retained, add to this the sum of all the ages, and then divide by the total number of workers.

b. It would be reasonable to use any of the possible choices to get an indication of how the ages of those laid off compare with those that would occur by chance alone.

However, reducing a set of numbers to a summary statistic may involve loss of information, and typically there will be several choices, sometimes with no obvious best choice. ("Which is best" turns out to be a surprisingly complicated question. The answer is based on which summary statistic is more likely to "catch" a company that does, indeed, discriminate on the basis of age. Using the average age (or an equivalent summary statistic) tends to make better use of the information in the sample than the others.)

E9. "If it is July 4, it is very unlikely to be snowing in Kansas. Therefore, this probably isn't July 4." The hypothesis is that it is July 4, so we begin by assuming that. We then examine the data (it's snowing in Kansas), and because it's unlikely to be snowing on July 4 in Kansas, we reject the hypothesis that it is July 4.

E10. **a.** There are $\binom{10}{2} = 45$ possible pairs. The partial listing given in the problem suggests computing this as $9 + 8 + \ldots + 3 + 2 + 1 = 45$.

b. Only four pairs give an average age of 59.5 or older:

25 33 35 38 48 **55** 55 55 56 **64**
25 33 35 38 48 55 **55** 55 56 **64**
25 33 35 38 48 55 55 **55** 56 **64**
25 33 35 38 48 55 55 55 **56 64**

c. Thus, the probability of getting an average of 59.5 or more is $4/45 \approx .09$.

d. The evidence of age bias is somewhat weak—weaker than in the *Martin* example, for which the probability was .05.

Review

Homework	
Essential	E11, E13
Recommended	E14, E15
Optional	E12

Review Exercises

E11. **a.** The data for Compound B include more of the larger values, but the two data sets are pretty well mixed together. Students will argue both ways; some will say Compound B is better because it has more of the higher values, and some will say that there is no obvious winner.

b.

a   b
  a   b   a   ab b   a   b
|—————————————————————————————————————|
.30   .50   .70   .90   1.10 1.30 1.50
        Volume Increase (in liters)

a = volume increase for Compound A
b = volume increase for Compound B

The points for Compound B tend to fall more on the right side of the plot, so it appears that Compound B gives larger measurements than Compound A.

c. Compound A mean = 0.746; Compound B mean = 1.002, for a difference of 0.256. Because the Compound B mean exceeds the Compound A mean, some students will think of this as sufficient evidence to claim that Compound B is better at opening the lungs than Compound A. They are forgetting about variability, indicated by the overlap in the distributions!

E12. To explore the effects of poverty, the variables you might look at include literacy rate, fertility rate, rate of malnutrition, percentage of dwellings with indoor plumbing, number of people per room, percentage of children who have been vaccinated for various diseases, and infant mortality.

E13. **a–b.** Here are the results of 50 trails of a simulation to find the difference between the means.

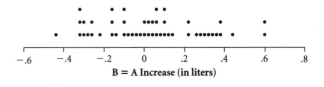

−.6   −.4   −.2   0   .2   .4   .6   .8
              B = A Increase (in liters)

c. The observed difference of 0.256 was exceeded 11 times out of the 50. This is a high fraction and points to a conclusion that the 0.256 value could well be the result of chance alone.

E14. **a.** There are six sets of three that give an average of 58 or more:

25 33 35 38 48 **55 55** 55 56 **64**

25 33 35 38 48 **55** 55 **55** 56 **64**

25 33 35 38 48 **55** 55 55 **56 64**

25 33 35 38 48 55 **55 55** 56 **64**

25 33 35 38 48 55 **55** 55 **56 64**

25 33 35 38 48 55 55 **55 56 64**

b. The probability of getting an average age of 58 or more by choosing three ages at random is $6/120 = .05$.

c. Answers will vary, depending on the results of Activity 1.1. The probabilities differ because their result from Activity 1.1 was from a simulation and so is an estimate of the exact answer computed in part b. Unless the number of repetitions is quite large, there can be a considerable difference.

E15. There are still 120 possible subsets of three, but there are many more ways to get an average as large as the observed average of 55, so the probability is substantially higher than in the actual case, and therefore the evidence of age bias is much weaker. (There are in fact 10 possible ways to get an average age of 55, so the exact probability is $10/120 \approx .83$.)

2

EXPLORING DISTRIBUTIONS

Overview

Goals

The overall goal of Chapter 2 is to provide a systematic way to uncover information through displaying and summarizing distributions of univariate data. Students will get a sound knowledge of the basic concepts and tools for exploring distributions and an understanding of how the tools compare. If students merely memorize the set of graphical and numerical techniques, they will have missed the point. The type of information uncovered through exploratory techniques should prompt students to ask questions that can be answered by the inferential techniques in later chapters.

In this chapter, students will learn

- to make and interpret plots for displaying univariate data: dot plot, histogram, stemplot, and boxplot
- to compute and interpret measures of center: mean and median
- to compute and interpret measures of spread: interquartile range and standard deviation
- to examine the effects of a linear transformation of the data on measures of center and spread
- to understand the use of normal density curves as models for data distributions
- to calculate probabilities connected with the normal distribution using standard units (z-scores) and a table of the standard normal distribution

Content Overview

Understanding what data represents is most easily seen by clearly distinguishing between *variables* and *cases.* A variable is that feature being measured, and a case is that object or person on which the measurement is made. In the spreadsheet data in Display 2.24, the variables are the column headings, (gestation period, average longevity, etc.) and the cases are the row headings (baboon, grizzly bear, etc.). For each case (type of mammal), measurements are made of gestation period, average longevity, and so forth.

Types of Variables

Categorical variables specify the group (category) to which a case belongs. Whether a mammal is considered wild or not and whether a mammal is considered to be a predator or not are the two categorical variables in Display 2.24. Coding wild as "1" and domestic as "0" is convenient but arbitrary. We could just as well have used "W" and "D" rather than "1" and "0." The 0–1 coding is convenient because the sum of the Wild column gives the number of mammals that are wild.

A *quantitative variable* assigns a numerical value or measurement to each case. Gestation period (in days), average longevity (in years), maximum longevity (in years), and speed (in mph) are the quantitative variables in Display 2.24.

Displaying Distributions

The set of values a variable takes on across the cases, along with the frequency with which each value occurs, produces a *distribution* of the data. Display 2.33 shows the distribution of the categorical variable describing whether a mammal is wild or not. Display 2.29 shows the distribution of the quantitative variable of mammal speeds. In fact, almost every plot in Chapter 2 displays a distribution of a single variable. Distributions are the key to statistical investigations. (Later, probability distributions and sampling distributions will be added to the array of distributions essential for statistics.) **One of the first steps in understanding statistics is learning to think in terms of distributions and where the value that is of interest to you fits into the appropriate distribution.** A picture may be worth a thousand words, but a statistical graphic is worth even more. Often it is the only way to see essential properties of a distribution. Thus, modern statistics is highly graphical. So stress the importance of graphical summaries and displays in the process of understanding distributions.

These are the standard plots used to display a single variable:

Categorical Variables	**Quantitative Variables**
Bar graph	Dot plot
	Stemplot (stem-and-leaf plot)
	Histogram
	Cumulative frequency plot
	Boxplot (box-and-whiskers plot)

For categorical variables:

Bar graph: A bar graph shows the frequencies (or relative frequencies) for the various categories of a categorical variable. Display 2.33 is a bar graph of the distribution of wild versus domestic mammals in the data set of Display 2.24. Note that the bars do not have to be arranged in any particular order because the horizontal axis is not a numerical scale. (See also Display 2.35.)

For quantitative variables:

Dot plot: A dot plot has a small dot above a real number line to mark the value for each case. Section 2.1 introduces students to distributions and their properties by using easily understood dot plots, which were introduced in Chapter 1. Dot plots quite nicely show the shape of a distribution, and you can use them for either large or small data sets.

Stemplot or stem-and-leaf plot: Display 2.29 gives a stemplot of the mammal speeds. Stemplots have the advantage of preserving at least two digits of the actual numerical values of the data. They are most useful for data sets of small to moderate size and can be made quickly by hand.

Histogram: A histogram places a bar above intervals of values of a variable, with the height of a bar indicating the frequency (or relative frequency) of the cases for that interval. Display 2.26 shows a histogram of the mammal speed data. Histograms do not preserve the exact numerical values in the data set. They are most useful for data sets of moderate to large size and are best made by a computer.

Cumulative frequency plot: A cumulative frequency plot (or cumulative relative frequency plot) shows the number (or proportion) of the values in a data set that are a given size or smaller. See Display 2.55.

Boxplot: A five-number summary consisting of the extremes, the quartiles, and the median can be plotted on a real number line, with the quartiles connected by a box, to form a boxplot or *box-and-whiskers plot* for the data. Boxplots do not give detailed information on shape, as found in other plots described above, but do provide a quick summary of location, spread, and possible skewness. See Display 2.50.

These plots all give some indication of the shape, center, and spread of the data. You should choose the one (or two) that best meets the needs of the situation. In most cases, you should try more than one to see which works best.

Describing Distributions

Here are the key strategies for describing distributions.

For categorical variables: Focus on the frequency or relative frequency. The data for categorical variables, as pictured in a bar graph, are summarized in a table of frequencies. Categorical variables will be covered in Chapters 6, 8, and 10.

For quantitative variables: Focus on shape, center, and spread.

Shape is described in terms of general shape, *symmetry* versus *skewness,* and in terms of the possible presence of *outliers, clusters,* and *gaps.* These terms, with the possible exception of *outlier,* are only loosely defined, and a great deal of judgment can be necessary when describing the shape of a distribution.

Center is a location for the data distribution on the real number line. The center is at the line of symmetry for a symmetric distribution, but more options present themselves for skewed distributions. The two common measures of center are the *median* and the *mean* (or average), both of which lie at the line of symmetry for symmetric distributions. For skewed distributions, the median will lie close to the bulk of the data points, whereas the mean will lie closer to the tail. The *mode,* or most common value, is the location of the highest bar on a histogram. It will play almost no part in this book, except that distributions with two peaks will be called *bimodal.*

Spread is a measure of the variability in a data set. If the median is an appropriate measure of center, then the distance between the quartiles (*interquartile range*) is typically an appropriate measure of spread. If the quartiles are close to the median, there is little variability in the data; if at least one of the quartiles is far from the median, there is considerable variability in the data. If the mean is an appropriate measure of center, then the standard deviation is typically an appropriate measure of spread. The standard deviation measures the "typical" distance between the values and their mean. It is a good measure of the typical deviation from the mean when the data distribution has a single peak and is reasonably symmetric.

A Systematic Approach to Exploring Univariate Data

Any data exploration should follow the steps of

$$\text{plot} \rightarrow \text{shape} \rightarrow \text{center} \rightarrow \text{spread}$$

That is, choose an appropriate plot, describe the shape, and find a measure of center appropriate to the shape and a measure of spread that agrees with the measure of center.

Ultimately, which measure of center and spread to use depends on the purpose for computing a summary statistic. If the purpose is simply to describe a distribution, it is most informative to use the mean and standard deviation for distributions that are approximately normal in shape and the median and interquartile range for skewed distributions.

In the Final Analysis

Being able to choose appropriate graphical and numerical summaries of data and being able to write or verbalize a coherent summary of what the data show is more important than mastering details of computation that a calculator or computer can handle.

Instructional Methods

Because one goal of this chapter is to have students learn to display and summarize sets of data, even large sets of data, it is important that they have practice doing just that. Now is the time for students to begin learning how to use their graphing calculators and statistical software. Statistical software enables students to construct plots quickly, accurately, and flexibly.

Statistics must be taught using data from the real world, so it is important that you review the discussion, practice, and exercise items for their suitability for your class. Statistics is an incredibly powerful tool in the social sciences and in the life sciences, and this text draws from many areas of these disciplines. Consequently, some contexts may be too sensitive for some of your students. Only you can make that decision. We recommend that you routinely review the social contexts of the material before presenting it.

Move through this chapter as quickly as possible. The amount of time you'll need will depend on how much statistics your students have previously learned in their high school mathematics curriculum.

Students may not become thoroughly comfortable with several of the concepts in this chapter, such as standard deviation and transforming data. These ideas will be revisited in later chapters, and by the end of the course students will have mastered them.

Time Required

Traditional Schedule			Block	4 x 4 Block
Section 2.1				
1–2 days	Day 1	Overview, Activity 2.1, uniform, normal	1.5 days	1 long, 1 short
	Day 2	Skewed, bimodal, summary, exercises		
Section 2.2				
1–2 days	Day 1	Dot plot, histogram, stemplot	1.5 days	1 long, 1 short
	Day 2	Activity 2.2, bar graph, summary, exercises		
Section 2.3				
5–6 days	Day 1	Mean, median	5 days	2 long, 2 short
	Day 2	Quartiles, five-number summaries, boxplots, modified boxplots		
	Day 3	Percentiles, cumulative frequency plots		
	Day 4	Activity 2.3, standard deviation		
	Day 5	Properties of summary statistics, recentering and rescaling		
	Day 6	Influence of outliers, summaries from a frequency table, summary, exercises		
Section 2.4				
2–3 days	Day 1	Unknown value and percentage problems, standard normal curve	2 days	1 long, 2 short
	Day 2	Determining z-scores, solving unknown value and percentage problems		
	Day 3	Central intervals, summary, exercises		
Review				
1 day			1 day	1 day

Materials

Section 2.1: For Activity 2.1, a tennis ball (a dead one is fine) and a centimeter ruler for every two students

Section 2.2: For Activity 2.2, a yardstick or meterstick

Section 2.3: For Activity 2.3, a ruler for each group of four students

Section 2.4: None

Suggested Assignments

Classwork			
Section	**Essential**	**Recommended**	**Optional**
2.1	Activity 2.1 D1, D2, D4 P1, P2, P4–P6	D3a P3, P7	D3b (must do Activity 2.1 before D3b), D5–D7
2.2	D8, D12–D15, D17 P9–P11, P13–P15	D9, D10, D16 P8, P12, P16	Activity 2.21 D11
2.3	D18, D20, D22–D30, D33–D36 P17, P19–P21, P23–P25, P27, P29, P30, P32, P34, P35	Activity 2.3 D19, D31, D37 P18, P22, P28, P31, P33, P36	D21, D32 P26
2.4	D39, D40, D42, D43, D45, D46 P38–P42, P44, P46–P48	D38, D41, D44 P37, P43, P45	

Homework			
Section	**Essential**	**Recommended**	**Optional**
2.1	E1–E5	E6, E7, E10, E11	E8, E9
2.2	E12, E16, E20	E13, E14, E19, E22	E15, E17, E18, E21
2.3	E24, E26–E29, E33, E35, E40	E23, E25, E30, E37, E38, E41–E43	E31, E32, E34, E36, E39, E44
2.4	E46–E48, E52, E54, E56	E45, E49–E51, E53, E55	
Review	E57–E59, E62, E63, E65, E67, E69, E71	E60, E66, E74	E61, E64, E68, E70, E72, E73, E75, E76

2.1 The Shapes of Things: Visualizing Distributions

Objectives

- to learn the basic shapes of distributions of data—uniform, normal, skewed
- to describe the characteristics of the shape of a distribution, including symmetry, skewness, modes, outliers, gaps, and clusters
- to describe a uniform distribution using the range and the frequency
- to estimate graphically the mean and standard deviation of a normal distribution and use them to describe the distribution
- to estimate graphically the median and quartiles and use them to describe a skewed distribution

Mastery of the mean, median, quartiles, and standard deviation is not expected until later sections of this chapter.

Important Terms and Concepts

- *basic shape of a distribution:* rectangular or uniform, normal, skewed right, skewed left
- *characteristics of the shape of a distribution:* symmetric, skewed, bimodal, outliers, gaps, clusters
- *measures of center:* mean, median
- *measures of spread:* standard deviation, quartiles

Lesson Planning

Class Time

One to two days. We suggest that you move quickly through this section.

Materials

For Activity 2.1, a tennis ball (a dead one is fine) and a centimeter ruler for every two students

Suggested Assignments

Classwork		
Essential	**Recommended**	**Optional**
Activity 2.1* D1, D2, D4 P1, P2, P4–P6	D3a P3, P7	D3b (must do Activity 2.1 first), D5–D7

*This activity is highly recommended because it demonstrates to students the variability inherent in even careful measurement of the same thing.

Homework		
Essential	**Recommended**	**Optional**
E1–E5	E6, E7, E10, E11	E8, E9

Lesson Notes: The Shapes of Things

The dot plots in this section were made by statistical software. Because of the limitations of the resolution of the computer screen, the dot plot in Display 2.3, for example, has places for 10 vertical lines of dots on which to plot the values from 0 through 0.20. Students don't need to worry about the exact rounding rule used by the software.

Activity 2.1: Measuring Diameters

Activity 2.1 introduces students to the concept of measurement error. The term *error* is not used in the sense of "mistake" but rather in the sense of "variation."

Throughout the course, students will gather data and combine their individual responses into a large data set. Make sure that students understand that variation generally occurs in the process of gathering data and may not represent an error on the part of anyone associated with the process. Variation occurs from one measurement of an object to another measurement of the same object, and from one object to another object. Variation also occurs in chance processes. For example, if you flip a fair coin, you expect that you will get 50% heads and 50% tails. However, you may get 6 heads out of 10 flips or 29 heads out of 50 flips just by chance.

1. Methods will vary. Some students will hold the tennis ball between two books and measure the distance between the books. Others might wrap a string around the ball, measure the length of the string, and then divide by π.

2. Answers will vary. Most measurements should be between about 60 and 70 mm.

3. This plot and print-out summarize the data for 25 student measurements (in millimeters) of the diameters of tennis balls. Each pair of students had their own ball, so there may be a little ball-to-ball variation. Most of the variation, however, is due to measurement error; it is difficult to measure the diameter of a sphere.

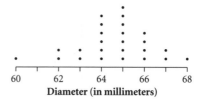

	N	MEAN	MEDIAN	TRMEAN	STDEV	SEMEAN
Diameter	25	64.640	65.000	64.652	1.655	.331

	MIN	MAX	Q1	Q3
Diameter	61.000	68.000	64.000	66.000

4. Like the one in step 3, distributions should be somewhat symmetrical and mound-shaped, which is typical of distributions of measurement errors.

5. Answers will vary. A typical result would be "about 65 mm, give or take about 2 mm or so."

6. Sources of variability include differences from tennis ball to tennis ball, differences in method of measurement, and error in reading or placing the centimeter scale. The variability could be reduced by using just one tennis ball, by all groups using the same method of measuring, and by all groups being trained in the method before starting. The variability cannot be eliminated entirely. As an example of why, suppose the diameter actually was 65.5 mm. When measuring to the nearest millimeter, some groups would report 65 and others 66 depending on whether they judged the measurement to be slightly under or slightly over 65.5 mm.

Lesson Notes: Uniform or Rectangular Distribution

The area over the closed interval $0.2 \leq x \leq 0.4$ or $[0.2, 0.4]$ is the same as over the open interval $0.2 < x < 0.4$ or $(0.2, 0.4)$ because the area over a single point is 0.

Discussion

As in Chapter 1, discussion questions were written to guide you in leading a class discussion of the previous material. You don't need to cover every one or cover them in order if your students lead the discussion in a different direction. Many questions will require you to provide significant help. The questions weren't designed for students to write out answers, except perhaps some notes to use in studying for exams.

D1. Answers will vary for this question. For part a, for example, each answer should involve the number of occurrences or frequency of some phenomenon that is attached to the days of the week. The important thing here is to discuss each suggested answer so that students learn what constitutes a distribution and what doesn't. For part a, students might suggest the temperature on each day of the week. That wouldn't be a distribution because the value on the y-axis would not be a frequency. However, a good example might be the number of days in the past year that the temperature rose above 70 degrees for each day of the week. That generates a distribution that is most likely uniform. Most suggestions will generate some discussion—and that's the idea. For example, a student might suggest that the number of, say, visits to McDonald's would have a uniform distribution over the days of the week. With class discussion, he or she should soon realize that there are more visits on Saturday than on, say, Wednesday, so this would not be a good example.

a. A good example would involve something that is equally likely to occur on each day of the week, such as the birthdays of classmates or the number of shooting stars seen in the night sky.

b. Possible examples are the last digits of phone numbers of students in the class or the last digit of the height in millimeters of members of the class.

D2. **a.** Possible examples include the number of automobile accidents or the number of visits to the doctor because both occur more frequently in winter in most places. Shooting stars are more likely in some months than others, a notable meteor shower occurring each August. Because February has fewer days, almost anything should occur less frequently in February.

b. A possible example is the number of bills paid each day of the month in a given family, which tend to be clustered around given days of the month, such as payday.

c. Possible examples include the frequency of students in the class with that digit as the last digit of their age or the frequency of days in a year that the traffic deaths in a small town reached that number.

d. Possible examples include the number of trips to the beach a person makes in a lifetime on that day or the number of people who attend the local movie theater on that day.

Practice

As in Chapter 1, practice questions are designed for students to do individually to make sure each student understands the preceding material. Usually, these will be done as "seat work"; other times, they will be part of the homework.

P1. An example plot follows. The number of deaths per month is fairly constant across the months, with about 190,000 per month. The exception is January, which shows a higher number of deaths than the other months.

The up-and-down nature of the plot appears to be a result of the fact that some months have more days than others. However, the up-and-down pattern should have been broken from July to August, which have the same number of days.

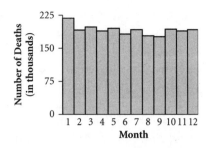

P2. **a.** With a perfect uniform distribution on [0, 2], the value 1.0 would divide the values in half.

b. 0.5, 1.0, and 1.5

c. 0.5 and 1.5

d. 0.15

e. 0.05 and 1.95

Lesson Notes: Normal Distribution

The term *normal* should not be applied casually to any distribution that is mound-shaped and symmetric. Instead, use terms like *round-shaped, approximately normal, bell-shaped,* and so forth to describe the shape of a data distribution. The normal distribution has a precise definition, and the equation of a normal curve is

$$y = \frac{1}{\sigma\sqrt{2\pi}} e^{-0.5\left(\frac{x-\mu}{\sigma}\right)^2}$$

This equation is completely determined by the two parameters of the distribution—the mean, μ, and standard deviation, σ. The integral below gives the area under this curve below a specified value a on the x-axis.

$$\text{area} = \int_{-\infty}^{a} \frac{1}{\sigma\sqrt{2\pi}} e^{-0.5\left(\frac{x-\mu}{\sigma}\right)^2} dx$$

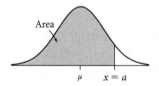

This function does not have a closed-form anti-derivative, so the definite integral can be evaluated only by numerical methods.

The section on the normal distribution on pages 27 to 29 contains an introduction to the standard deviation. The approach here is entirely graphical. Students learn that the distance from the center of a normal curve to either inflection point is one standard deviation and that the region within one standard deviation of the mean contains about two-thirds of the values. This approach fits with their interpretation of other measures of spread:

Range: The interval between the minimum and maximum contains 100% of the data.

IQR: The interval between the first and third quartiles contains 50% of the data.

SD: The interval between one *SD* below and one *SD* above the mean contains two-thirds of the data if the distribution is normal.

No formula is given at this time for the standard deviation. We have found that if the formula is given too early, students concentrate on questions like "Why do we divide by $n - 1$ rather than by n?" and "Why are we squaring things?" and "Where did the square root come from?" Try to get students to think graphically about the standard deviation at this stage so they will be comfortable with it as a measure of spread before encountering the formula in Section 2.3.

The region within one standard deviation of the mean actually encloses closer to 68% of the values than two-thirds, which you may want to tell your students at this point or wait until this comes up in Section 2.4.

Discussion

D3. **a.** The weight of a typical penny is about 3.11 grams, give or take 0.04 grams or so.

b. Answers will vary depending on measurements from your class. The mean should be about 65 mm and the standard deviation about 1.7 mm.

Practice

P3.

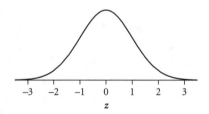

P4. Student estimates will differ somewhat from the actual means and standard deviations given here.

a. A typical SAT verbal score is roughly 500, give or take about 100 or so.

b. A typical ACT score is about 20, give or take 5 or so.

c. A typical college-aged woman is about 65 inches tall, give or take 2.5 inches or so.

d. A typical professional baseball player in the 1910s had a single-season batting average of about .260 or .270, give or take about .040 or so.

Lesson Notes: Skewed Distribution

In this section, students will be estimating quartiles graphically, not computing them. Computation will begin in Section 2.3. For now, have students think graphically about quartiles so they understand the concept.

Discussion

D4. **a.** This distribution is strongly skewed right. Most islands are quite small; Cuba and Hispaniola are comparatively very large. There is a wall at 0 because no island can be smaller than that, but many are close.

b. This distribution should be skewed right because some countries, such as the United States, have a per capita income that is much higher than most other countries. There is a wall near 0 because average per capita incomes can't go below that, but for many countries the per capita income is very small.

c. This distribution should not be skewed at all. Lengths like this typically form a distribution that is approximately normal.

d. This distribution probably will be skewed left. There is a wall at 1 hour—no student can take longer than that, and most students will work on an exam for the entire hour or close to it. A few students, however, will leave early.

e. This distribution will be skewed right. Some emperors reigned a long time but most for a moderate number of years. There is a wall at 0 years.

D5. Variables that tend to have a few large values and many relatively small ones include sizes of corporations (in either dollars or people) and land areas of the states. A variable that is actually a maximum also tends to be skewed right, such as maximum speeds of different models of cars or the most expensive shirt in each of the stores in a large mall.

D6. Variables that tend to have many large values and a few relatively small ones include scores on an easy exam, ages of residents of a retirement home, and anything that is actually a minimum, like the lowest priced shirt in each of the stores in a large mall.

D7. Toward the right, because it is very common to have a wall at 0 because most quantities must be positive.

Practice

P5. **a.** IV   **b.** II   **c.** V
    d. III   **e.** I

P6. Students should make a plot that is skewed right. Here is a histogram of the actual distribution:

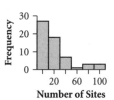

P7. There are 61 GPAs, so about 15 should fall into each quarter. The lower quartile is about 2.9, the median about 3.35, and the upper quartile about 3.7. The middle 50% of the students had GPAs between 2.9 and 3.7, with half above 3.35 and half below. (If the class were made up of older students, the distribution of GPAs might shift away from 4.0 and become less skewed. Students with more classes to their credit will have a harder time maintaining a high GPA.)

Lesson Notes: Bimodal Distribution and Other Features: Outliers, Gaps, and Clusters

In Section 2.3, students will get a rule to use to identify a value as an outlier. At this point, the purpose of introducing the term is to provide more tools for students to use in describing distributions. Although the mode is not an important summary statistic, the idea of *bimodal* as a description of a distribution should be in the AP Statistics student's vocabulary.

There are no discussion problems or practice problems provided for these two short sections. If you have time, you could use E10 and E11 for that purpose.

Exercises

Exercises were designed for students to do as homework. Most can be done either individually or in groups.

E1. **a.** This distribution is strongly skewed left. The actual distribution follows. Students will often have the height of the bar for 85+ taller than that for 75–84, confusing actual number of deaths with probability of death. There are fewer people in the 85+ category than in the 75–84 category, so fewer of them die.

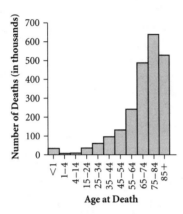

Source: *Statistical Abstract of the United States*, 1997, Table 130.

b. This distribution will be strongly skewed right. Most people get their driver's licenses at the earliest possible age or quite close to it.

c. The distribution of SAT scores for a large number of students should be approximately normal.

d. Selling prices of new cars should show a few very expensive models (like Corvettes) and a large number of relatively inexpensive (but not cheap!) ones (around $15,000 to $20,000). The distributions should be skewed toward the larger values.

E2. **a.** skewed right (toward larger values)
b. bimodal; developing countries tend to have higher birth rates than do developed countries.
c. Approximately normal is a good answer, but in fact the distribution is slightly skewed right. The dot plot shown next gives the heights in inches of the U.S. women's soccer team that won the World Cup in 1999.

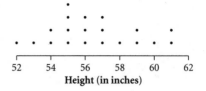

d. roughly uniform
e. skewed left (toward smaller values)

E3. **a.**

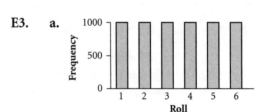

b.

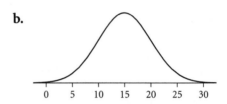

c. There are many possible answers. One such set of numbers is 1, 2, 3, 4, 9, 11, 13, 14, 17, 19, 21, 22, 23, 23, 24, 26, 27, 28, 29, 30. This boxplot represents one possible sketch.

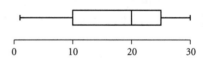

d. There are many possible answers. One such set of numbers is 0, 10, 20, 30, 80, 120, 150, 160, 170, 190, 210, 400, 500, 600, 700, 1300, 1500, 1800, 2400, 2900. This boxplot represents one possible sketch.

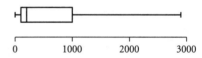

E4. The last digits of social security numbers are essentially random digits, so they should be fairly uniform over the range 0 to 9, as these are. Here we would say that the distribution is approximately uniform with about six students with each digit from 0 to 9.

E5. a. A case is one of the approximately 92 officers who attained the rank of colonel in the Royal Netherlands Air Force. There is only one variable: the age at which the officer became a colonel.

b. This distribution is skewed left with no outliers, gaps, or clusters. The median is 52 years, and the quartiles are 50 and 53. So we would say that the middle half of the ages are between 50 and 53, with half above 52 and half below.

c. In questions like this, students aren't expected to "guess" the "right" answer. Instead, they are expected to generate many possibilities that could then be investigated. For example, some military services have an "up or out" rule. It may be the case in the Royal Netherlands Air Force that if you haven't been promoted to colonel by your 55th birthday, you must retire. The armed services have very little use for 55-year-old privates. Alternatively, there might be a mandatory retirement at age 55. A third possibility is age discrimination against older people in the service.

E6. a. A case is one of the 125 seasons. The only variable is the number of inches of rain. Note: Rainfall is given by "seasons" rather than by years because Los Angeles has almost no rain from May through October. The rainy season is late fall through early spring. To give rainfall by year would be to break each of these natural seasons into two parts.

b. This distribution is skewed right with no obvious outliers. The three peaks suggest three groups of data points; perhaps weather conditions cause dry, normal, or rainy years. The median is 13, and the quartiles are 10 and 19. So we say that half the values are above 13 and half are below, with the middle half between 10 and 19.

c. The number of inches of rain cannot go below 0, so that is a natural wall. However, it appears that about 4 inches of rain is the effective minimum. There may be some characteristic of the weather that makes it almost impossible to go below that.

E7. The distribution is approximately normal, except that it has too many outliers and is a bit too "peaked" to be traced by a normal

curve. Because it is roughly symmetric, we can say that the distribution is centered at about 98.

E8. The up-and-down pattern looks fairly random, but we now see that births tend to be more frequent in the summer (July, August, and September). You may want to mention to students that they should always check plots to see where the scale begins. Although this plot shows more detail, if someone did not notice that the plot has been cut off at the bottom, they would think that the variation from month to month is larger than it actually is.

E9. The plot appears next (the first plot) with a scale beginning at 170. In this plot, January looks even more unusually high. As mentioned in P1, the up-and-down nature of the plot appears to be a result of the fact that some months have more days than others. However, the up-and-down pattern should have been broken from July to August, which have the same number of days. Now we can see the additional fact that the number of deaths seems to be generally declining over the months until October when it goes back up. Apparently, there are more deaths in the colder months. This becomes especially clear if we let October be month #1 and September be month #12, as was done in the second plot.

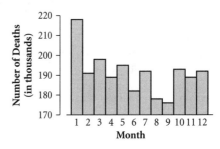

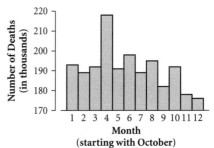

E10. **a.** The Nielsen data consist of 101 cases—the 101 television shows. Each case has two variables associated with it—the number of viewers who watched each show and the network on which it was shown. The number of viewers is a quantitative variable because it is a measured quantity or value. The network is a categorical variable because each show falls into exactly one of six categories (ABC, CBS, FOX, NBC, UPN, or WB).

b. As is often the case, the basic shape of the distribution of Nielsen ratings isn't clear-cut. The distribution is somewhat skewed right as the values rise rapidly from the left and taper off toward the right. There is a wall at 0—a show cannot have a negative number of viewers, no matter how awful it is.

The values in this distribution are all clumped together, with the exception of three high values for *Seinfeld, Seinfeld Clips,* and *ER*. These three highest values are widely separated from the bulk of the ratings. There are no gaps or clusters other than those created by the three highest values.

c. The median is 10.15. The spread is large, especially if you consider the three highest ratings. However, this large range is due to an outlier—*Seinfeld*. The middle half of the shows are fairly close together, grouped between ratings of about 6 and 13. (Actual values are 6.18 and 12.78.)

d. It had about seven times as many viewers as a typical show.

e. First, note that the scales on the two dot plots are different. The distribution for the regular week fits none of the basic shapes.

There appear to be two outliers, the bulk of the shows cluster around 7, and a cluster of shows have ratings less than 3.5. During the *Seinfeld* week, except for the outliers, the shows were more uniformly distributed. About 7 million people watched a typical show during the regular week, which is about 3 million people less than during the *Seinfeld* week. During the *Seinfeld* week, not only were there three shows watched by huge numbers of people, but also, in general, more people watched the programs. Even excluding the outliers, the spread for the regular week was less than for the *Seinfeld* week.

E11. **a.** ABC is approximately symmetrical and mound-shaped. CBS is slightly skewed right. FOX is more strongly skewed right. NBC is rather rectangular except for three outliers. UPN has very few shows (and very few viewers), and all but one are stacked on one point. WB is slightly skewed right. There are no outliers with the exception of NBC. There are no clusters or gaps.

b. The median for FOX is around 7 or 8. For NBC, the median is higher at about 12 or 13. The quartiles for FOX are about 6 and 14, and for NBC, they are about 9 and 16. So the middle half of the ratings have about the same spread for the two networks. The ratings are centered highest for NBC and lowest for UPN.

c. NBC has the most variability, and UPN has the least.

d. Answers will vary. A reasonable ranking would be NBC, CBS, ABC, FOX, WB, and UPN, based on their centers.

2.2 Graphical Displays for Distributions

Objectives

- to learn the difference between a case and a variable and between quantitative and categorical variables
- to make and interpret the most common graphical displays: histogram, relative frequency histogram, stemplot (stem-and-leaf plot), bar graph, and dot plot

There should be a shared emphasis between making and interpreting graphical displays. On the AP Statistics exam, interpretation of plots is crucial, but occasionally students are asked to make a plot as well as interpret it. They must remember to include scales and labels, not just copy the "bare" plot from their calculator.

Important Terms and Concepts

- case, quantitative variable, categorical variable
- histogram
- relative frequency and relative frequency histogram
- stemplot
- bar graph

Lesson Planning

Class Time

One to two days. Again, we recommend moving quickly through this section. If your students are taking the Advanced Placement exam, you may wish to save some of the recommended practice problems and exercises to use for review right before the exam.

Materials

For Activity 2.2, a yardstick or meterstick

Classwork		
Essential	**Recommended**	**Optional**
D8, D12–D15, D17	D9, D10, D16	Activity 2.2
P9–P11, P13–P15	P8, P12, P16	D11

Homework		
Essential	**Recommended**	**Optional**
E12, E16, E20	E13, E14, E19, E22	E15, E17, E18, E21

Lesson Notes: Variables and More About Dot Plots

In this lesson, continue to emphasize that distributions, however they are displayed, should be described in terms of center, shape, and spread, and all plots should have scales on the axes. Popular graphing calculators do not include a dot plot option in their plot menus. However, a program can be loaded into your calculator. A dot plot program is found in the calculator guide. Boxplots appear in Section 2.3.

Discussion

D8. Quantitative variables are gestation period (in days), average longevity (in years), maximum longevity (in years), and speed (in mph). Categorical variables are whether a mammal is considered wild or not and whether a mammal is considered to be a predator or not.

D9. **a.** Of the 18 mammals for which speeds are given, 12 have speeds that end in 0 or 5.
b. Two-tenths of the 18 mammals, or 3.6
c. The most likely explanation is that the speeds are actually estimates for the wild mammals. Who is going to measure the speed of a grizzly bear in the wild? The speeds that don't end in 0 or 5 are for the dog, fox, giraffe, horse, pig, and squirrel. For these mammals, with the possible exception of the giraffe, you can see how speed could be measured accurately. (And it certainly is in horse races and dog races.)

Practice

P8. Quantitative variables are year of birth, year of hire, RIF stage, and age. Categorical variables are row number, job title, and pay category (hourly or salaried). Month of birth and month of hire fall somewhat in between and are best called "ordered categories." Months are ordered and can be represented by numbers 1, 2, 3, . . . , 12 that can be meaningfully compared—they tell you whose birthdays come earlier in the year, for example. On the other hand, no one ever computes the mean or standard deviation of birth months as they might with age.

P9. The distribution is skewed right with no obvious gaps or clusters. There is a wall at 0 days because no mammal can have a smaller gestation period. The elephant is the only outlier. About half of the mammals have a gestation period of more than 160 days, and half have a shorter period. The middle half have gestation periods between 63 and 284. Large mammals have the longer gestation periods.

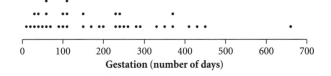

Lesson Notes: Histograms

Graphing calculators generally put a value that falls on a boundary into the bar on the right. If you plot a histogram on a TI-83, for example, and press TRACE, you will see that the interval always includes the left endpoint and never the right endpoint.

Discussion

D10. The histograms are somewhat mound-shaped. In each histogram, the mammal speeds center around 40 miles per hour with a standard deviation of about 20 miles per hour. The bar width doesn't make a lot of difference for this data set, except that in the first histogram there is some hint of two peaks rather than one.

D11. The narrower bars cover a smaller interval on the real number line. Thus, you can state more precisely which speeds are in a given bar than you can when they are wider. If you made all histograms with very narrow bars, they would essentially be dot plots and you could have hundreds or thousands of bars. In a histogram, you combine nearby values into bars so that you can have fewer bars, making the overall shape easier to see. On the other hand, if the bars are too wide, you may miss gaps and clusters.

D12. No, the "skyline" of the histogram remains the same. Only the scale on the vertical axis changes. The histogram has a vertical scale from 0 to some integer, whereas the relative frequency histogram has a vertical scale from 0 to 1. From a relative frequency histogram, you cannot tell how many cases there are in each bar. From a frequency histogram, it is harder to judge relative frequency.

Practice

P10. The shape of the maximum longevity distribution is quite different from that for average longevity. The average longevity distribution is skewed right with two possible outliers at 35–40 and 40–45. The distribution of maximum longevity is more uniform but with a peak at 20–30 years and an outlier at 70–80 years. As must be the case, the center of the distribution of maximum longevity is much higher than the center of the distribution of average longevity—about 30 years compared to about 15 years. The

spread of the distribution of maximum longevity is also much larger.

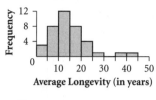

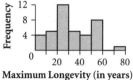

P11. The shapes do not change.

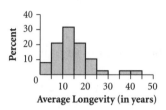

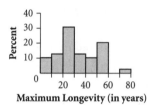

P12. The value at which the histogram balances (the mean) will be smaller than the value that divides the area into two equal parts (the median). If the distribution were symmetric, the mean and the median would be the same. However, here the outlying values tend to decrease the mean, but they don't affect the median. Specifically, if the values in the interval 40–48 were moved up to lie in the interval, say, 52–60, the median would be unchanged, but the mean would increase.

Lesson Notes: Stemplots

John Tukey (United States, 1915–2000), a statistician at Bell Labs, invented the *stemplot* about 30 years ago. He also invented the boxplot and other useful techniques for exploratory data analysis. Because these techniques were invented so recently and are meant to be used for informal exploration, you will find variation from source to source about how they are constructed.

An efficient way to make a stemplot is to record the data as it appears in the list to create unordered leaves. Once all of the data have been recorded, redo the plot, ordering the leaves.

For more information on stemplots, consult *Exploring Data* by James M. Landwehr and Ann E. Watkins (D. Seymour Publications, 1995).

If your students will be taking the AP exam, it is also useful to discuss the Minitab stemplot in Display 2.32 in the student text on page 46 and to note that graphing calculators do not have the capability to make this plot without a specific program.

You may wish to have students display a histogram and a stemplot of the same data set and to compare and contrast the two displays, listing advantages and deficiencies (if any) of each plot.

Discussion

D13. The stem-and-leaf plot shows a mound-shaped distribution in the middle with gaps at either end; the 11 and 12 at the low end and the 70 at the high end may be outliers. The median is 37, and the middle half of the values fall between 30 and 42. The stemplot gives more detail than the histogram.

D14. The leftmost column gives the number of values in the stemplot up to and including that row. Below the median, the counting is done from the bottom up. For example, the 8 at the beginning of the seventh row means that by the end of that row, with value 42, there are 8 values so far in the stemplot, counting from the bottom row up.

D15. This plot was made by Minitab statistical software. "Leaf Unit = 10" means that the leaf gives the tens place of the number and the stem gives the hundreds place. So, for example, the last line represents one number that falls in the interval 660 to 669.

```
Stem-and-leaf of Gestation N = 38
Leaf Unit = 10              N* = 1
  6   0   123334
 13   0   5666699
 17   1   0001
 (4)  1   5568
 17   2   02334
 12   2   5588
  8   3   3
  7   3   566
  4   4   02
  2   4   5
  1   5
  1   5
  1   6
  1   6   6
        6|6 represents a number in
        the interval 660-669 days
```

Practice

P13. The plots are shown here:

```
Stem-and-leaf of Ave Long  N = 38
Leaf Unit = 1.0            N* = 1
  3    0   134
 11    0   55567788
(12)   1   000222222222
 15    1   55555556
  7    2   0000
  3    2   5
  2    3
  2    3   5
  1    4   1
        4|1 represents 41 years
```

```
Stem-and-leaf of Max Long  N = 39
Leaf Unit = 1.0
  1    0   4
  4    0   588
  8    1   3344
  9    1   8
 16    2   0000334
 (5)   2   67778
 18    3   0004
 14    3   7
 13    4   0
 12    4   557
  9    5   00000344
  1    5
  1    6
  1    6
  7    0   0
        7|0 represents 70 years
```

```
Back-to-back stem-and-leaf plot
   Ave Long  |   | Max Long
         431 | 0 | 4
    88776555 | 0 | 588
222222222000 | 1 | 3344
    65555555 | 1 | 8
        0000 | 2 | 0000334
           5 | 2 | 67778
             | 3 | 0004
           5 | 3 | 7
           1 | 4 | 0
             | 4 | 557
             | 5 | 00000344
             | 5 |
             | 6 |
             | 6 |
             | 7 | 0
```

5|2|6 represents an animal with an average life span of 25 years and an animal (not necessarily the same) with a maximum life span of 26 years.

As also seen in the histograms students made in P10, the values of average longevity are generally smaller and have a slight skewness toward the larger values. The distribution of maximum longevity is more spread out and is more uniform in shape.

Note, again, that there is evidence of estimating to the nearest 5 or 10. Of the 38 values of average longevity, half end in 5 or 0. Of the 39 values for maximum longevity, 17 end in 5 or 0.

P14. There aren't enough values to get a good idea of the shapes of the two distributions. However, it appears that there is an outlier on the high side for the predators and two outliers on the low side for the nonpredators. The median of the predator distribution, 40.5, is larger than for the nonpredators, 33.5. The spreads are about the same. The most striking thing about the two distributions is that there are no slow predators. That certainly makes sense because a slow predator wouldn't catch much prey.

Activity 2.2: Do Units of Measurement Affect Your Estimates?

This activity is optional. It has several purposes. The first is to give students practice in choosing an "appropriate and meaningful way to display data." Use this activity and similar ones as an opportunity to discuss with students what makes a display appropriate. It is very important that students start to learn how to make good decisions based on the data they are dealing with.

This activity also provides the opportunity to begin the discussion of the importance of random assignment in any experiment. Finally, you can use the activity to begin discussing the concept and the possibility of bias in measurement. That is, some methods of measurement are more likely to result in estimates that are too high (or too low) compared to other methods.

1. There will be several occasions when you must split your class randomly. The purpose of randomization is to create groups that are as similar as possible with the exception of the variable of interest. Here are some ways to split the class randomly.

a. Have a slip of paper for each student in the class—half marked "feet" and half marked "meters." Mix them up, and have each student draw a slip.

b. Have students count off, and then randomly assign the evens to one group and the odds to the other. Decide by flipping a coin which group uses feet and which uses meters. Although this method is quick to use, it does not ensure a random division because there may be some pattern in the way students are seated (such as boy, girl, boy, . . .).

c. Another way to split the class quickly is to have each student flip a coin, and those with heads estimate in feet while those with tails

estimate in meters. This is random, but you may not end up with groups approximately equal in size.

2. Watch to be sure that students who measure in meters do not estimate in feet and then convert to meters.

3. To compare the two sets of estimates, you should convert the estimates in meters to feet or vice versa. The formula for converting meters, *m*, to feet, *f*, is $f = 0.305m$. The formula for converting feet to meters is $m = 3.28f$.

4. An interesting set of data to compare your results with is given in Hand, et al., *Small Data Sets* (Chapman and Hall, 1994), p.2, where a similar experiment was done in Australia. For those students, meter was the familiar unit, of course. Histograms of the two groups are shown below. The length of the room in question was 13.1 meters, or 43 feet. Both of these distributions have centers remarkably close to the true value, and both are similarly skewed. Using 1 meter = 3.28 feet, the third histogram shows the meter data rescaled to feet. Now you can see that estimating in meters produced much more variation than estimating in feet.

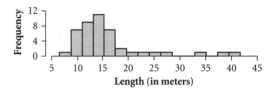

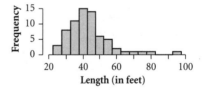

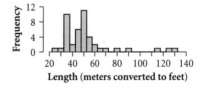

5. It's possible that there are some differences between students on the two sides of the room. For example, students on the right side of the room might have a better view of the length than students on the left side, or perhaps students on one side of the room have to walk farther from the door to their desks and consequently have a better sense of the size of the room. When there is any possibility of bias like this—and there almost always is—it's best to randomize.

Lesson Notes: Bar Graphs for Categorical Data

Quantitative variables are either continuous or discrete. If the numerical data can take on any value on a given interval, the variable is *continuous* and the data are called *measurement data.* Examples of continuous variables are height, weight, inflation rate in countries of the world, and blood pressure.

If the numerical data cannot take on every value within its range, the variable is *discrete,* and the data are also called discrete. Examples of discrete data are the number of cylinders in a car (which can only take on whole number values) and the sizes of a collection of wrenches (which can only take on values that are multiples of $\frac{1}{16}$ inch).

Data that are actually discrete are often treated as continuous. For example, when you measure a person's height, you must do so to, say, the nearest centimeter. That makes the data discrete, although the underlying distribution is continuous. Because they are always whole numbers, test scores such as the SAT or ACT are discrete but are often treated as measurement data. Looked at this way, there are no continuous real-world variables because the limitations of measuring instruments make all variables discrete.

Many statisticians say that a histogram should be used only for measurement data, not for discrete data. However, histograms are often suitable for discrete data if there are many values, as with ages or household income.

For bar graphs, the order of the bars, technically, is irrelevant. However, in many situations, one particular ordering might make more sense than other orderings. Sometimes alphabetical ordering of the categories is most reasonable, as when the categories are the 50 states. Sometimes ordering by height of the bar is most reasonable. Sometimes the categories have a natural ordering, as in Display 2.34 in the student text. See also D16, discussed next.

Categories can be coded using integers such as 0 or 1, as with predator/nonpredator and domestic/wild mammals, but these numbers are used merely for convenience and are not analyzed as measurements. The data are still categorical data.

Discussion

D16. The ordering of the bars in Display 2.35 is completely arbitrary and could have been done in the opposite order. The categories in the education data in Display 2.34, however, represent increasing amounts of education and should be kept in order to see the pattern in the frequencies. Two types of categorical variables are those that have ordered categories and those that have unordered categories. A non-numerical example of ordered categories is small, medium, and large, as in shirt sizes.

D17. a. The heights are the number of mammals in Display 2.24 that fall into that category. For example, the first bar shows that there are about 8 nonpredators that are domestic.
b. Looking at the middle set of bars, for predators, the second bar is taller than the first. Thus, a predator is more likely to be wild than domestic.
c. Looking at the first set of bars, for nonpredators, you can see that a nonpredator is also more likely to be wild because the second bar is taller than the first bar. However, for nonpredators, the first bar is a larger fraction of the second bar than is the case for predators. Thus, a predator is more likely to be wild than is a nonpredator.

Note: The way the bar graph is set up makes it easy to make the comparison asked for in part b but difficult to make the comparison in part c. You may wish to ask students to make a bar graph that makes it easy to answer part c. A two-way table like the one shown here can be helpful in summarizing the data on different categorical variables before making the bar graph.

	Nonpredator (0)	Predator (1)	Totals
Domestic (0)	8	2	10
Wild (1)	19	10	29
Totals	27	12	39

Practice

P15. The cases are the individual male members of the labor force aged 25 and older, and the variable is their educational attainment. The distribution shows an increasing proportion of males through the first four levels of education with a huge jump at the high school graduation level. After high school, the proportions in each education category decrease regularly with increasing education levels, except for a spike at bachelor's degree.

The distributions for males and females have much the same shape, but females have lower proportions in categories 1 and 2 and higher proportions in all the other categories except 6, 8, and 9. The female labor force overall is a bit better educated than is the male labor force.

Relative frequency bar graphs are better for this comparison because the number of males and the number of females in the labor force are different.

P16.

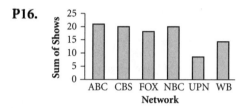

Exercises

E12. A case is a student in your class. The quantitative variables are age, number of siblings, and number of miles he or she lives from school. The categorical variables are hair color and gender.

E13. E13 could be done as a class discussion or a class activity if you have students collect their own pennies.

a. These data are the ages of a set of pennies collected by a statistics class. A case is a penny. The variable is the age of the penny.
b. The shape is strongly skewed right. (In fact, the shape is characteristic of a geometric distribution, which students will study in Chapter 7.) The median is 8 years, and the spread is quite large, with the middle half of the ages of pennies falling between 3 and 15 years. However, it is not terribly unusual to see a penny that is more than 30 years old. (Typically, students predict that the shape will be normal.)
c. There are about the same number of pennies produced each year. Supposing that a penny has the same chance of going out of circulation each year, you would get a shape something like this one, with the height of each vertical line being a certain percentage of the previous one. The age of 0 is lower

than the age of 1 because the data were collected partway through the current year.

E14. a. Answers will vary depending on whether students think domestic or wild mammals live longer and what they think about the variability in the two classes.

b.
```
 Domestic |   | Wild
        4 | 0 | 13
       85 | 0 | 556778
    22220 | 1 | 0022222
        5 | 1 | 5555556
        0 | 2 | 000
          | 2 | 5
          | 3 |
          | 3 | 5
          | 4 | 1
        1 | 5 | represents 15 years
```

c. Both distributions appear to be slightly skewed to the right with possible outliers on the high side. The median of both distributions is 12, but the spread of the distribution for wild mammals is quite a bit larger. The middle half of the domestic mammals have an average longevity approximately between 8 and 12 years. The middle half of the wild mammals have an average longevity between 7.5 and 15.5 years.

E15. These are bar graphs. Answers will vary. In general, between 1992 and 1996, the number of outlets of five major fast-food chains in the United States grew by about 20% to 30%, but the average revenue stayed about the same or even went down.

E16. **I.** Graph D, because on an easy test most people get high scores.
II. Graph A, because the distribution of heights has two modes (mothers and daughters).
III. Graph C, because most countries in the Olympics get no medals at all and only a very small number of countries get multiple medals.
IV. Graph B, because the weights should be mound-shaped. Most chickens will be clustered near a central weight with decreasing numbers having lower or much higher weights.

E17. The three histograms for average longevity are shown next with bar widths of 4, 8, and 16 years, respectively. At a bar width of 4, you can see a somewhat mound-shaped distribution with some skewness to the right, a pattern which is preserved at a bar width of 8.

At a bar width of 16, the mound-shaped part disappears and the distribution only looks highly skewed.

The histograms for maximum longevity show a bimodal distribution at a bar width of 4; the bimodality is mostly obscured by the time the bar width gets to 16.

For both sets of data, a bar width of 16 is clearly too large, but both 4 and 8 work well. Note that in the stemplot in the answer to P13, the bar width is essentially 5.

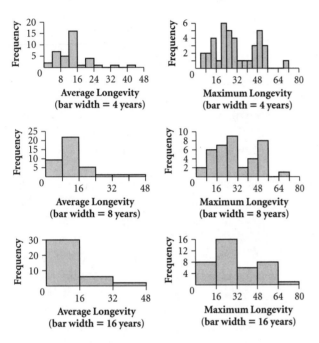

E18. **a.** The simulated means themselves have a mean of 46.62 years and a standard deviation of 6.16 years. Student estimates will differ somewhat. (The normal density curve that most closely corresponds to the histogram is shown here.)

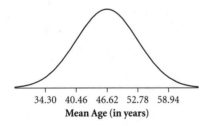

Mean Age (in years)

b. About 67%, about 95%; 100%. However, student estimates will vary, depending on their estimates of the mean and standard deviation.

c. From the histogram, it appears that about 50 of the 1000 sample means, or 5%, had an average age of 58 or more.

E19. **a.** For the SAT I Math scores in 1999–2000, the mean was 514 and the standard deviation was 113. Students may estimate that the mean is about 500 because that is near the center of the distribution and that the standard deviation is about 100 because about two-thirds of the values lie between 400 and 600.

b. About 67%; about 95%; 100%

c. Answers will vary based on student estimates in part a.

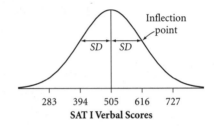

E20. **a.**

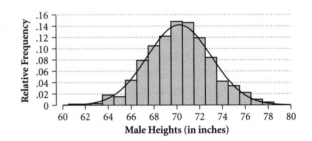

b. The mean is 70.2 inches, and the standard deviation is 2.8 inches. Estimates from students should be within 1 inch of those.

c. About .93, although student estimates will probably be a few percentage points different (about ±.05). Note that it is more efficient to find the proportion above 74 inches and then subtract from 1 or 1 − (.005 + .01 + .022 + .034).

d. .163 or (.002 + .002 + .003 + .018 + .015 + .044 + .079). Students' estimates will probably be a bit different (±.12).

e. Because the width of each bar is 1, the height and the area are the same. This is not true of every histogram. For example, see Display 2.41, which shows SAT I Math scores.

f. A normal distribution is a smooth continuous curve that has a domain of −∞ to +∞. The histogram of heights consists of distinct bars with flat tops and has a domain of only 60.5 to 78.5.

E21. For the United States, there is a population bulge around the ages of 30 to 50 for both men and women with decreasing percentages in the age groups above 50. For Mexico, the largest segments of the population are young children, with a regularly decreasing pattern in percentage of the population as the age increases. In both countries, there are more infant boys than infant girls. However, this reverses at the oldest ages, especially in the United States, where there are far more older women than older men.

E22. Students may find examples of bar graphs where the scale does not start at 0, making differences in the bars appear larger than they actually are. They may find examples of bar graphs where the scale does start at 0 and thus obscures differences that are important in the heights of the bars. They may find examples of "picture" graphs where a three-dimensional picture makes, for example, one quantity that is twice as big as another look like it is 8 times as big, and so on. The classic book, *How to Lie with Statistics* by Darrell Huff (Norton, 1993), originally published in 1965, is still informative and entertaining reading. More up-to-date examples can be found in Edward R. Tufte, *The Visual Display of Quantitative Information* (Graphics Press, 1983).

2.3 Measures of Center and Spread

Objectives

- to compute and interpret the mean and median
- to compute the five-number summary and the interquartile range and to identify outliers
- to make and interpret boxplots
- to interpret percentiles and read cumulative relative frequency plots
- to compute and interpret the standard deviation
- to compute summary statistics from a frequency table
- to learn the effect on summary statistics of a linear transformation of the data
- to learn which summary statistics are resistant to outliers

In this section, students study the common measures of center (mean and median) and the common measures of spread (interquartile range and standard deviation). One of the main goals of the section is to help students realize that every measure of center should be accompanied by a corresponding measure of spread. A related goal is to convince students that the standard deviation is a reasonable measure of variation from the mean for data that are approximately normal.

Important Terms and Concepts

- *measures of center* or *averages:* mean, median
- *measures of spread:* interquartile range (*IQR*), standard deviation, variance
- *five-number summary:* quartiles, minimum, maximum
- boxplot and modified boxplot
- percentiles
- cumulative frequency plots
- *linear transformations:* recentering and rescaling
- *outliers:* resistant to v. sensitive to
- frequency table
- formulas for the mean and standard deviation of a frequency table

Lesson Planning

Class Time

Five to six days

Materials

For Activity 2.3, a ruler for each group of four students

Suggested Assignments

Classwork

Essential	Recommended	Optional
D18, D20, D22–D30, D33–D36 P17, P19–P21, P23–P25, P27, P29, P30, P32, P34, P35	Activity 2.3 D19, D31, D37 P18, P22, P28, P31, P33, P36	D21, D32 P26

Homework

Essential	Recommended	Optional
E24, E26–E29, E33, E35, E40	E23, E25, E30, E37, E38, E41–E43	E31, E32, E34, E36, E39, E44

Lesson Notes: Measures of Center

The symbol $\bar{x}$ may be new to many of your students. Summation notation is introduced gradually in this text, and you probably will not need additional work with it.

Discussion

D18. **a.** mean: 2   median: 2
b. mean: 3   median: 2
c. mean: 4   median: 2
d. mean: 100   median: 2

The median is unchanged because increasing the largest number doesn't change the fact that 2 is the number in the center. The mean gets larger when any number is increased.

D19. **a.** As in D18, the mean is more affected by an outlier. In order to be the balance point, the mean has to move upward with the largest number because the mean increases if any number increases. In order to be the value in the center, the median doesn't have to change at all.

b. The distribution for the predators is skewed right, so the median is smaller than the mean. The distribution for the nonpredators is skewed left, so the median is larger than the mean. Because the nonpredators have generally smaller values to begin with, the means are farther apart than the medians.

c. There is a fairly large gap in the distribution between ages 38 and 48. When the larger values were removed, the central value or median had to "jump" that gap and became much smaller. This illustrates that the median can be quite unstable when there are only a few values in a distribution or when there are gaps.

Practice

P17. **a.** mean: 2.5   median: 2.5
b. mean: 3   median: 3
c. mean: 3.5   median: 3.5
d. mean: 49.5   median: 49.5
e. mean: 50   median: 50

P18. The mean height will increase by about 4 inches. The median should not change much because it will still be one of the 3rd graders, who all are about 4 feet tall.

P19. **a.** The measures of center for the life expectancies are

	Mean	Median
Africa	53.59	5
Europe	73.61	73

b. For Africa, the median is smaller than the mean because of the skewness toward the larger values. For Europe, the mean is about the same as the median.

Lesson Notes: Measuring Spread Around the Median: Quartiles and *IQR*

A good way to show the need to connect a measure of spread with a measure of center is with this example: Two AP Statistics classes took the same test, and the median score for both classes was found to be 78. Can we conclude that the classes performed in the same way given only that their medians are equal? Two dot plots with the same center, 78, but very different spreads should convince the students of the need for more information than the center provides. For example,

> Class 1: 78, 78, 78, 78, 78, 78, 78, 78, 78, 78
> Class 2: 60 62 64 72 76 | 80 82 90 91 92

Students may have been introduced to quartiles previously. If not, be sure to use many visual displays such as the ones on page 58 of the student text to assist them in seeing the idea.

A common mistake students make is to divide the range into four equal parts. For example, with the data 60, 62, 64, 72, 76, 80, 82, 90, 91, and 92, a student may divide the range of 32 into fourths, or 8, and get

> $\text{Min} = 60$
> $Q_1 = 68$
> $Q_2 = 76$
> $Q_3 = 84$
> $\text{Max} = 92$

Note that the correct quartiles are 64, 78, and 90.

On the AP Statistics exam, students are expected to understand, for example, that the first quartile is the number that divides the first and second quarters. It is incorrect to say something like, "My test score was really low. It fell in the first quartile." It would be correct to say, "It fell below the first quartile" or "It fell in the lowest quarter of all scores."

Discussion

D20. a. The middle half of the speeds of domestic mammals are between 30 and 40. The spread for wild mammals is a bit larger—the middle half of the speeds are between 27.5 and 43.5. Half of the domestic mammals have speeds above 37 and half below. The median for wild mammals, again, is almost the same, at 36. Note that in each case the median is closer to the upper quartile than the lower quartile, indicating that the distribution of speeds may be skewed left.

b. The wild mammals are more likely to be predators than are the domestic animals (see D17), and the speeds of predators have the larger *IQR* (see Display 2.31).

D21. Detective Seymour has received "quite a few" descriptions of the suspect from various eyewitnesses. These descriptions varied so much that Detective Seymour felt that the average was useless. For example, suppose he had four eyewitnesses, two of whom said the murderer was $5'7''$ tall and two of whom said the murderer was $5'8''$ tall. In this case, it would be perfectly reasonable for Detective Seymour to believe that the murderer was close to $5'7\frac{1}{2}''$ tall. However, if his four eyewitnesses said the murderer was $5'$, $5'4''$, $5'9''$, and $6'5''$, it wouldn't be reasonable for him to make any conclusion about the murderer's height even though the average is still $5'7\frac{1}{2}''$.

Practice

P20. a. quartiles: 2 and 5   *IQR*: 3
    b. quartiles: 2 and 6   *IQR*: 4
    c. quartiles: 2.5 and 6.5   *IQR*: 4
    d. quartiles: 2.5 and 7.5   *IQR*: 5

P21. a. The quartiles and medians are marked in bold on this plot.

```
Predators|  |Nonpredators
        1| 0|34
       75| 0|556788
    22222| 1|0002222
       65| 1|555555
         | 2|0000
        5| 2|
         | 3|
         | 3|5
         | 4|1
```

1|5 represents 15 years

b. The distribution of the average longevity of predators is mound-shaped, centered at about 12 years, with 50% of the values falling between 7 and 15 years. The distribution of the average longevity of nonpredators is centered at exactly the same place and has about the same spread, but it has two outliers on the high side.

Lesson Notes: Five-Number Summaries, Outliers, and Boxplots

Quartiles

Some textbooks and software packages use rules for finding quartiles that differ somewhat from that in *Statistics in Action*. For example, when there is an odd number of values, the median may be included in each half when computing the quartiles. Some software packages (such as Minitab and DataDesk) use the formula $\frac{(n+1)}{4}$ for the position of the first quartile. Texas Instruments calculators use the rule given in *Statistics in Action*.

It is not important for students to understand all of these various rules. They need to know the basic idea that the quartiles, with the median, divide the data into four parts with roughly the same number of values.

For large sets of data, the rule that is used makes little difference. For smaller sets of data, especially those with gaps, it can make quite a difference. For those types of data sets, a five-number summary is inappropriate, as in this example:

Consider the data set of the number of hours of TV per week a group of 8th graders said they watched on Monday through Friday nights during the school year: {1, 1, 2, 8, 9, 10, 19, 20}.

Two five-number summaries can be calculated:

Statistics in Action (TI-83)	Minitab
Min = 1	Min = 1
Q1 = 1.5	Q1 = 1.25
Med = 8.5	Med = 8.5
Q3 = 14.5	Q3 = 16.75
Max = 20	Max = 20

Outliers

Why is the number 1.5 used in the definition of outlier? According to John Tukey, who defined outliers this way, the reason is that 1 is too small and 2 is too large. That is, if you use the value 1, you get too many values defined as outliers that don't seem to be outliers. If you use 2, values that you think should be outliers aren't defined as outliers. Although the 1.5 rule is somewhat arbitrary, it works well in practice due to the remarkable intuition of an expert data analyst. There are methods of defining outliers other than the $1.5 \cdot IQR$ rule, but the $1.5 \cdot IQR$ method is a convention that many statisticians employ.

Different software packages use different symbols to mark outliers, and some mark outliers more than $3 \cdot IQR$ from the quartiles differently from those only $1.5 \cdot IQR$ from the quartiles. In addition, some software packages and many calculators orient the boxes horizontally.

Boxplots display skewness and show the existence of outliers in distributions. This fact makes it the most useful plot in Chapter 9 for deciding whether the conditions for the *t*-test have been met. Once the students have computed the five-number summary and constructed both regular and modified boxplots for several examples, students who will be taking the AP Statistics exam should know how to do this on their calculators and should be able to read the print-outs of common statistical software.

Discussion

D22. It gives the value of the quartiles, not their position; the median.

D23. **a.** 50%; 25%; 25%

b. A boxplot for a data set that is extremely skewed right would have a lower whisker that is shorter than the bottom half of the box, which is shorter than the top half of the box, which is shorter than the upper whisker. A boxplot for a data set that is extremely skewed left would have a lower whisker that is longer than the lower half of the box, which is longer than the upper half of the box, which is longer than the upper whisker. A boxplot for a data set that is symmetric would have whiskers of equal length, and the two halves of the box would be of equal length.

c. The *IQR* is equal to the length of the box. The range is the distance from the end of one whisker (or outermost outlier) to the end of the other whisker (or outermost outlier).

d. From a boxplot, you can see the five-number summary exactly and outliers are clearly marked. These must be estimated from a histogram and can be difficult to estimate. From a histogram, you can estimate the mean by estimating a balance point for the distribution. You cannot do this with a boxplot. A histogram will reveal the frequency of the data within an interval. You do not know the exact values, but you know how many are within the given boundaries.

You know a lower and upper bound but not necessarily the exact least and greatest value. You know where there are clusters of data and where there are gaps. With a boxplot, you get a sense of the basic shape of the distribution, but you cannot see clusters or gaps.

Practice

P22. **a.** *Seinfeld, Seinfeld Clips,* and *ER*
b. *Touched by an Angel*
c. The actual histogram is shown here:

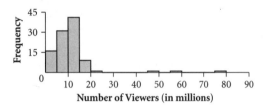

P23.

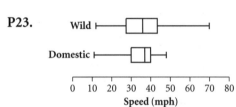

P24. **a.** The five-number summary for the average longevity of this set of mammals is

minimum: 1
lower quartile (Q_1): 8
median: 12
upper quartile (Q_3): 15
maximum 41

Once again, software packages may give quartiles slightly different from those done by hand. Here are the results from Minitab:

```
Variable    N    N*  Mean Median TrMean StDev SEMean
Ave long   38     1 13.13  12.00  12.32  8.00   1.30

Variable  Min   Max    Q1     Q3
Ave long 1.00 41.00  7.75  15.00
```

b. $IQR = 15 - 8 = 7$
c. $Q_1 - 1.5 \cdot IQR = 8 - 1.5(7) = -2.5$. There are no outliers on the lower end.
d. $Q_3 + 1.5 \cdot IQR = 15 + 1.5(7) = 25.5$. The life spans of 35 years for the elephant and 41 years for the hippopotamus are outliers. The largest value that isn't an outlier is 25. This is where the upper whisker will end.

P25.

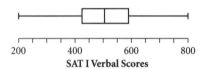

P26. Yes. There will be no lower whisker, for example, if the minimum and the first quartile are equal. This set of data has no lower whisker:

$$\{1, 1, 1, 1, 2, 3, 5, 6, 7, 12, 14, 16\}.$$

Lesson Notes: Percentiles and Cumulative Frequency Plots

We say that a given score is at, say, the 74th percentile if 74% of the scores in the distribution lie *at or below* the given score.

Discussion

D24. **a.** about the 23rd percentile
b. about 325 to 700; about 290 to 745
c. about 480

D25. 90%; between the 2.5th percentile and the 97.5th percentile

Practice

P27. The quartiles are about 425 and 590; the median is about 505; the *IQR* is about $590 - 425 = 165$. The minimum of 200 and the maximum of 800 complete the five-number summary. A boxplot is shown here:

Lesson Notes: Measuring Spread About the Mean: The Standard Deviation

Activity 2.3: Comparing Hand Spans: How Far Are You from the Mean?

The activity "Comparing Hand Spans" familiarizes students with the concept of a measure of variation from the mean. They also learn that several such measures may be defined. Students should be in groups of four or five for this activity.

1–3. Measurements, means, and dot plots will vary.

4. The major source of variability is that everyone in the group has a different hand span, depending on the size of their hand and on their flexibility. The other source of variability is in the uncertainty of the measurement of a given hand. That is, if different people measure the same hand, they may get different values. Also, if the same hand is measured at different times, the measurement for that hand span may be a little different each time.

5. Answers will vary.

6–8. Groups will tend to invent the mean absolute deviation (*MAD*):

$$MAD = \frac{\sum |x - \bar{x}|}{n}$$

The *MAD* is easily understood and a reasonable measure of spread for describing a distribution of data but has almost no importance in statistical theory. Sometimes a group will invent a statistic defined as the number of group members whose hand span is not equal to the mean (the number of "misses"). Other groups may suggest the largest difference from the mean.

The Standard Deviation

Have students calculate the standard deviation by hand a few times (using a table for organization) so that the formula is more meaningful for them.

Two questions will surface when students see the formula for the standard deviation: Why do we square the deviations instead of taking the absolute value, and why and when do we divide by n and by $n - 1$?

Why do we square rather than take the absolute value? In Activity 2.3, students may invent the mean absolute deviation (*MAD*):

$$MAD = \frac{\sum |x - \bar{x}|}{n}$$

as a method of measuring spread. Intuitively, this is a perfectly reasonable measure and much simpler than the standard deviation. Why, then, don't statisticians use it?

There are two main uses of statistics that we should try to keep separate when deciding what summary measures to use. The first is exploratory, in which we are just trying to describe key features of the data. The second is inferential, in which we are trying to infer something about a larger population (sample survey) or about treatments (experiments). In the exploratory sense, many measures of variability will work (interquartile range, mean absolute deviation, standard deviation, etc.), depending on the nature of the data. In fact, the standard deviation is not always useful for describing distributions of real data. It works well as a measure of spread only for data distributions that

are approximately normal in shape. If the distribution is skewed, the *IQR* is usually a better choice.

However, the standard deviation cannot be avoided (at least easily avoided) when one is using classical inference for means. The sampling distribution of the sample mean is approximately normal (given a reasonable sample size) with standard deviation equal to the population standard deviation divided by the square root of sample size. Thus, confidence intervals and test statistics for means require a good estimate of the population standard deviation, which is provided by the sample standard deviation.

In short, in exploratory analysis, we can do anything reasonable after viewing the shape of the data distribution. In inference, we use the sample standard deviation as an estimate of the population standard deviation because we are forced into the normal model by the laws of probability.

One reason that the standard deviation comes up so often in statistical theory is that squaring rather than taking the absolute value has an important characteristic. Have students examine the difference among the graphs of $y = |x|$, $y = |x| + |x - 2|$, $y = |x| + |x - 2| + |x - 4|$, and so on. Observe that the graphs are composed of segments and rays and the pattern varies depending on the number of terms. Then explore $y = x^2$, $y = x^2 + (x - 2)^2$, $y = x^2 + (x - 2)^2 + (x - 4)^2$, and so on. Observe that in each case the graph is a parabola. If the situation is to be analyzed mathematically, squaring is simpler than absolute values.

Why do we divide by $n - 1$ rather than by n? Essentially, the reason for dividing by $n - 1$ is to adjust for working with a sample. As mentioned earlier, the population standard deviation in inferential statistics is estimated by the sample standard deviation. The variability in a random sample tends to be less than in the entire population. Thus, you divide by $n - 1$ rather than by n to increase the sample variability a bit. As the sample size increases, it makes little difference whether you divide by n or by $n - 1$. This issue will be investigated more fully in Chapter 5 along with the discussion of sampling distributions.

Discussion

D26. Yes, this seems reasonable. Some values are more than this distance from the mean, and some are less. In addition, many of the deviations are close to the value of the standard deviation.

D27. Each of these, except the variance, has the same units as the data—*years*. The variance is in *years*².

D28. Dividing by a slightly smaller number makes the standard deviation a bit larger.

D29. In both cases, the formulas involve the square root of a sum of squared differences. To compute the standard deviation, find the differences, square, average, and take the square root. To find the distance between two points, find the differences, square, add, and take the square root. For example, suppose that you have a set of three values, say, {1, 4, 10}, with mean 5. Then, except for dividing by the sample size, the standard deviation is the same thing as the distance in space between the point (1, 4, 10) and the point of the mean (5, 5, 5):

$$\sqrt{(1-5)^2 + (4-5)^2 + (10-5)^2}$$

Thus, the measure of distance in statistics, the standard deviation, has almost exactly the same form as the measure of distance in Euclidean geometry. Perhaps this reason, above all others, helps convince students that the standard deviation is a natural measure of spread.

Practice

P28. The mean is 4.4, and the deviations from the mean are shown in this table. The sum of these deviations is 0. To get the standard deviation, find the $(n-1)$ average of the squared deviations, $\frac{41.2}{4} = 10.3$, and take the square root to get about 3.21.

Value x	Deviation from Mean: $x - \bar{x}$	Squared Deviations: $(x - \bar{x})^2$
1	−3.4	11.56
2	−2.4	5.76
4	−0.4	0.16
6	1.6	2.56
9	4.6	21.16
Sum	**0**	**41.20**

P29. **a.** i. 0, because all of the deviations from the mean are 0

   b. iii. 0.577

   c. iv. 1.581

   d. vii. 5.774. Note that the values are 10 times as far from the mean as those in part b,

so the standard deviation is 10 times as large.

   e. ii. 0.058. Note that the values are one-tenth as far from the mean as those in part b, so the standard deviation is one-tenth as large.

   f. v. 3.162. Note that the values are twice as far apart as those in part c, so the standard deviation is twice as large.

   g. vi. 3.606. It may be hard for students to distinguish part f from part g. If so, they should compute the standard deviation to check their answer.

Lesson Notes: Which Summary Statistic?

Discussion

Plotting the data is the first step to making good decisions about summary statistics. Many students may ask for "rules." There are very few hard and fast rules when it comes to data analysis.

D30. Multiply the number of houses by the mean value by the tax rate. The total is equal to the number of values times the mean. If you know the number of houses, you can easily convert between the mean value and the total value.

D31. Income is strongly skewed right. A few people make a lot of money, whereas most people are clustered together toward the low end. Consequently, the mean looks larger than most people think is "typical." The median tells you that half of the residents earn more and half earn less. Another reason the median may be given is that the median income is probably easier to estimate.

D32. **a.** If you knew the upper quartile, you could make the seats wide enough for 75% of the people. The maximum wouldn't do much good because it would be so large that it would be too expensive to make every seat that size. Perhaps the best thing would be to know (say) the 95th percentile, so you could make the seats wide enough for 95% of the people.

   b. If you want the best price, you need to know the minimum.

   c. If you tend to study less than most people, the lower quartile of the study time needed by students at that college would give you a good indication of how much time you will need. If you are typical, you might like to know the median. If you tend to study more than most people, you might like to know the upper quartile.

Practice

P30. The mean is larger than the median because house values tend to be skewed right—some houses cost a lot more than most houses in a community. Very few houses cost a lot less. To get the total property taxes, multiply the number of houses by the mean value by the tax rate to get ($392,059)(9,751) (0.0115) = $43,964,124. This is an average of $4,508.68 per house. (This assumes that the assessed value is equal to the price. California's Proposition 13 makes the situation more complicated because many houses are assessed at quite a bit under the actual value.)

P31. **a.** Medians were used in this story because the distribution of car ages is strongly skewed right. There are more brand-new cars on the road than cars of any other age (because cars of any other age have been disappearing due to accidents and mechanical problems). A few people drive very old cars. A story that appeared in the same newspaper tells of such a couple—the husband drives a 1971 Blazer, and the wife drives a 1966 Mustang.
b. The article says that the year 1970 was "before the Big Three auto makers were challenged by a flood of well-built Japanese imports" and quotes an expert as saying vehicles are proving more durable. Another reasonable explanation that students might give is that people are choosing to spend their income on other things or that they are forced to spend their income on other things. Again, encourage students to generate lots of possibilities.

Lesson Notes: The Effects of Recentering and Rescaling

Discussion

D33. **a.** mean: 188 pesos; *SD:* 47 pesos
b. median: $10; Q_1: $5; Q_3: $20

Practice

P32. **a.** Divide each of the summary statistics by 12 so then the mean is 4 feet, the median is 3.75 feet, the standard deviation is 0.2 feet, and the interquartile range is 0.25 feet.
b. The mean is 50 inches, and the median is 47 inches. The standard deviation and interquartile range do not change.
c. The mean is $4\frac{1}{3}$ feet, the median is $4\frac{1}{12}$ feet, the standard deviation is 0.2 feet, and the interquartile range is 0.25 feet.

P33. **a.** mean: 2; *SD:* 1
b. mean: 12; *SD:* 1 (same as in part a)
c. mean: 20; *SD:* 10 (10 times that in part a)
d. mean: 110; *SD:* 5 (5 times that in part a)
e. mean: −900; *SD:* 100 (100 times that in part a)

Lesson Notes: The Influence of Outliers

Although it is always true that removing a value that is larger than the rest of the values in a data set will decrease the mean, it does not necessarily decrease the standard deviation. The reason is that if the mean decreases, it changes all of the deviations from the mean. It's also possible to remove the only outlier in a set of data only to create a new outlier!

Discussion

D34. **a.** The mean is affected by the outliers. Whether the effect is moderate or not depends on the context. To compute the mean, first add the values. An unusually large value will increase this sum quite a lot. Outliers tend to have greater influence in small samples than in large ones.
b. The numerical value of an outlier does not affect the median because the size of the largest or smallest value doesn't affect which value is in the center. But removal of an outlier from a data set may cause some change in the median because of a change in the sample size.

D35. **a.** Yes. The range is greatly affected by an outlier because it is computed by subtracting the largest and smallest values.

b. Yes. Generally, the standard deviation is affected greatly by an outlier. To compute the standard deviation, first square the differences from the mean. If one of these differences is large, squaring it makes it even larger.

c. No. An outlier does not affect the interquartile range because the quartiles aren't affected by the size of the maximum or the minimum.

Practice

P34. a. Outliers occur above $-30 + 1.5(21) =$ 1.5. Hawaii, at 12, is an outlier.

b. The count will decrease by 1 to become 49.

```
Summary of Lowest Temperature without Hawaii
No selector
        Percentile   25
            Count    49
             Mean    -41.5
           Median    -40
           StdDev    16.2
              Min    -80
              Max    -2
            Range    78
Lower ith %tile      -51
Upper ith %tile      -32
```

The minimum, median, quartiles, and interquartile range should remain the same or about the same. With a sample of size 50, removing one data value will have little effect on the median but could have greater effect on the quartiles as they are, in essence, the medians of samples of size 25. The mean should go down by a bit more than one degree because the difference between Hawaii's temperature and the mean is about −52 degrees and there are 49 states remaining. The standard deviation should go down only slightly, but this is difficult to predict. The range will decrease from 92 degrees to about 80 degrees. The maximum will decrease from 12 to a little less than zero.

Lesson Notes: Summaries from a Frequency Table

The formulas in this section provide a foundation for calculating the mean and standard deviation of probability distributions.

On some calculators, such as the TI-83, you can put the values from a frequency table into, say, list L_1. Then put the frequencies into list L_2. Using the command 1-VAR STAT L1, L2 will give the summary statistics for the frequency table. Similarly, you can make a histogram.

Discussion

D36. a. Skewed right, or toward the larger values. There is a wall at 0 because no family can have fewer than zero children.

b. Because there are 100 families, the median is at position $\frac{(100 + 1)}{2} = 50.5$ between family 50 and 51. For 1967, the 50th and 51st families both occur in the category of 3 children, so 3 is the median.

c. For 1967, the computation for mean is shown below.

D37. The formula uses multiplication as a short cut for addition. Instead of adding the value x a total of f times, you can just multiply x by f. The symbol n stands for the sample size or 100, x is the value or number of children, and f is the frequency or number of families that have that particular number of children. Again, the formula substitutes multiplication for repeated addition.

Practice

P35. a. For 1997, the mean is shown at the bottom of page 49. You can find the standard deviation for 1997 by realizing that there are 15 deviations of $(0 - 2.3)$, 22 deviations of $(1 - 2.3)$, and so on. The standard deviation is also shown on page 49. The standard

---

Lesson 2.3, D36c

$$\bar{x} = \frac{0 \cdot 5 + 1 \cdot 10 + 2 \cdot 21 + 3 \cdot 28 + 4 \cdot 17 + 5 \cdot 7 + 6 \cdot 4 + 7 \cdot 3 + 8 \cdot 5}{100}$$

$$= \frac{324}{100}$$

$$= 3.24$$

$$SD = 1.89$$

deviation for 1997 is 1.84, which is a bit less than that for 1967, which is 1.89.

b. For 1997, the 50th and 51st families both occur in the category of 2 children, so that is the median, one fewer than in 1967.

c. The quartiles are at positions 25.5 and 75.5. Counting in from the top of the 1967 table, the 25th and 26th families both occur in the category of 2 children, so that is the first or lower quartile. For 1967, the quartiles are 2 and 4. For 1997, the quartiles are 1 and 3. In both cases, the *IQR* is 2.

d. The median number of children for 1997 is 2, 1 fewer than in 1967; the mean also went down by about 1 child per family, from 3.2 to 2.3. The distributions kept the same shape and about the same spread.

Note about outliers and skewed distributions: Note that both the 1967 and 1997 distributions have values identified as possible outliers even though no value is separated from the rest of the distribution. For 1997, an outlier would be more than

$3 + 1.5(2) = 6$ or less than $1 - 1.5(2) = -2$. An outlier is a family with more than 6 children. For 1967, any outlier would have to lie below $2 - 1.5(2) = -1$ or above $4 + 1.5(2) = 7$. So two families would be identified as outliers, those with 8 children. A distribution with long tails will usually have values identified as outliers even though they are not separated from the rest of the values.

P36. **a.** The mean is about 10.

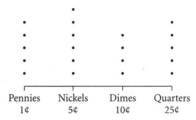

Number of Coins and Their Value

b. The mean is shown below.

c. The standard deviation is closest to 10.

d. The standard deviation is shown below.

Lesson 2.3, P35a

Mean:

$$\bar{x} = \frac{0 \cdot 15 + 1 \cdot 22 + 2 \cdot 25 + 3 \cdot 18 + 4 \cdot 10 + 5 \cdot 2 + 6 \cdot 4 + 7 \cdot 2 + 8 \cdot 2}{100}$$

$$= \frac{230}{100}$$

$$= 2.3$$

Standard Deviation:

$$SD = \sqrt{\frac{(0 - 2.3)^2 \cdot 15 + (1 - 2.3)^2 \cdot 22 + \cdots + (8 - 2.3)^2 \cdot 2}{99}} \approx 1.84$$

Lesson 2.3, P36b

$$\bar{x} = \frac{\sum x \cdot f}{n} = \frac{1 \cdot 5 + 5 \cdot 6 + 10 \cdot 4 + 25 \cdot 5}{20} = \frac{200}{20} = 10$$

Lesson 2.3, P36d

$$s = \sqrt{\frac{\sum (x - \bar{x})^2 \cdot f}{n - 1}}$$

$$= \sqrt{\frac{(1 - 10)^2 \cdot 5 + (5 - 10)^2 \cdot 6 + (10 - 10)^2 \cdot 4 + (25 - 10)^2 \cdot 5}{99}}$$

$$\approx 9.4$$

Exercises

E23. **a.** Either could be used depending on the purpose of computing a measure of center. If, as is typical, there are a few expensive homes mixed in with many modestly priced homes, then the mean price will be larger than the median price. So real estate agents usually report the median price because it is lower and it tells people that half the prices are lower and half are higher. The tax collector would be interested in the mean price because the mean times the tax rate times the number of houses gives the total taxes collected.

b. As always, the answer depends on the purpose for computing a measure of center. Most likely, the reason here is to establish the total crop in Iowa for the year. In that case, it is best to find the mean yield per acre. This mean could be multiplied by the total acres planted in corn to approximate a total yield. An individual farmer probably would want to know the median as it gives the better indication of whether his or her yield was typical.

c. Again, the purpose of computing the measure of center determines which one you would use. Survival times are usually strongly skewed right. Telling a patient only the mean survival time would give too optimistic a picture. The smaller median would inform the person that half the people survive longer and half shorter. On the other hand, if you are the physician and must allocate your time by estimating the total number of hours you will be caring for your patients with this disease, the mean would be better. You would then multiply the mean number of survival days by the number of patients you have by an estimate of the number of hours each day that each patient takes.

E24. **a.** boxplot 3
b. boxplot 1
c. boxplot 2

E25. The back-to-back stemplot is better because there are only a few values, so you may as well see them.

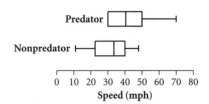

E26. The third boxplot cannot be the plot for both classes combined because the minimum test score for the second period is about 10, and that would be the lowest for the combined set also.

E27. The seventh value is 10, as you can see from solving

$$25 = \frac{x + 24 + 47 + 34 + 10 + 22 + 28}{7}$$

E28. **a.** II has the largest standard deviation, and III has the smallest.
b. II and III

E29. The second data set is the same as the first except that each value is 4 more, so the spreads are the same. The standard deviation of the recentered values, then, is also about 30.

E30. The set of heights of all female NCAA basketball players will have the larger mean because basketball players tend to be taller than other athletes, in general. The set of all female NCAA athletes will have the larger standard deviation because it will include tall, medium, and short athletes, whereas the set of all basketball players will include mostly tall athletes.

E31. **a.** The mean length of a generation. You would divide 300 years by the mean length of a generation to get the number of generations.
b. The average speed. You multiply the average speed by the time to get the distance.
c. Yes, if you know the number of trees. The average volume is $\pi r^2 h = \pi \cdot 3^2 \cdot 45 \approx$ 1272 ft^3. To get the total volume, multiply by the number of trees.

E32. **a.** Replace the 15 with a 1.
b. Replace the 32 with a 10.
c. There is no way to get an outlier.

E33. **a.** To make the histogram, students need only copy the histogram in the student text and then use the formula

$$C = \frac{5}{9}(F - 32)$$

to convert the numbers on the *x*-axis from °F to °C. The scale would then go from 36.67 to 58.89.

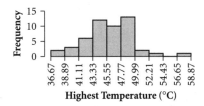

Highest Temperature (°C)

b. Note that the standard deviation is the tricky one: You just multiply by $\frac{5}{9}$. For each of the others, you subtract 32 and then multiply by $\frac{5}{9}$.

Variable	N	Mean	Median	TrMean	StDev
Highest	50	45.61	45.56	45.53	3.72

Variable	Min	Max	Q1	Q3
Highest	37.78	56.67	43.33	47.78

c. Yes, there is an outlier on the high side. The *IQR* = 4.45, and 1.5(*IQR*) = 6.675. So $Q_3 + 1.5 \cdot IQR = 54.455$, and the maximum is larger than that—so definitely an outlier. $Q_1 - 1.5 \cdot IQR = 36.655$, and the minimum is bigger—so none on the lower end.

E34. **a.** **i.** 6.325 v. 6.667
   ii. 2.000 v. 2.010
   iii. 0.632 v. 0.633

b. No, as *n* gets larger, the difference between *s* and σ goes to 0.

E35. **a.** 3.11 grams
b. 0.04 gram
c. Yes, most of the weights are between 3.07 and 3.15.

E36. The mean is 73.154, and the standard deviation is 3.065.

E37. Of the 36 salaried workers, 18 were kept and 18 were laid off. The 18 salaried workers who were laid off had a median age of 53.5 and quartiles 42 and 61. The 18 salaried workers who were kept had a median age of 48 with quartiles 37 and 55. So the median age of the workers laid off was 5.5 years older, but the distributions had about the same *IQR*.

Salaried Worker's Ages

Kept		Laid Off
	2	3
9	2	
421	3	012
7	3	
2	4	2
8887	4	9
443	5	0234
975	5	669
10	6	134
	6	69

6|9 represents 69 years

E38. The maximum value must be an outlier. The length of the box is the *IQR*, and Q_3 lies at the top of the box. An outlier lies beyond $Q_3 + 1.5(IQR)$. This point can be estimated from the boxplot by imagining stacking one-and-a-half boxes to the right of the box as illustrated here. The top of these boxes is less than the maximum value.

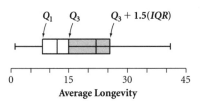

Average Longevity

E39. There are three outliers in Display 2.52 but only two in Display 2.74. The explanation is that the boxplot for the average longevity of domestic mammals creates its own outlier because the spread in longevity in these mammals is otherwise so small. There is no reason to expect that the outliers of subsets of a set of data will be the same as in the set of data itself.

E40. The standard deviation is 0 because the numbers don't vary.

E41. First, subtract 5478 from every number, leaving

0.1	0.3	0.3	0.9	0.4	0.2

The mean of these numbers is 0.3667, so the mean of the original numbers is 5478.3667. The standard deviation is about 0.280. Because recentering doesn't change the standard deviation, that's the standard deviation for the original set of numbers, too.

E42. Let the mean of the original set of data be

$$\bar{x} = \frac{x_1 + x_2 + x_3 + x_4 + x_5}{5}$$

Then the mean of the transformed data is the result of the equation shown below.

E43. If $\bar{x}$ is the mean of the original set of data, then the standard deviation is shown below.

   You know from E42 that the mean of the transformed data is $\bar{x} + c$. Then the standard deviation of the transformed data is shown below.

E44. Mean: 1.36
      Median: 0
      First quartile: 0
      Third quartile: 1

The *IQR* is 1, so the 8 values larger than $1 + 1.5(1) = 2.5$ are outliers. This results in an odd-looking boxplot with no median line and no whiskers.

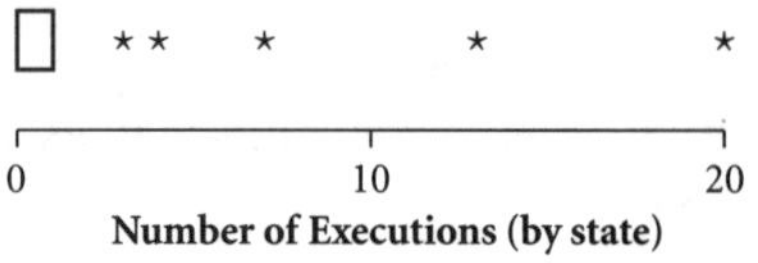

Number of Executions (by state)

Lesson 2.3, E42

$$\frac{(x_1 + c) + (x_2 + c) + (x_3 + c) + (x_4 + c) + (x_5 + c)}{5}$$

$$= \frac{x_1 + x_2 + x_3 + x_4 + x_5 + 5c}{5}$$

$$= \frac{x_1 + x_2 + x_3 + x_4 + x_5}{5} + \frac{5c}{5}$$

$$= \bar{x} + c$$

Lesson 2.3, E43

Standard Deviation of Original Data:

$$s = \sqrt{\frac{(x_1 - \bar{x})^2 + (x_2 - \bar{x})^2 + (x_3 - \bar{x})^2 + (x_4 - \bar{x})^2 + (x_5 - \bar{x})^2}{4}}$$

Standard Deviation of Transformed Data:

$$\sqrt{\frac{\big((x_1 + c)\big) - (\bar{x} + c)^2 + \big((x_2 + c) - (\bar{x} + c)\big)^2 + \big((x_3 + c) - (\bar{x} + c)\big)^2 + \big((x_4 + c) - (\bar{x} + c)\big)^2 + \big((x_5 + c) - (\bar{x} + c)\big)^2}{4}}$$

$$= \sqrt{\frac{(x_1 + c - \bar{x} - c)^2 + (x_2 + c - \bar{x} - c)^2 + (x_3 + c - \bar{x} - c)^2 + (x_4 + c - \bar{x} - c)^2 + (x_5 + c - \bar{x} - c)^2}{4}}$$

$$= \sqrt{\frac{(x_1 - \bar{x})^2 + (x_2 - \bar{x})^2 + (x_3 - \bar{x})^2 + (x_4 - \bar{x})^2 + (x_5 - \bar{x})^2}{4}}$$

$$= s$$

2.4 The Normal Distribution

Objectives

- to learn to convert values to z-scores (standardize)
- to learn to convert z-scores to values in the original units (unstandardize)
- to find areas under the standard normal curve
- to use a table of the normal distribution to estimate proportions and probabilities of events that come from a population that is normally distributed
- to find the value that is located at a given percentile of the normal distribution

Important Terms and Concepts

- standard normal curve
- z-scores or standard units

Lesson Planning

Class Time

Two to three days

Materials

None

Suggested Assignments

Classwork		
Essential	**Recommended**	**Optional**
D39, D40, D42, D43, D45, D46 P38–P42, P44, P46–P48	D38, D41, D44 P37, P43, P45	

Homework		
Essential	**Recommended**	**Optional**
E46–E48, E52, E54, E56	E45, E49–E51, E53, E55	

Lesson Notes: Solving the Unknown Problems and Calculator Use

With a graphing calculator, a student can circumvent most of the procedures in this section. How much of that process should still be taught in the introductory statistics course is an open question.

Consequently, your biggest decision in this lesson is deciding when to show students how to use their calculator to find areas under normal curves. If your students aren't taking the AP Statistics exam, once they understand the concept of a *z*-score as the number of standard deviations from the mean, you may want to move to the calculator right away. Specifically, once you finish P43, skip over P44–P45 and use the calculator from that point on (rather than *z*-scores and the table) to answer all questions.

Students who will be taking the AP Statistics exam should be able to work through the process step-by-step, including the use of the table, because they may be asked for the results of any one step of this process. However, it is even more important that they are able to use their calculator because it will be quicker and more accurate for most questions.

To find the area between the values x_1 and x_2 under a normal curve with mean μ and standard deviation σ on a TI-83, use the command

$$\text{normalcdf}(x_1, x_2, \mu, \sigma)$$

To find the value x in a normal distribution with mean μ and standard deviation σ that gives an area of P below x, use the command

$$\text{invNorm}(P, \mu, \sigma)$$

If you omit values for μ and σ, the calculator assumes they are 0 and 1.

Answers in this section may differ slightly depending on whether students use a calculator or the table of the normal distribution.

Discussion

D38. **a.** This is an unknown percentage problem.

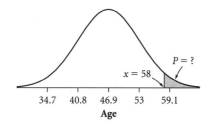

Practice

P37. **a.** This is an unknown percentage problem. You need to find the percentage of scores over 1300.

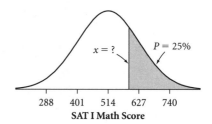

b. This is an unknown value problem—you must find the value, not the percentage. You need to find the value that cuts off the bottom 75% of the distribution.

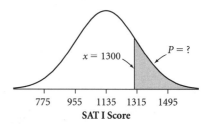

b. This is an unknown value problem. You need to find the age that cuts off the largest 2.5%.

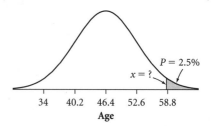

Lesson Notes: The Standard Normal Distribution

All normal distributions can be transformed to a normal distribution with mean 0 and standard deviation 1 by the *z* transformation,

$$z = \frac{x - mean}{SD}$$

That is, when you compute a *z*-score, you are rescaling so that the mean of the new distribution is 0 and the standard deviation is 1. A *z*-score, then, tells how many standard deviations from the mean a value lies. This distribution, pictured on the next page, is called the *standard normal distribution*.

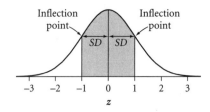

Inflection point — Inflection point

SD   SD

-3 -2 -1 0 1 2 3
z

Students should make a sketch of the standard normal curve before they do any calculations.

Table A on page 701 of the appendix of the student text gives the areas in this standard normal distribution. After converting to z-scores, students can use this table to find the proportion of values that fall into a given region of any normal distribution.

Discussion

D39. **a.** .8413 or 84.13%; .9943 or 99.43%
   b. .1587 or 15.87%; .0057 or 0.57%
   c. .9332 or 93.32%
   d. .6827 or 68.27% (.6826 using Table A)

D40. **a.** 0
   b. The lower quartile is the z-score that has 25% of the values below it. Looking in the center of the table, the z-score with a percentage closest to 25 is −0.67.
   c. A percentage of 95 lies right between z-scores of 1.64 and 1.65, so the best answer is z = 1.645.
   d. IQR = 1.349 or 1.34

Practice

P38. **a.** −0.47   **b.** −0.23
   c. 1.13   **d.** 1.555

P39. **a.** .0129   **b.** .0475
   c. .3446   **d.** .7881

P40. **a.** .9279 − .0721 = .8558 or 85.58%.
   b. .9987 − .0013 = .9974 or 99.74%.

P41. **a.** The z-score that has 5% of the values below it is −1.645, and the z-score that has 5% of the values above it is 1.645. So the interval is −1.645 to 1.645.
   b. −1.96 to 1.96

Lesson Notes: Standard Units

The use of z-scores, or standard units, for a comparison is appropriate whenever you have two comparable normally distributed variables with different means and/or standard deviations.

Unless the distributions are approximately normal, z-scores should not be used to compare two values in the distribution. Percentiles, however, can always be used. (See E51 on page 70 in the student book.)

Discussion

D41. **a.** $\dfrac{(200 - 80)}{60} = 2$ hours

   b. Subtract (recenter), and then divide (rescale). That is, how far from the exit? How many hours is that?

D42.
$$z_{heart} = \frac{90 - 289}{54} = -3.69$$
$$z_{cancer} = \frac{84 - 200}{31} = -3.74$$

The death rate for heart disease is 3.69 standard deviations below the mean. The death rate for cancer is 3.74 standard deviations below the mean. Thus, these rates are about equally extreme, but the death rate for cancer is slightly more extreme. (They are quite extreme because of Alaska's relatively young population.)

Practice

P42. The death rate for cancer is more standard deviations below the mean, so it is a bit more extreme.
$$z_{heart} = \frac{240 - 289}{54} = -0.91$$
$$z_{cancer} = \frac{166 - 200}{31} = -1.10$$

P43. **a.** The death rate for cancer is more standard deviations above the mean, so it is more extreme.
$$z_{heart} = \frac{365 - 289}{54} = 1.41$$
$$z_{cancer} = \frac{257 - 200}{31} = 1.84$$

   b. The death rate for heart disease in Colorado is more extreme than the death rate for cancer in Texas.
$$z_{heart} = \frac{184 - 289}{54} = -1.94$$
$$z_{cancer} = \frac{161 - 200}{31} = -1.26$$

P44. **a.** 2 **b.** 1 **c.** 1.5
        d. 3 **e.** −1 **f.** −2.5

P45. **a.** 30 **b.** 22
        c. 85 **d.** −9.5

Lesson Notes: Solving the Unknown Percentage Problem and the Unknown Value Problem

Discussion

D43. **a.** The *z*-score for the height 68 is $\frac{(68 - 70.1)}{2.7} = -0.78$. The area under the normal curve to the left of this point is .2177. Thus, about 21.77% of U.S. males between 18 and 24 are less than 68 inches tall.

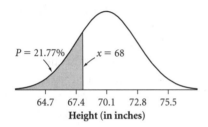

Height (in inches)

b. From part a, .2177 of the men are below the height of 68 inches. Similarly, the *z*-score for a height of 67 inches is −1.15, and so .1251 of the men are below that height. The proportion in between is .2177 − .1251 = .0926.

   So about .0926(13,000,000) = 1,203,800 are between the two heights.

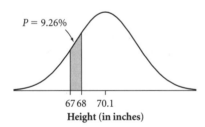

Height (in inches)

c. A percentile of 90 corresponds to a *z*-score of about 1.28. Using the formula,

$$x = mean + z \cdot SD = 70.1 + 1.28(2.7)$$
$$= 73.56$$

or, alternatively, solving

$$1.28 = \frac{x - 70.1}{2.7}$$
$$x = 73.56$$

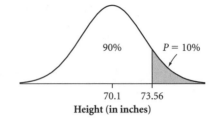

Height (in inches)

D44. The shape will not change. The mean will be $\frac{70.1}{12} \approx 5.84$ feet, and the *SD* will be $\frac{2.7}{12} = 0.225$ feet.

D45. 176 ± (1.645)30 or 126.65 mg/dl and 225.35 mg/dl.

Practice

P46. **a.** The *z*-score for the height 72 is $\frac{(72 - 70.1)}{2.7} = 0.70$. The area under the normal curve to the right of this point is $1 - .7580 = .2420$. Thus, about 24% of U.S. males between 18 and 24 are taller than 72 inches.

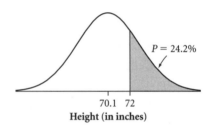

Height (in inches)

b. The *z*-score for the 35th percentile is −0.385. The height that corresponds to that *z*-score is

$$x = mean + z \cdot SD = 64.8 + (-0.385)2.5$$
$$\approx 63.84 \text{ inches}$$

P47. 1100 ± (1.96)180 or roughly 747 and 1453

Lesson Notes: Central Intervals for Normal Distributions

Discussion

Some textbooks call this the "Empirical Rule."

D46. **a.** 289 ± 1.645(54) or about 200 to 378
        b. 289 ± 1.96(54) or about 183 to 395
        c. 200 ± 1.645(31) or about 149 to 251

Practice

P48. **a.** The *z*-score is −0.91, which is not outside either interval.
        b. The *z*-score is −1.10, which is not outside either interval.

c. The z-score is −3.69, which is outside both intervals.

d. The z-score is −3.74, which is outside both intervals.

Exercises

E51 and E52 are important exercises to discuss as many students forget that z-scores can be used to estimate proportions only when the distribution is approximately normal.

E45.

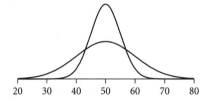

E46. 68%; 95%; 16%; 84%; 97.5%; 2.5%

E47. **a.**   **i.** .6340 (calculator: .6319)
  ii. .0392 (calculator: .0395)
  iii. .3085 (calculator: .3101)

b. The middle 95% of scores range from, approximately,

$$505 − 1.96(111) ≈ 287$$

to

$$505 + 1.96(111) ≈ 723$$

E48. The z-score that has an area of .80 below it is about $z = .84$.

Unstandardizing,

$$x = mean + z \cdot SD = 511 + .84(112) ≈ 605$$

The college should send letters to students who get 605 or more on the exam.

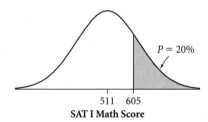

SAT I Math Score

E49. First, find the percentage of men who qualify.

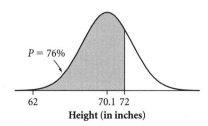

Height (in inches)

$$z = \frac{x − mean}{SD} = \frac{62 − 70.1}{2.7} = −3$$

$$z = \frac{x − mean}{SD} = \frac{72 − 70.1}{2.7} ≈ 0.70$$

The area between these z-scores is about .76. About 76% of men aged 18 to 24 in the United States meet the height qualifications to be a flight attendant for United Airlines.

Next, find the percentage of women who qualify.

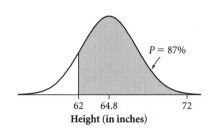

Height (in inches)

$$z = \frac{x − mean}{SD} = \frac{62 − 64.8}{2.5} = −1.12$$

$$z = \frac{x − mean}{SD} = \frac{72 − 64.8}{2.5} = 2.88$$

The area between these two z-scores is about .87.

About 87% of women aged 18 to 24 in the United States meet the height qualifications to be a flight attendant for United Airlines, a higher percentage than men.

E50. **a.** About .0000270786, or 0.00270786%, are as tall or taller than Karl Malone. There are only about 352 men aged 18 to 24 who are at least as tall.

b. About .001717, or 0.1717%, are as tall or taller than Michael Jordan. There are only about 22,324 men aged 18 to 24 who are at least as tall.

c. About .000000017136, or 0.0000017136%, are as tall or taller than Shaquille O'Neal. You would expect to find less than 1 man (or .22) this tall in the 18- to 24-year-old age group.

d. The estimates will be too small.

E51. You cannot use the normal distribution to solve this problem because the distribution of ages of cars is not approximately normal. In fact, it is strongly skewed right.

E52. **a.** The distribution is probably skewed right because it's not possible for the length of a reign to be much more than 1 standard deviation below the mean.

b. The z-score for 0 is $\frac{(0 - 18.5)}{15.4} = -1.20$, so about .1151 of the reigns.

c. If all values in the distribution must be positive and two standard deviations or less below the mean is less than 0, the distribution isn't approximately normal.

E53. **a.** about 145 points

b. about 25 points

c. From the graph, the middle 95% of the values appear to lie between about 90 and about 200. Using the mean and standard deviation from parts a and b, this interval is about 95 to 195.

d. The z-score for 150 is 0.20, and the area to the right of this point is .4207. The z-score for 190 is 1.80, and the area to the right of this point is .0359. A weakness here is that next year's teams may not look like a random sample from the set of teams since 1939. Modern teams place more emphasis on scoring than did the teams from an earlier era.

E54. **a.** .1587

b. 8.16

c. Solving $-1.34 = \frac{6 - mean}{3}$, you get mean = 10.02.

d. Solving $0.25 = \frac{12 - 10}{SD}$, you get $SD = 8$.

E55. **a.** The z-scores for the quartiles are ± 0.67. Thus, $Q_1 = 6.65$ and $Q_3 = 13.35$.

b. The mean must be 150 because it lies midway between the quartiles in a normal distribution. Then $SD \approx 44.78$.

c. Solving $-0.67 = \frac{100 - mean}{10}$, you get mean = 106.7. Then, because the quartiles are symmetric about the mean, $Q_3 = 113.4$.

d. Because the quartiles are symmetric about the mean, $Q_1 = 9$. Then $SD \approx 1.5$.

E56. **a.** Using the plot, a score of 425 appears to be at about the 22nd percentile. Assuming a normal distribution, the z-score for 425 is -0.72, giving a percentile of 23.58. These are fairly close.

b. From Display 2.55, the 40th percentile appears to be about 480. The 40th percentile under a standard normal curve has a z-score of -0.25, which translates to a test score of

$x = mean + z \cdot SD \approx 505 - 0.25(111) \approx 477$

Again, these are quite close, which gives some evidence in support of the normality of the scores.

c. Answers will vary somewhat. From the plot, the median appears to be about 510. In a normal distribution, the median should be close to the mean, or 505. The mean and median here are close.

d. The quartiles are about 430 and about 585, giving an *IQR* of about $585 - 430 = 155$.

From the standard normal curve, the quartiles have z-scores of approximately -0.67 and $+0.67$ and the median has a z-score of 0. Thus, the approximate quartiles for the exam scores with mean 505 and standard deviation 111 are

$$Q_1 = 505 - 0.67(111) \approx 431$$
$$Q_3 = 505 + 0.67(111) \approx 579$$

The normal model is looking good!

Review

You may wish to save some or all of these exercises to use as review before the AP Statistics exam.

Review Exercises

E57. **a.**
```
Stem-and-leaf of Number     N = 51
Leaf Unit = 1.0

    16    0   0000000111122244
    25    0   566778899
   (5)    1   00013
    21    1   5
    20    2   244
    17    2   66
    15    3   03
    13    3   579
    10    4   2
     9    4   58
     7    5   14
     5    5
     5    6
     5    6
     5    7   2
     4    7   69
   HI  95, 232
        0|5 stands for 5 tornadoes
```

b. Minimum:　　0

Q_1:　　　　2

Median:　　10

Q_3:　　　35

Maximum:　232

c. Outliers fall below $2 - 1.5(35 - 2) = -47.5$ or above $35 + 1.5(35 - 2) = 84.5$. There are two outliers, Florida and Texas.

d.

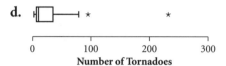

e. Both plots show the strong skewness in the data and the outlier of Texas. In the stemplot, you can see that half the states have less than 10 tornadoes. The cleanness of the boxplot makes it clear how much of an outlier Texas actually is. (Of course, it is a very large state, which helps explain why it is an outlier.) However, you can't see from the boxplot at all that so many states have at most 1 tornado. Because the stemplot has a reasonable number of values in it and is consequently easy to read while carrying almost the complete values, it is reasonable to select it as the most informative.

f. The distribution of numbers of tornadoes is strongly skewed right with two outliers, Florida at 95 and Texas at 232. The median number of tornadoes is 10 with the middle half of the states having between 2 and 35.

E58. Outliers would lie below $1170 - 1.5(1340 - 1170) = 915$ or above $1340 + 1.5(1340 - 1170) = 1595$.

E59. **a.** Median:　23 or 24 cents

b. Q_1:　　about 10 cents

　　Q_3:　　about 70 cents

　　IQR:　　$70 - 10 = 60$ cents

c. Skewed right

d. No, because the data are obviously skewed, as you can see from the summary computed in parts a and b.

E60. **I.** B　　**II.** D

III. A　　**IV.** C

E61. Important warning in this exercise: Percentiles are not *score/total* but a measure of position relative to the number of scores.

a. The mean of the scores on Test I is 15.5, and the standard deviation is 3.028. The score of 19 has a z-score of 1.16 and is at the 90th percentile, relative to the other 9 scores.

b. The mean of the scores on Test II is 6.4, and the standard deviation is 8.708. The score of 18 has a z-score of 1.33 but is only at the 80th percentile, relative to the other 9 scores.

c. Answers will vary, and rightfully so. The student who got a 19 on Test I did better than all but one other student in the class. However, the student who got an 18 on Test II did *much* better than all but two students in the class.

E62. **a.** The state with the lowest average income in dollars in 1980 had an average income of $6,926.

b. There are no outliers for 1980. There is at least one outlier for 1994 because $Q_3 + 1.5(IQR) = 22{,}542 + 5{,}598 = \$28{,}140$, which is less than the maximum of $30,721. Thus, the state with the maximum income is an outlier. There may be other states as well on the high end that are outliers.

c. No. Alabama remains below the lower quartile of the distribution, but you cannot say exactly where in the lowest quarter it lies. It is tempting to find Alabama's relative position using z-scores, but there is no indication that these incomes are normally distributed and that it is appropriate to use z-scores for comparison only in that case.

E63. The stems represent the first three digits of the year. The leaves represent the final digit of the year. The distribution of record lows is relatively uniform over the years since 1890. The distribution of record highs is also relatively uniform, except for a spike during the 1930s, when records were set for low temperatures in many states. Those years were also overrepresented in record highs. The center and spread of the two distributions are about the same.

E64. **a.** Each value is the instructional time in mathematics in a given school. (Only schools that have all 9th graders in the same mathematics course are plotted.)

b. Norway and Singapore have no variation by school in instructional time in mathematics. These countries may mandate instructional time for every school in the country.

c. The median instructional time in mathematics is about the same for the United States as the overall median. In addition, the variation from school to school is about average for the countries in the plot. There are no schools in the United States with an unusually large or small amount of instructional time.

E65. a. Guesses may vary. In actual fact, Region 1 is Africa, Region 2 is South and Central America, Region 3 is Asia, and Region 4 is Europe. The outlier for Asia is Bangladesh. The outlier for Africa is Angola (Egypt is the country with 99% in Africa).

b. Distributions 1, 2, and 4 are skewed left.

c. The dot plots are in the same order as the boxplots, A being Africa, B South and Central America, C Asia, and D Europe.

d. The outlier shown in the boxplot in Region 1 doesn't appear to be an outlier in the dot plot. Region 4 does not look skewed in the dot plot even though it appears so in the boxplot. The number of countries plotted is small, and the values vary a lot, so the locations of the quartiles might change quite a bit with small changes in the data. Dot plots give the better picture here.

E66. The mean grade is 2.98 with a standard deviation of 1.33.

E67. a. The median number of deaths is 47. Half of the cities have fewer than 47 pedestrian deaths per year, and half have more.

b. The quartiles are 28.5 and 88.5. An outlier is a city whose number of deaths exceeds $88.5 + 1.5(88.5 - 28.5) = 178.5$ or is less than $28.5 - 1.5(88.5 - 28.5) = -61.5$, which is impossible. There are three outliers, Chicago, Los Angeles, and New York. One explanation is the large populations these cities have; these are the three largest cities in the United States.

c. Student plots and explanations will vary. A stemplot is a very good choice. It reveals the three outliers and shows that the distribution is skewed right.

```
Stem-and-leaf of NumDeath N = 41
Leaf Unit = 1.0
   2    1   79
  11    2   023457889
  19    3   33456777
  (3)   4   378
  19    5   118
  16    6   6
  15    7   69
  13    8   045
  10    9   268
   7   10   017
   4   11
   4   12   0
HI 180, 299, 310
        11|7 represents 17 deaths
```

d. Note what happened in part b. If the data were presented in rates per 100,000 population, these three cities might not be outliers. In fact, their rates of pedestrian death might be relatively small.

E68. a. 1267

b. Bacon himself

c. For Bacon and for Connery, $n = 263,484$. The mean Bacon number is 2.8. The mean Connery number is only 2.6. Connery is the better center. Also, Connery has only 974 actors who are outliers, that is, those with Connery numbers of 5–7 (not counting the outlier "0," himself), whereas Bacon has 2237 outliers (those with Bacon numbers of 5–8) not counting himself. That is, there are more people at a far remove from Bacon than at a far remove from Connery.

d. Students should realize that the numbers must be equal. In fact, it is 2: Sean Connery was in *The Untouchables* (1987) with Kevin Costner, who was in *JFK* (1991) with Kevin Bacon.

E69. a. Except for a slight bulge around .220, the batting averages look quite normal in their distribution.

b. The mean is about .270, and the standard deviation is about .030.

c. about .200 to .320

E70. **a.** Again, the histogram of batting averages looks quite normal in shape with center at about .260. The standard deviation is approximately .040. Quite a few regular players hit under .200 in the National League. In fact, .200 has a z-score of -1.5, and this is about the 7th percentile of a normal density curve.

b. The batting averages in both leagues have distributions that are approximately normal in shape. The American League has a higher mean (by about .010) and less spread.

c. As seen above, the z-score corresponding to .200 in the National League is $z = -1.5$. The corresponding batting average, x, in the American League would still be 1.5 standard deviations below the mean, or

$$x = .270 - (1.5)(.030) = .225$$

E71. **a.**

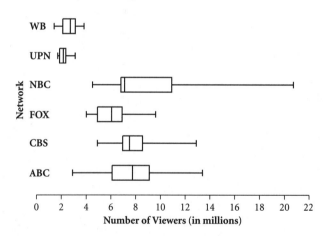

b. These boxplots are made with Fathom.

E72. No, this is true only for normal distributions. For example, the set of values $\{2, 2, 4, 6, 8, 8\}$ is symmetric and has mean and median both equal to 5. The standard deviation is about 2.76. Only two, or one-third, of the values are within one standard deviation of the mean.

E73. There are many possible responses. An example is $\{1, 1, 1, 1, 1, 2, 2, 10\}$, which has mean 2.375 and standard deviation of about 3.11. One standard deviation below the mean is less than 0.

E74. **a.** Developing countries have lower life expectancies than do developed countries. Thus, Region 1 must be Africa (developing countries, for the most part) and Region 3 must be Europe (developed countries). The Middle East, Region 2, has a mixture of developed and developing countries.

b. A is for Region 3 (Europe); B is for Region 1 (Africa); C is for Region 2 (Middle East).

E75. **a.** With *Seinfeld*, the midrange is $\frac{(2.32 + 76.26)}{2} = 39.29$. Without *Seinfeld*, the midrange is $\frac{(2.32 + 58.53)}{2} = 30.425$. The midrange is not resistant and is extremely sensitive to outliers because it is computed using only the maximum and minimum.

b. The total of the ratings without the *Seinfeld* episode is $(101)11.187 - 76.26 = 1053.627$. So the mean rating is $\frac{1053.627}{100} \approx 10.54$.

E76. **a.** Students will need to remove the top 2 longevities and the bottom 2 longevities from the data set and compute the mean of the remaining 35 animals. The trimmed mean is 30.5114.

b. Yes, because most outliers are removed before computing the trimmed mean.

Table A   Standard Normal Probabilities

Table entry for *z* is the probability lying below *z*.

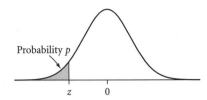

Probability *p*

z	.00	.01	.02	.03	.04	.05	.06	.07	.08	.09
−3.8	.0001	.0001	.0001	.0001	.0001	.0001	.0001	.0001	.0001	.0001
−3.7	.0001	.0001	.0001	.0001	.0001	.0001	.0001	.0001	.0001	.0001
−3.6	.0002	.0002	.0001	.0001	.0001	.0001	.0001	.0001	.0001	.0001
−3.5	.0002	.0002	.0002	.0002	.0002	.0002	.0002	.0002	.0002	.0002
−3.4	.0003	.0003	.0003	.0003	.0003	.0003	.0003	.0003	.0003	.0002
−3.3	.0005	.0005	.0005	.0004	.0004	.0004	.0004	.0004	.0004	.0003
−3.2	.0007	.0007	.0006	.0006	.0006	.0006	.0006	.0005	.0005	.0005
−3.1	.0010	.0009	.0009	.0009	.0008	.0008	.0008	.0008	.0007	.0007
−3.0	.0013	.0013	.0013	.0012	.0012	.0011	.0011	.0011	.0010	.0010
−2.9	.0019	.0018	.0018	.0017	.0016	.0016	.0015	.0015	.0014	.0014
−2.8	.0026	.0025	.0024	.0023	.0023	.0022	.0021	.0021	.0020	.0019
−2.7	.0035	.0034	.0033	.0032	.0031	.0030	.0029	.0028	.0027	.0026
−2.6	.0047	.0045	.0044	.0043	.0041	.0040	.0039	.0038	.0037	.0036
−2.5	.0062	.0060	.0059	.0057	.0055	.0054	.0052	.0051	.0049	.0048
−2.4	.0082	.0080	.0078	.0075	.0073	.0071	.0069	.0068	.0066	.0064
−2.3	.0107	.0104	.0102	.0099	.0096	.0094	.0091	.0089	.0087	.0084
−2.2	.0139	.0136	.0132	.0129	.0125	.0122	.0119	.0116	.0113	.0110
−2.1	.0179	.0174	.0170	.0166	.0162	.0158	.0154	.0150	.0146	.0143
−2.0	.0228	.0222	.0217	.0212	.0207	.0202	.0197	.0192	.0188	.0183
−1.9	.0287	.0281	.0274	.0268	.0262	.0256	.0250	.0244	.0239	.0233
−1.8	.0359	.0351	.0344	.0336	.0329	.0322	.0314	.0307	.0301	.0294
−1.7	.0446	.0436	.0427	.0418	.0409	.0401	.0392	.0384	.0375	.0367
−1.6	.0548	.0537	.0526	.0516	.0505	.0495	.0485	.0475	.0465	.0455
−1.5	.0668	.0655	.0643	.0630	.0618	.0606	.0594	.0582	.0571	.0559
−1.4	.0808	.0793	.0778	.0764	.0749	.0735	.0721	.0708	.0694	.0681
−1.3	.0968	.0951	.0934	.0918	.0901	.0885	.0869	.0853	.0838	.0823
−1.2	.1151	.1131	.1112	.1093	.1075	.1056	.1038	.1020	.1003	.0985
−1.1	.1357	.1335	.1314	.1292	.1271	.1251	.1230	.1210	.1190	.1170
−1.0	.1587	.1562	.1539	.1515	.1492	.1469	.1446	.1423	.1401	.1379
−0.9	.1841	.1814	.1788	.1762	.1736	.1711	.1685	.1660	.1635	.1611
−0.8	.2119	.2090	.2061	.2033	.2005	.1977	.1949	.1922	.1894	.1867
−0.7	.2420	.2389	.2358	.2327	.2296	.2266	.2236	.2206	.2177	.2148
−0.6	.2743	.2709	.2676	.2643	.2611	.2578	.2546	.2514	.2483	.2451
−0.5	.3085	.3050	.3015	.2981	.2946	.2912	.2877	.2843	.2810	.2776
−0.4	.3446	.3409	.3372	.3336	.3300	.3264	.3228	.3192	.3156	.3121
−0.3	.3821	.3783	.3745	.3707	.3669	.3632	.3594	.3557	.3520	.3483
−0.2	.4207	.4168	.4129	.4090	.4052	.4013	.3974	.3936	.3897	.3859
−0.1	.4602	.4562	.4522	.4483	.4443	.4404	.4364	.4325	.4286	.4247
0.0	.5000	.4960	.4920	.4880	.4840	.4801	.4761	.4721	.4681	.4641

Table A   Standard Normal Probabilities (continued)

Table entry for z is the
probability lying below z.

Probability p

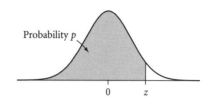

z	.00	.01	.02	.03	.04	.05	.06	.07	.08	.09
0.0	.5000	.5040	.5080	.5120	.5160	.5199	.5239	.5279	.5319	.5359
0.1	.5398	.5438	.5478	.5517	.5557	.5596	.5636	.5675	.5714	.5753
0.2	.5793	.5832	.5871	.5910	.5948	.5987	.6026	.6064	.6103	.6141
0.3	.6179	.6217	.6255	.6293	.6331	.6368	.6406	.6443	.6480	.6517
0.4	.6554	.6591	.6628	.6664	.6700	.6736	.6772	.6808	.6844	.6879
0.5	.6915	.6950	.6985	.7019	.7054	.7088	.7123	.7157	.7190	.7224
0.6	.7257	.7291	.7324	.7357	.7389	.7422	.7454	.7486	.7517	.7549
0.7	.7580	.7611	.7642	.7673	.7704	.7734	.7764	.7794	.7823	.7852
0.8	.7881	.7910	.7939	.7967	.7995	.8023	.8051	.8078	.8106	.8133
0.9	.8159	.8186	.8212	.8238	.8264	.8289	.8315	.8340	.8365	.8389
1.0	.8413	.8438	.8461	.8485	.8508	.8531	.8554	.8577	.8599	.8621
1.1	.8643	.8665	.8686	.8708	.8729	.8749	.8770	.8790	.8810	.8830
1.2	.8849	.8869	.8888	.8907	.8925	.8944	.8962	.8980	.8997	.9015
1.3	.9032	.9049	.9066	.9082	.9099	.9115	.9131	.9147	.9162	.9177
1.4	.9192	.9207	.9222	.9236	.9251	.9265	.9279	.9292	.9306	.9319
1.5	.9332	.9345	.9357	.9370	.9382	.9394	.9406	.9418	.9429	.9441
1.6	.9452	.9463	.9474	.9484	.9495	.9505	.9515	.9525	.9535	.9545
1.7	.9554	.9564	.9573	.9582	.9591	.9599	.9608	.9616	.9625	.9633
1.8	.9641	.9649	.9656	.9664	.9671	.9678	.9686	.9693	.9699	.9706
1.9	.9713	.9719	.9726	.9732	.9738	.9744	.9750	.9756	.9761	.9767
2.0	.9772	.9778	.9783	.9788	.9793	.9798	.9803	.9808	.9812	.9817
2.1	.9821	.9826	.9830	.9834	.9838	.9842	.9846	.9850	.9854	.9857
2.2	.9861	.9864	.9868	.9871	.9875	.9878	.9881	.9884	.9887	.9890
2.3	.9893	.9896	.9898	.9901	.9904	.9906	.9909	.9911	.9913	.9916
2.4	.9918	.9920	.9922	.9925	.9927	.9929	.9931	.9932	.9934	.9936
2.5	.9938	.9940	.9941	.9943	.9945	.9946	.9948	.9949	.9951	.9952
2.6	.9953	.9955	.9956	.9957	.9959	.9960	.9961	.9962	.9963	.9964
2.7	.9965	.9966	.9967	.9968	.9969	.9970	.9971	.9972	.9973	.9974
2.8	.9974	.9975	.9976	.9977	.9977	.9978	.9979	.9979	.9980	.9981
2.9	.9981	.9982	.9982	.9983	.9984	.9984	.9985	.9985	.9986	.9986
3.0	.9987	.9987	.9987	.9988	.9988	.9989	.9989	.9989	.9990	.9990
3.1	.9990	.9991	.9991	.9991	.9992	.9992	.9992	.9992	.9993	.9993
3.2	.9993	.9993	.9994	.9994	.9994	.9994	.9994	.9995	.9995	.9995
3.3	.9995	.9995	.9995	.9996	.9996	.9996	.9996	.9996	.9996	.9997
3.4	.9997	.9997	.9997	.9997	.9997	.9997	.9997	.9997	.9997	.9998
3.5	.9998	.9998	.9998	.9998	.9998	.9998	.9998	.9998	.9998	.9998
3.6	.9998	.9998	.9999	.9999	.9999	.9999	.9999	.9999	.9999	.9999
3.7	.9999	.9999	.9999	.9999	.9999	.9999	.9999	.9999	.9999	.9999
3.8	.9999	.9999	.9999	.9999	.9999	.9999	.9999	.9999	.9999	.9999

RELATIONSHIPS BETWEEN TWO QUANTITATIVE VARIABLES

Overview

Goals

The overall goal of Chapter 3 is to develop a systematic way to uncover information about bivariate (two variable) data. We can pursue this goal as we did in Chapter 2 for univariate data: by using graphical displays and then finding a measure of center and spread to summarize the distribution. The basic plot used is the scatterplot. The basic summary measures are the regression line (which can be thought of as the measure of center) and the correlation (which can be thought of as the measure of spread).

The five sections of this chapter will teach students

- to make a scatterplot and determine what its shape tells about the relationship between the two variables
- to find and interpret the equation of the least squares regression line
- to find and interpret the correlation coefficient
- to use diagnostic tools such as residual plots to determine whether the linear regression line is appropriate or a transformation is needed first
- to make transformations that re-express a curved relationship as a linear one

Content Overview

Statistical Software

Statistical software is important for this chapter—one of the most computationally intensive in this textbook. Students can use statistical software to construct scatterplots quickly, accurately, and flexibly. But more to the instructional point, they can use the software to change the location of points and then observe the corresponding change in the correlation and the regression line to further their understanding of the properties of these two measures.

A Note on Terminology

The language of correlation and regression has not been standardized. The words in the following chart are sometimes used interchangeably.

Terminology

Concept	Words Used
A bivariate relationship	relationship
	association
	correlation (used only when the trend is linear)
A summary line	regression line
	trend line
	model
	fitted line
	least squares line
The degree of spread of the points about the line	correlation
	measure of strength of the relationship
	noise
	scatter
	variation
	precision

Comparing One Variable and Two Variable Distributions

In comparing two variable distributions with one variable distributions, it is sometimes helpful to think of the parallels between exploring a distribution and exploring a relationship. You may want to discuss the following table with your students, which you can show them on the overhead projector or give them as a handout.

	Chapter 2 One Variable	Chapter 3 Two Variables
Key Idea	Distribution	Relationship (association)
Plots	Dot plot	Scatterplot
	Stemplot	
	Boxplot	
	Histogram	
Shape	Unimodal/bimodal	Linear or curved
	Symmetry/skewness	Varying strength
	Clusters, gaps, and outliers	Clusters, gaps, and outliers
Ideal Shape	Normal	Linear (oval/ellipse)
Measure of Center	Mean	Regression line
	Median	
Measure of Spread from the Center	Standard deviation	Correlation
	Interquartile range	

Time Required

Traditional Schedule			Block	4 x 4 Block
Section 3.1				
1–2 days	Day 1	Describing a scatterplot	1 day	1 long
	Day 2	Summary, exercises		
Section 3.2				
2–3 days	Day 1	Activity 3.1, lines as summaries and prediction	2 days	1 long, 1 short
	Day 2	Least squares regression		
	Day 3	Summary, exercises		
Section 3.3				
2–3 days	Day 1	Activity 3.2, formula, relation to slope	2 days	2 long
	Day 2	Cause and effect, interpreting r^2		
	Day 3	Regression to the mean, summary, exercises		
Section 3.4				
1–2 days	Day 1	Activity 3.3, influence, residual plots	1.5 days	1 long, 1 short
	Day 2	Summary, exercises		
Section 3.5				
3–4 days	Day 1	Activity 3.4, power transformations, log-log transformations	3 days	2 long, 1 short
	Day 2	Log transformations		
	Day 3	Exponential growth and decay		
	Day 4	Activity 3.5, summary, exercises		
Review				
1–2 days			1.5 days	1 long, 1 short

Materials

Section 3.1: None

Section 3.2: For Activity 3.1, a ruler with a millimeter scale and a textbook for each pair of students

Section 3.3: For Activity 3.2, a measuring tape, a yardstick, or a meterstick for each pair of students

Section 3.4: For Activity 3.3, a piece of paper for recording data

Section 3.5: For Activity 3.4, a copy of the sheet of triangles (Display 3.80) for each student. For Activity 3.5, a paper cup and 200 pennies for each student (or each pair of students).

Suggested Assignments

Classwork

Section	Essential	Recommended	Optional
3.1	D1, D2 P1	P2	
3.2	Activity 3.1 D3–D5, D7 P3–P5, P7, P8	D6 P6, P9	
3.3	D8, D10, D11, D14, D15 P10–P12, P14–P16	Activity 3.2 D9, D12, D13, D16, D17 P13, P17	D18–D22 P18, P19
3.4	Activity 3.3 D23–D29 P21–P23	P20	
3.5	Activity 3.4, Activity 3.5 D30–D33, D35, D37, D40–D42 P24–P26, P28, P30–P34	D34, D36, D38, D39, D43, D44 P27, P29	

Homework

Section	Essential	Recommended	Optional
3.1	E1, E5	E2, E4, E9	E3, E6–E8
3.2	E11, E12, E16	E10, E13, E14, E21, E22	E15, E17–E20
3.3	E23, E25–E27, E29, E30, E33, E37	E24, E31, E32	E28, E34–E36, E38, E39
3.4	E40, E41, E43, E44, E46–E48	E42, E45, E51, E52	E49, E50
3.5	E53, E54, E56, E58, E60, E62	E59, E61	E55, E57, E63
Review	E64, E66, E67, E70, E71, E73, E75	E65, E68, E72, E74, E78, E79	E69, E76, E77, E80–E84

3.1 Scatterplots

Objectives

- to make a scatterplot and describe its basic shape in terms of linearity, curvature, clusters, and outliers
- to describe whether the trend in a scatterplot is positive or negative
- to describe whether the strength of the relationship is strong, moderate, or weak and whether the strength is constant across all values of x
- to decide whether the pattern in a scatterplot can be generalized to other cases and to propose possible explanations for the pattern

Important Terms and Concepts

- bivariate data
- scatterplot
- *shape of a cluster on a scatterplot:* linear or curved
- *trend:* positive or negative

- *strength of an association or relationship:* strong, moderate, or weak
- constant strength versus varying strength

Lesson Planning

Class Time

One to two days

Materials

None

Suggested Assignments

Classwork		
Essential	**Recommended**	**Optional**
D1, D2 P1	P2	

Homework		
Essential	**Recommended**	**Optional**
E1, E5	E2, E4, E9	E3, E6–E8

Lesson Notes: Interpreting Scatterplots

Discussion

D1. **a.** Display 3.1 illustrates the commonsense idea that people born earlier typically become employed before people who were born later. Display 3.2 shows the same idea but uses *age* instead of *birth year*. A larger birth year means a smaller age, so the relationship in Display 3.2 is the reverse of Display 3.1: Older people were hired earlier and younger people are hired later, so the association is negative.

b. All the points are in the lower-right half of the plot because people cannot be hired until they are about 18 years old. Specifically, a person's year of birth must be at least 18 years before the year of hire so all points (but one) are below the line $y = x - 18$. The one point below this diagonal line is a person who was hired into the company at a very young age during the 1940s. Although there is a lot of variation, in general people were born 25 or 30 years before they were hired.

c. No, this is not correct. The ages plotted are not the ages of the employees when they were hired but their age when layoffs began. This idea will be explored further in E5.

Lesson Notes: Describing the Pattern in a Scatterplot

Linearity

It is often very difficult for students to get used to the idea that any scatterplot where the points fall fairly uniformly within an oval is called "linear." Linear does not mean that all points lie on or even near a line. For example, the points in the next scatterplot have a linear relationship even though they are not clustered closely about the line.

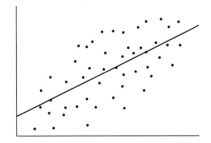

On the other hand, the points on this next scatterplot do *not* follow a linear pattern even though they are clustered rather closely to the line. This pattern is curved.

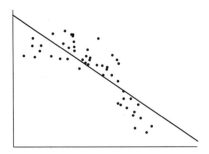

Outliers in Two-Variable Relationships

The question of what is an outlier in a scatterplot is more complicated than with univariate data, where we could use the $Q_1 - 1.5 \cdot IQR$ or $Q_3 + 1.5 \cdot IQR$ rule as a guideline for identifying possible outliers. There are several kinds of outliers in a scatterplot:

- a point with an extreme value of x or an extreme value of y or both
- a point that does not follow the general trend

In this next plot, the point represented by the **x** is an outlier in the sense that it has an extreme x-value. However, its y-value is not extreme and this point follows the curved pattern.

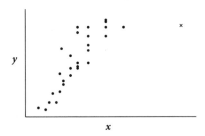

In the next plot, the point represented by the **x** has neither an extreme x-value nor an extreme y-value. However, it does not follow the general trend and is considered an outlier.

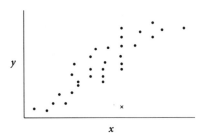

Varying Strength (Heteroscedasticity)

Instead of using the word "heteroscedasticity," you can substitute "fan-shaped" or other synonyms for the word. But students like the way this word sounds, and it is fun to use in class. It is pronounced just as it is spelled: "hetero-sce-das-ticity," where "sce" is pronounced like the "si" part of "sit" and "das" is pronounced so it rhymes with "class."

If a plot is not heteroscedastic, it is homoscedastic, which means "having the same variance." (See page 72.)

Discussion

D2. **a.** For these data, the cases are the states and the variables are the number of people per 1000 living in dorms and the proportion of the state population living in urban areas.

The shape of the cluster is linear (roughly oval or elliptical), except for four points (VT, WV, RI, and MA) that lie relatively far away from the main body of data. Vermont, a rural state, has a large number of colleges and a higher dorm proportion than would be anticipated. Rhode Island and Massachusetts also have a relatively high proportion living in dorms, but they are essentially urban states. West Virginia is a highly rural state with a moderate proportion of dorm residents.

The trend is negative, as a larger proportion of people living in urban areas tends to mean a smaller proportion in dorms.

There is a lot of variability in dorm proportions for any particular proportion living in urban areas, and thus the strength of the association between the two variables is only moderate. Other than the four apparent outliers, the strength is relatively constant across all values of x.

This scatterplot shows the data for all of the 50 states, so there is no larger population to generalize to. What you see is all there is for this particular year. However, it is

reasonable to generalize to a previous or subsequent year.

A possible explanation for this pattern is that states with a high proportion of the population living in urban areas also have a high proportion of their colleges located in urban areas. In an urban area, there is little need for students to live in dorms. They can commute from home or get off-campus housing in nearby apartments. Thus, for highly urbanized states, a lower proportion of students need to live in dorms.

b. The positive trend in the original data comes from the fact that states with a large number of people tend to have a large number of colleges and universities and a large number of people living in urban areas. A possible explanation for the negative trend in the proportion data is given in part a.

Practice

P1. **a.** You may have to remind students that a scatterplot without labels and units on the axes is meaningless. Emphasize the importance of appropriate labeling.

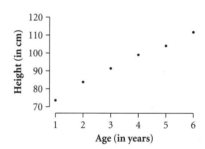

b. These data are not very interesting to describe. The x-axis shows ages from 1 to 6 years, and the y-axis shows an average height of children at each age. The shape is linear, the trend is positive, and the strength is very strong. That is, the scatterplot shows a very strong positive linear trend. Students may mention that the average child grows about 8 cm per year.

Describing Bivariate Data

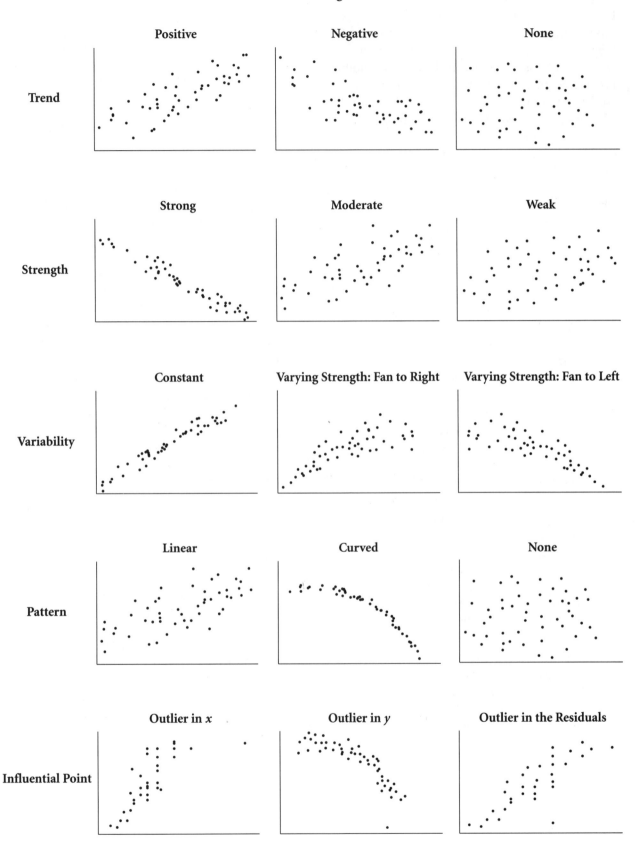

c. The linear trend could reasonably be expected to hold for another year. However, *height* could not be expected to increase at this rate to age 50, as people typically stop growing around age 20.

d. In the background, there is something called "growing up" that happens over time during the early years of life. That is, an increase in age is associated with an increase in height.

P2. **a.** The worst record for baggage handling during this period is America West, and United has the lowest on-time percentage among the airlines.

b. Airlines with a high percentage of on-time arrivals and a low rate of mishandled baggage would fall in the upper left of the plot. Thus, Delta is "best" for mishandled baggage; Northwest is best for percentage on-time arrivals.

c. False. United's baggage mishandling rate of 7.6 was not twice Southwest's rate of a little over 5.03. It appears to be twice because the scale on the *x*-axis starts at 3.5, not 0.

d. The relationship between the two variables is negative and moderate. The negative relationship shows that an airline that is "bad" on one variable tends to be "bad" on the other as well.

e. No. These are the largest carriers in the United States. (The airlines included in this plot are all of the U.S. carriers with at least 1% of total domestic scheduled-service passenger revenues.) The other airlines that might be added would be small, regional carriers. There is no reason to expect their pattern to be the same as that of the large national airlines. If we were to plot these same airlines for the previous or following year, it would probably look much the same but would likely be quite different from a plot of similar variables for 10 years ago. At the time this teacher's guide went to press, United had the best on-time record.

Exercises

E1. Plot a shows a positive relationship that is moderately strong and linear. There is greater variation at the smaller values of *x* than there is at the larger values of *x*, so there is varying strength. Some students may see, instead, a strong relationship with several outliers above the general trend.

Plot b shows a negative relationship that is moderately strong and linear, again with larger variation at the smaller values of *x*. Some students may see a strong negative trend with several outliers below the general trend.

Plot c shows a positive relationship that is moderate and linear. There is one point that lies a short distance from the bulk of the data.

Plot d shows a negative relationship that is moderate and linear. Again, there is one outlier.

Plot e shows a positive relationship that is strong and linear. As students will learn, the one outlier has dramatic influence on the strength of this relationship.

Plot f shows a negative relationship that is very strong and curved. Again, one point lies in the general pattern but far away from the remainder of the data, which accentuates the strong relationship. Another outlier lies below the bulk of the data on the left.

Plot g shows a negative relationship that is strong and curved. The two points at either end of the array accentuate the curvature.

Plot h shows a positive relationship that is strong and curved. Again, the outlier on the extreme right accentuates the curved pattern and would have dramatic influence on where a trend line might be placed.

E2. **a.** Positive and strong: As eggs get bigger, both length and width increase proportionally.

b. Positive and moderate: Most students tend to score relatively high on both parts of the exam or score relatively low on both parts of the exam.

c. Positive and strong: Trees produce one new ring each year.

d. Positive and strong (but curved): The area is equal to the square of a side.

e. Positive and strong: The number of representatives is proportional to the population of a state.

f. Positive and weak: Large countries tend to have large populations, but there are notable exceptions such as Canada and Australia. Also, some small countries in area have very large populations, such as Indonesia.

g. Negative and strong (but curved): Winning times tend to improve (get smaller) over the years.

E3. **a.** ii

b. iv (The larger states—mainly in the West—tend to have fewer people per square mile.)

c. iii

d. i (Heavier cars tend to get lower gas mileage.)

E4. **a.** North Dakota 4% and Iowa 5%; about 81% of New Jersey and Connecticut students took the SAT, and they averaged 513 and 509, respectively.

b. The overall trend is negative, moderately strong, and curved. The white space in the middle of the scatterplot suggests two groups of states—one with low percentages and high average scores and another with high percentages and low average scores. There is one state that stands out from the rest—West Virginia, with only 19% taking the SAT and a relatively low average of 511.

c. Yes, the distribution of the percentage taking the SAT looks bimodal because there is a cluster of percentages below 10 and a second around 60 to 70. Ask students to visualize all of the points dropping onto the x-axis so that they can see this distribution. A histogram of percentages is shown here.

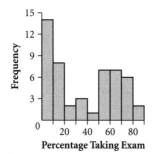

Percentage Taking Exam

The distribution of SAT scores is possibly bimodal. There appears to be a cluster of scores around 500 and another cluster around 560. This time, ask students to visualize all the points dropping onto the y-axis so that they can see this distribution.

The histogram of the average scores is shown next. Even though we can see two peaks around 500 and 560, the shape is more skewed right than bimodal.

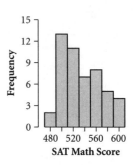

SAT Math Score

d. There are no more states to add, so this is the complete picture for the given year. What you see is all there is. You might generalize, however, to the previous year and the next year. In fact, the plot over the last 20 or so years looks similar to this one. These numbers do not change rapidly from year to year.

e. The Midwestern states are predominantly ACT states. In these states, only small percentages of students take the SAT, and these tend to be the better students who are trying for admission to exclusive colleges, perhaps outside the Midwest. If only a few students in a state are taking the SAT, they are probably the best students in the state and their average scores would then be higher than the average scores for other states. Thus, as the percentage of students taking the SAT increases, the average score tends to decrease. Although this explanation makes sense, we cannot be sure from these data alone.

In case students are interested in the scores for their state, the table on the following page gives the SAT verbal score, SAT math score, and the percentage taking the test in 2000. You can get current data on the College Board's Web site: www.collegeboard.com.

State	Verbal	Math	Percentage Taking Exam
Alabama	559	555	9
Alaska	519	515	50
Arizona	521	523	34
Arkansas	563	554	6
California	497	518	49
Colorado	534	537	32
Connecticut	508	509	81
Delaware	502	496	66
Florida	498	500	55
Georgia	488	486	64
Hawaii	488	519	53
Idaho	540	541	16
Illinois	568	586	12
Indiana	498	501	60
Iowa	589	600	5
Kansas	574	580	9
Kentucky	548	550	12
Louisiana	562	558	8
Maine	504	500	68
Maryland	507	509	65
Massachusetts	511	513	78
Michigan	557	569	11
Minnesota	581	594	9
Mississippi	562	549	4
Missouri	572	577	8
Montana	543	546	23
Nebraska	560	571	9
Nevada	510	517	34
New Hampshire	520	519	72
New Jersey	498	513	81
New Mexico	549	543	12
New York	494	506	77
North Carolina	492	496	64
North Dakota	588	609	4
Ohio	533	539	26
Oklahoma	563	560	8
Oregon	527	527	54
Pennsylvania	498	497	70
Rhode Island	505	500	71
South Carolina	484	482	59

(continued)

State	Verbal	Math	Percentage Taking Exam
South Dakota	587	588	4
Tennessee	563	553	13
Texas	493	500	52
Utah	570	569	5
Vermont	513	508	70
Virginia	509	500	67
Washington	526	528	52
West Virginia	526	511	19
Wisconsin	584	597	7
Wyoming	545	545	12
National Average	505	514	44

E5. **a.** The cases are the individual employees at the time of the layoffs, and the variables are the age at hire and the year of hire. The triangular shape of this plot indicates heteroscedasticity. The direction of the cloud is upward to the right, showing weak positive association between *age at hire* and *year of hire*. There are no points in the upper-left side of the plot because these employees would have reached retirement age.

b. This plot does not help us decide this question. Because so many people who were hired in the early years (and even recently) would have retired, we do not know whether older people were hired then or not. To determine whether age discrimination in hiring may have existed, we need a plot of the age at hire of all people hired, not just those who remained at the time of layoffs.

c. From this plot, it appears that people hired earliest were more subject to layoff, not necessarily the older employees. Everyone hired before the early 1960s was laid off, but not all of the older people were laid off. Perhaps, then, it was higher salaries because of seniority or obsolete job skills that resulted in a greater proportion of older employees being laid off.

E6. **NOTE:** If your students aren't working with computers, you may wish to provide them with copies of the three scatterplots on the next page. ∎

All three have positive association, but *circumference* appears to have the strongest positive association with *hat size*. Students may discover this rule: *hat size* is equal to *circumference* divided by π and then rounded to the closest eighth.

Note that the measurements tend to come aligned in vertical strips, indicating that the students made the measurements only to the nearest quarter of an inch.

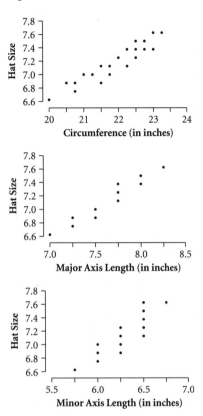

E7. **NOTE:** A computer should be used for this exercise. This open-ended investigation can be very time consuming if students do all three parts. We suggest that you assign just one of the three parts to each student (or small group of students) and have them share their results. Or you could also give each student a copy of the scatterplot matrix on page 84. This graphic was made on Minitab using the command **Matrix Plot** from the Graph menu. All of the relationships requested in this exercise are shown in one large plot. For example, the plots requested in part a, with *cost per hour* on the vertical axis, are shown across the bottom row. ■

a. *Cost per hour*

i. Students might point out that all of the associations are positive. As the variable on the *x*-axis increases, so does the cost per hour. Although all relationships are strong, the strongest are *cost per hour* versus *fuel consumption per hour* and versus *number of seats*. The other three relationships are weaker and show less constant strength. The scatterplot of *cost per hour* against *cargo space* is the most fan-shaped.

Relationships of *cost per hour* to *fuel per hour* and to *number of seats* are the most linear. The relationship of *cost per hour* to *speed* is the most curved. As *speed* increases, the *cost per hour* stays relatively constant up to about 460 miles per hour and then increases rapidly with increasing speed.

There appear to be no outliers in *cost per hour*. There is, however, one plane that is an outlier in *flight length*, the B747-400.

ii. It is true that the patterns in the plots show that bigger planes cost more per hour to operate, but this may be perfectly reasonable given that they carry more people and more cargo (and go faster).

One variable that might measure cost efficiency for the airplanes is *cost per hour per seat* (*cost/seats*). (Students may come up with others.) A plot showing this variable plotted against its denominator is shown on page 78. Notice *cost per hour per seat* remains somewhat constant (but with a lot of variability) across the number of passengers carried. That is, larger planes tend to cost about the same to fly a passenger for an hour as smaller planes. However, larger planes also tend to go faster and take less time to travel the same number of miles. Considering that, larger planes may be more efficient.

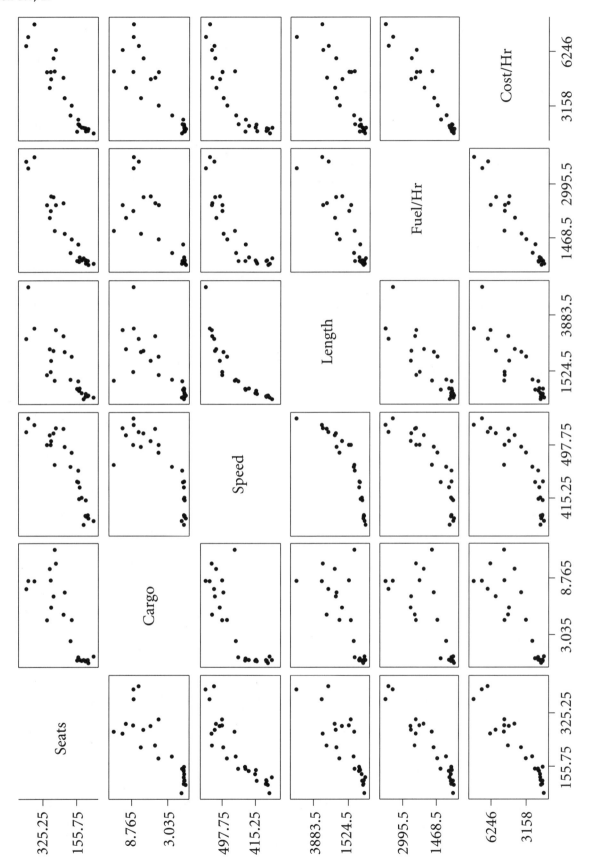

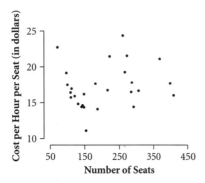

The next scatterplot shows *cost per passenger mile* (*cost/hr*, divided by *speed* (in mph) divided by *seats* or *number of passengers carried*) versus *number of seats*. Now we see that larger planes do tend to be somewhat more cost efficient per passenger mile. However, the relationship is weak.

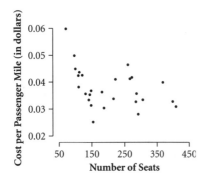

b. *Flight length*

i. Here are some things students might discover from their scatterplots or from the scatterplots in the fourth column of the scatterplot matrix:

Number of seats has a stronger relationship with *flight length* than does *cargo*. These are all passenger aircraft, and their primary purpose is to carry passengers. Cargo is added as space (and weight) is available. The weak relationship in the *cargo* versus *flight length* plot is due primarily to two aircraft, the large A300-600 (Airbus), used primarily to carry passengers and cargo over the short routes in Europe, and the B747-400, used to carry large numbers of

passengers (and relatively less freight) over the very long international routes.

Planes with the longest flight lengths (the B747s) have the most seats but are not at the top of the cargo carriers. This can be seen in the plots of *seats* and *cargo* versus *length*, but you have to look back at the data to identify the planes.

A description of the scatterplot of *speed* versus *flight length* follows.

Cases and variables: The cases are the planes in the data set, and the variables are the airborne speed in miles per hour and the length of flight in miles.

Shape: The shape shows a single cluster of points in a thin, curved array that opens downward, with one point (the B747-400) as an outlier on the *length* axis.

Trend: The direction of the relationship is positive.

Strength: The relationship is very strong; a pattern is quite obvious.

Generalization: It seems reasonable that a similar pattern might appear even if other planes were added to the study. The general pattern of *speed* versus *flight length* should not depend entirely on the specific planes being studied here.

Explanation: As the typical length of flight increases, airlines tend to use faster planes because it is inefficient to use a fast plane on a short flight and inconvenient for travelers to use a slow plane on a long flight. But there is a maximum speed that can be achieved by the designs used for commercial aircraft so that few planes fly much over 500 miles per hour. This causes the leveling off of the plot for the longer flights.

ii. The faster planes used on the longer flights use more fuel per hour, but they cover many more miles in an hour than do the slower planes. So perhaps they use less fuel per mile.

To compute *gallons of fuel used per mile,* we must divide *fuel* in gallons per hour by *speed* in miles per hour. This plot shows *fuel consumption* in gallons per mile plotted against *flight length.*

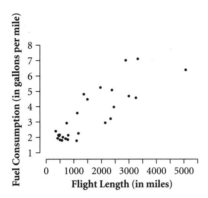

Apparently, the planes that are capable of flying longer distances use more gallons of fuel per mile than do planes that fly shorter distances. This isn't surprising, as they carry more passengers and cargo. Further, flying faster may take more gallons per mile (as with an automobile).

c. *Speed, seats, and cargo*

   i. Here are some things students may discover:

   The curvature is more pronounced in the relationship between *speed* and *cargo.* The slower (and smaller) planes carry little cargo, and the plane that carries the biggest cargo has only about medium speed. The planes that carry the biggest cargo carry only a moderate number of passengers.

   The A300-600 (Airbus) is unusually slow, both for the amount of cargo it carries (it has the largest cargo capacity of all the planes on the list) and the number of seats it has.

   ii. The flat part to the left of the plot of *cargo* versus *seats* reveals that passenger planes with a relatively small number of seats (up to nearly 200) carry very little cargo. The fan shape to the right reveals that as the planes get bigger and the number of seats increases beyond 200, the amount of cargo carried by these

planes also increases. However, the variation in the cargo-carrying capacity of a plane also increases as the number of seats increases.

E8. **NOTE:** This open-ended investigation requires a computer. This exercise involves issues that might be sensitive for some students. You have the chance to emphasize strongly that "association does not imply causation." ■

The four scatterplots needed are shown next. There appears to be little or no association between the percentage living below the poverty line and the percentage living in metropolitan areas. Likewise, there appears to be little association between the poverty rate and the percentage of Whites. The two outliers in this plot are regions with low percentages of Whites, namely, Washington, D.C. (high poverty rate) and Hawaii (low poverty rate).

The poverty rate is negatively associated with the percentage of high school graduates; as the latter goes up, the percentage living in poverty generally goes down. Finally, poverty appears to be only weakly associated with percentage of families headed by a single parent (with Washington, D.C., again as an outlier).

On the surface, it looks as though increasing graduation rates would have the largest effect on decreasing the poverty rate. Keep in mind, however, that the problem of poverty is much more complex than that, and many other variables are lurking in the background. Association is not the same as cause and effect. Simply increasing high school graduation rates, although it might be a good thing to do, will not automatically elevate all of those living below the poverty line to a better economic condition.

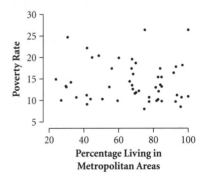

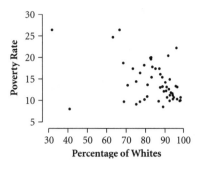

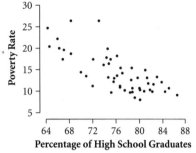

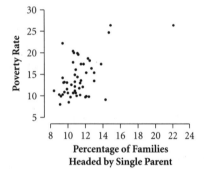

E9. **a.** Plots A, B, and C are basically linear. Plot D is not because of the seven universities in the lower right, which may be different from the rest. The first plot, of *graduation rate* versus *alumni giving rate,* gives some impression of downward curvature. However, if you disregard the point in the upper right, the impression of any curvature disappears.

Plots A, B, and C have just one cluster. Plot D, the plot of *graduation rate* versus *top 10% in high school,* has two clusters. Most of the points follow the upward linear trend, but the cluster of seven points in the lower right with the highest percentage of freshmen in the top 10% shows little relationship with the graduation rate.

Plots A and C have possible outliers. Plot A, the plot of *graduation rate* versus *alumni giving rate* has a possible outlier in the upper right. It is below the general trend and its *x*-value (but not its *y*-value) is unusually large. In Plot C, the plot of *graduation rate* versus *SAT 75th percentile,* the points toward

the upper left and the middle right should be examined because they are farther from the general trend than the other points, although neither their *x*-values nor their *y*-values are unusual. The point in the lower right of Plot D should also be examined, along with the other six points nearby.

b. The plot of *graduation rate* versus *alumni giving rate* has a positive linear trend. The plot of *graduation rate* versus *student/faculty ratio* has a moderately weak positive linear trend, with the graduation rates going down as the student/faculty ratios increase. The plot of *graduation rate* versus *SAT 75th percentile* again shows an increasing linear positive trend in the graduation rates as the SAT scores increase. The plot of *graduation rate* versus *top 10% in high school* shows wide variation in both variables, with little or no trend.

c. Among these four variables, it appears that the alumni giving rate is the best predictor of the graduation rate and SAT scores (as measured by the 75th percentile) is second best. However, both of these relationships are moderate and neither is a strong predictor of graduation rate. Ranking in high school class (as measured by the top 10%) is almost useless as a predictor of college graduation rate. The plot of *graduation rate* versus *alumni giving rate* owes part of the impression of a strong relationship to the point in the upper right. This plot shows some heteroscedasticity, with the graduation rate varying more with smaller alumni giving rates.

To help students understand the concept of strength, ask them, "If you look at the plot, do you see more trend or more variation?"

Students should understand that even though the relationship between, say, the graduation rate and the student/faculty ratio is negative, that's not what makes the student/faculty ratio a poor predictor of the graduation rate. Given a specific student/faculty ratio, we can predict a graduation rate. The problem is that there is a great deal of uncertainty about how close the actual rate would be to the predicted rate because the range of graduate rates is large for any given student/faculty ratio.

d. The relationships could change considerably when looking at all universities because these are highly rated universities, so the values of all variables tend to be "good." With a larger collection of universities, there may be more spread in the values of all variables and, most likely, more pronounced patterns.

To explain to students how this could be, show students the version that follows of the *graduation rate* versus *SAT 75th percentile* plot. On this plot, the squares represent the top 25 universities and the closed circles represent the next 25 most highly rated

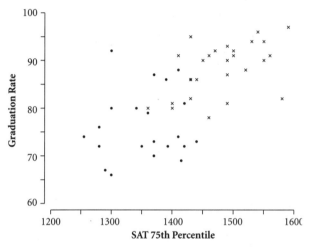

× Top 25%   • 26%–50%

universities. Note that if you look at either group, there is very little upward trend. However, putting the two groups together gives a stronger linear trend. If another group of 25 universities were added, the trend probably would be stronger. This phenomenon is sometimes called the effect of a restricted range.

e. Graduation rates may increase as SAT scores increase because better prepared students may be more successful in college courses, so a university with a greater number of prepared students will, on average, graduate a higher percentage of students. Alumni giving rates may increase as graduation rates increase because the university has produced happy alumni. These data do not "prove" this claim, however, because there are other possible explanations. These types of observational studies cannot prove claims; the proof of a claim requires an experiment, which is one of the topics of the next chapter.

You may wish to mention that these relationships hold for *universities* and that the data provide no evidence about whether the relationships hold for *individuals*.

Distributions and Relationships

	Chapter 2 One Variable	Chapter 3 Two Variables
Key Idea	Distribution	Relationship (association)
Plots	Dot plot Stemplot Boxplot Histogram	Scatterplot
Shape	Unimodal/bimodal Symmetry/skewness Clusters, gaps, and outliers	Linear or curved Varying strength Clusters, gaps, and outliers
Ideal Shape	Normal	Linear (oval/ellipse)
Measure of Center	Mean Median	Regression line
Measure of Spread from the Center	Standard deviation Interquartile range	Correlation

Describing Bivariate Data

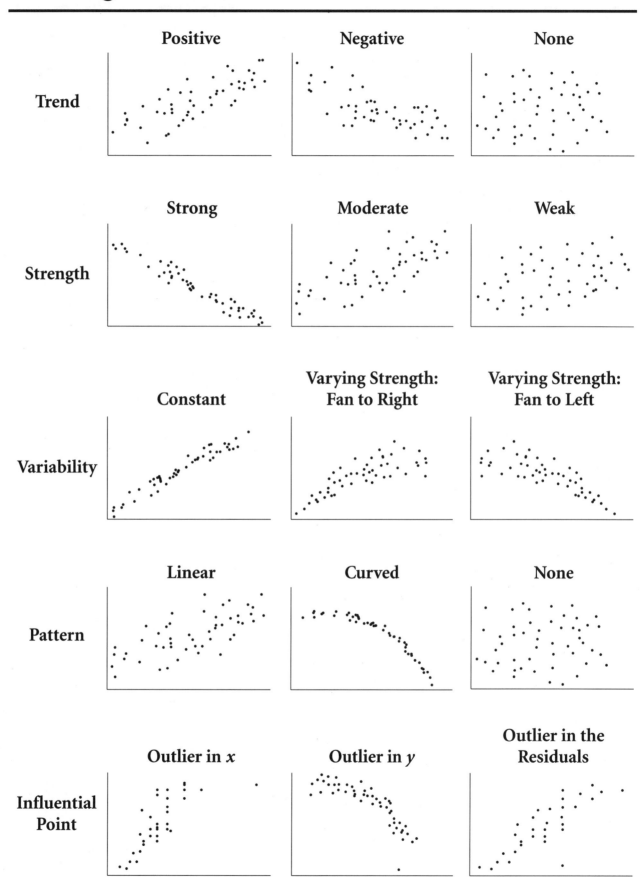

Matrix Plot of Aircraft Data

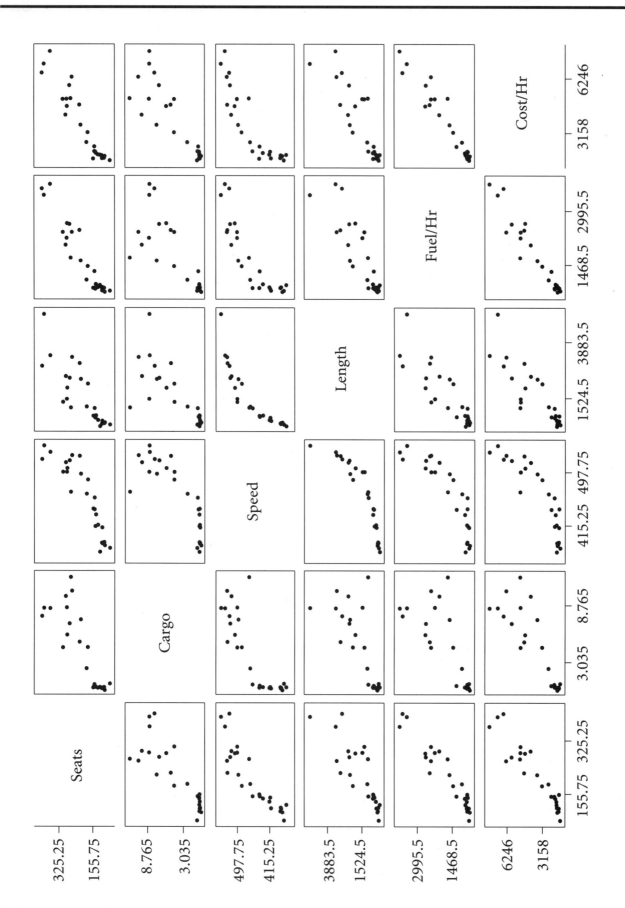

3.2 Getting a Line on the Pattern

Objectives

After reviewing the definition of slope and the slope-intercept form of a linear equation, students will learn

- to interpret the slope and y-intercept in the context of the situation
- to use a fitted line to model a relationship and to predict y when the value of x is known
- to understand that interpolation is more trustworthy than extrapolation
- to compute and interpret residuals and draw them on the scatterplot
- to understand that the least squares regression line minimizes the sum of the squared errors (residuals)
- to compute the least squares regression line
- to read regression output from various statistical software packages
- to understand various properties of the least squares regression line

Important Terms and Concepts

- slope; y-intercept
- least squares regression line; fitted line
- predictor or explanatory variable x
- predicted or response variable $\hat{y}$
- observed value y
- interpolation; extrapolation
- residual
- sum of squared errors (SSE)

Lesson Planning

Class Time

Two to three days

Materials

For Activity 3.1, a ruler with a millimeter scale and a textbook for each pair of students

Suggested Assignments

Classwork		
Essential	Recommended	Optional
Activity 3.1	D6	
D3–D5, D7	P6, P9	
P3–P5, P7, P8		

Homework		
Essential	Recommended	Optional
E11, E12, E16	E10, E13, E14, E21, E22	E15, E17–E20

Lesson Notes: Interpreting Slope

Most students should be able to find the equation of a line, given two points or a point and a slope. However, many may not have interpreted an equation of a line in the context of the situation, especially its slope. See Step 5 in Activity 3.1 for an example.

Why Do We Use $y = b_0 + b_1 x$ in Statistics Rather Than $y = mx + b$?

In multiple regression, there can be many explanatory variables: $x_1, x_2, x_3, \ldots, x\hat{n}$. This would occur, for example, if you want to predict college grade point average from a linear combination of variables such as high school GPA, number of Advanced Placement courses, SAT score, number of mathematics courses taken in high school, and so on. The fitted "plane" would then be of the form

$$\hat{y} = b_0 + b_1 x_1 + b_2 x_2 + b_3 x_3 + \cdots + b_n x_n$$

which is a straightforward generalization of

$$\hat{y} = b_0 + b_1 x$$

On the other hand, if we used the form $y = mx + b$, we have no obvious way to generalize the symbols to the case of more than one explanatory variable.

Notation on Calculators

When using a calculator to get a least squares regression line, there is a new wrinkle: The equation of the regression line may be written $y = a + bx$. So if your students are used to $y = mx + b$, with m as the slope and b as the intercept, warn them to be careful: b can be the slope. Alternatively (or additionally), a calculator may write the equation in the form $y = ax + b$.

Activity 3.1 Pinching Pages

The Pinching Pages activity can be done quickly and requires only a copy of the textbook and a ruler marked with millimeters for each student or pair of students. This activity gives students experience with an easily comprehended interpretation of the slope and y-intercept in context.

1–2. The following is a set of data for five "pinches" of a standard textbook. (The pages may have different thickness from the book your students have.) The thickness measurements are in millimeters. Note that "page" refers to a sheet of paper. Students who subtract *page numbers* instead of counting sheets will get estimates that are half the thickness of a sheet (because there are two "pages" per sheet).

Row	Pages	Thickness
1	50	6.0
2	100	11.0
3	150	12.5
4	200	17.0
5	250	21.0

3–4. This scatterplot shows a nearly straight line. It should be linear as an increase of one page adds a fixed amount to the thickness.

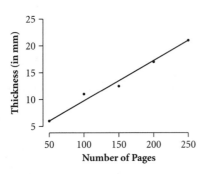

5. The line passes near the points (50, 6) and (250, 21), so its slope is about 0.075. Slope measures change in y, per unit change in x, and because a unit change in x is one page and y is thickness, this slope is an estimate of the thickness of one page. The y-intercept can be found by using any point near the line and solving for b_0:

$$6 = 0.075(50) + b_0$$

$$b_0 = 2.25$$

The y-intercept is the thickness if no pages are included, so it is the approximate thickness of the cover of the book.

You can write this equation as

$$thickness = y\text{-}intercept + slope\,(pages)$$

6. Because the points lie so close to the line, we believe the measurements are fairly precise. However, because we measured only to the nearest 0.5 millimeter, we expect some inaccuracy in each measurement—some will be too small and others too large. By using the line to estimate the slope, we are averaging out those errors.

7. If the measurements did not include the front cover, the line would be of the form $y = b_1 x$ because the thickness y would be 0 if no pages were included.

Discussion

D3. **a.** cost of purchase versus number of gallons purchased

b. miles driven versus number of gallons used

c. weight in pounds versus volume of the liquid

Practice

P3. Students should estimate that the slope is around 2. (The equation of the line is actually $cost/hr = 408 + 1.93\ fuel$.) This slope means that for every one gallon increase in fuel consumption per hour, the cost of flying the aircraft tends to go up about $2 per hour. This amount must be approximately the price of a gallon of fuel.

Lesson Notes: Lines as Summaries

The data for the doctors' incomes from Displays 3.16 and 3.17 of the student text are given in this table. The equation of the regression line of the average radiologist salary against year in Display 3.16 is actually

$$salary = -894.772 + 12.3817\ year$$

Note that the data are unavailable for the years 1983 and 1984.

When estimating the slope of the line in the example, we used two points on the line, (82, 120) and (92, 245), estimated off the plot. In this case, they are not the actual data because the actual value at 82 is not on the line we want to estimate, nor is the value at 92.

Year	Family Practioner	Radiologist	Ratio
82	71.4	133.3	1.87
85	77.9	144.3	1.85
86	80.3	168.8	2.1
87	91.5	180.7	1.97
88	94.6	188.5	1.99
89	95.9	210.5	2.19
90	102.7	219.4	2.14
91	111.5	229.8	2.06
92	111.8	253.3	2.27

Why Points Farther Apart Give Better Estimates of the Slope

Here is an example to show why picking points with values of x that are farther apart works better when estimating the slope. Suppose the equation of the line is actually $y = x$, so the slope is 1. Suppose also that your estimate of y tends to be off by about 5 units. If you select 1 and 2 as values for x, you might estimate the y-values to be -4 rather than 1, and 7 rather than 2. This gives an estimate for the slope of

$$\frac{(7 - (-4))}{(2 - 1)} = 11$$

which is wildly off. If you pick 1 and 101 as the values for x, you might estimate the y-values to be -4 and 106. This gives an estimate for the slope of

$$\frac{(106 - (-4))}{(101 - 1)} = 1.1$$

which is fairly close.

Discussion

D4. Answers will vary a little, but a summarizing line should come close to the points (92, 112) and (82, 70) for a slope of approximately

$$\frac{(112 - 70)}{(92 - 82)} = 4.2$$

This slope tells us that the income of family doctors was increasing at the rate of approximately \$4,200 per year across this time span, which is much less than the rate for radiologists.

The y-intercept can be found by solving

$$112 = b_0 + 4.2(92)$$
$$b_0 = -274.4$$

The equation of the line is
$$y = -274.4 + 4.2x$$

Practice

P4. The given fitted line comes close to the points (110, 240) and (72, 130), for a slope of

$$\frac{(240 - 130)}{(110 - 70)} = \frac{110}{40} = 2.75$$

This slope tells us that for every \$1,000 increase in the income of family doctors, the income of the average radiologist tended to increase by about \$2,750 per year. (Note that we already knew this from the information in the example and in D4. Radiologists' incomes went up about \$12,500 a year and family practice doctors about \$4,200, which is a ratio of about 3 to 1.)

The y-intercept can be found by solving

$$240 = b_0 + 2.75(110)$$
$$b_0 = -62.5$$

The equation of the line is
$$radiologist = -62.5 + 2.75\ family\ practitioner$$
The actual regression line is
$$y = -58.5 + 2.69x$$

Lesson Notes: Using Lines for Prediction

Typically, software writes equations using variable names instead of using x's and y's. For example, the equation $y = -905 + 12.5x$ could be written as $income = -905 + 12.5\ year$.

Students should be able to determine whether a regression model tends to *overestimate* or *underestimate* the value of y for particular values of x by viewing the residual plots of a regression equation. For example, if the observed value is above the line, the estimate is an underestimate because the predicted value on the line is below (less than) the observed value. As shown in Display 3.19 of the student text, a residual is the *vertical* distance between the actual value and the predicted value *at a particular value of the explanatory variable.*

Discussion

D5. **a.** Far below the line; the point lies on the line.
   b. The fitted line is too low. It lies below all of the points. Move the line up so that there are both positive and negative residuals.
   c. In the year 1900, the average income for family practitioners is estimated to be $-298,550$. (That's nearly \$300,000 less than zero!) This extrapolation obviously makes no sense. (Anyway, family practice as a specialty did not even exist in 1900.)

D6. The arithmetic is fine. The reasoning is an amusing example of the folly of extreme extrapolation. The equation is
$$length = 6460 - 1.375\ year$$

Practice

P5. **a.** The alumni giving rate (in percent) is the response variable, and the student/faculty ratio is the predictor or explanatory variable.
   b. As you can see from the plot shown here, a run of 4 in the direction of the x-axis corresponds to a drop of about 8 percentage points in the direction of the y-axis.

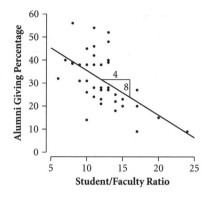

The slope of the fitted line is -2, which is equal to

$$\frac{rise}{run} = -\frac{8}{4} = -2$$

c. A university that has a student/faculty ratio of 0 (i.e., no students) would have a giving rate of 55%. This makes no sense. Extrapolation is not reasonable in this case.

d. The giving rate would be about 23%. The error probably is rather large because the points are not clustered closely about the line. There is quite a lot of variation around the line, especially for the universities with smaller student/faculty ratios. On the average, a prediction would be off by about 7 percentage points.

e. The point is just above the line, and the residual is about 1 or 2. The residual for the point with the highest giving rate is about $56 - 40 = 16$.

f. $y = 55 - 2(6) = 43$. The residual is $32 - 43 = -11$.

g. Because the line has a negative slope, the largest possible predicted giving rate occurs when the student/faculty ratio is as small as possible. The smallest the student/faculty ratio could be is 0 (if there were no students). This ratio gives a predicted giving rate of $55 - 2(0) = 55$. This is the largest possible predicted giving rate. The rate at Piranha State is larger than 55%, so the residual for Piranha State will be positive.

P6. **a.** Pizza Hut's Hand Tossed and Little Caesars Pan! Pan! have the fewest calories. Pizza Hut's Hand Tossed and Domino's Hand Tossed have the least fat. The right side of the graph contains pizzas with the most fat.

b. **i.** C **ii.** E **iii.** A
iv. B **v.** D

c. **i.** A: The line lies above all the points.
ii. E: The line lies below all the points.
iii. B: The line lies over most points on the left and under most points on the right.
iv. D: The line lies under most points on the left and over most points on the right.
v. C: This line fits best overall, going through the middle of the points on both the left and right.

Lesson Notes: Least Squares Regression Lines

Why the SSE?

Why do we minimize the SSE, the sum of the *squared* errors (residuals), not just the sum of the errors or the sum of the absolute value of the errors?

- Minimizing the sum of the residuals does not give a unique line. As students will see in E20, any line through the point of averages has residuals that sum to 0, and some of these lines clearly are not good models of the data.

  The same thing is true with the sum of the absolute errors. For example, consider the four points $(0, 0)$, $(0, 1)$, $(1, 1)$, and $(1, 2)$. The lines $y = 1$, $y = x$, $y = 1 + x$, $y = 2x$, and $y = 0.5 + 1.5x$ all have a sum of absolute residuals equal to 2.

- The sum of squared errors is a recurring theme in statistics. Students first met this idea with the standard deviation, which is constructed from the sum of the squared "errors" of the data points from the mean. The mean, in fact, is the measure of the center that minimizes the sum of the squared errors, much as the regression line is the "center" line that minimizes that sum.

- A nice formula results when we minimize the SSE. Although students may not appreciate it, the formula for the slope of the least squares regression line is easy to use, and it is easy to prove that it minimizes the sum of the squared errors. There is no simple formula for minimizing the sum of the absolute values of the residuals.

- A sum of squared errors is like our usual measure of Euclidean distance:

$$\sqrt{(x_1 - x_2)^2 + (y_1 - y_2)^2 + (z_1 - z_2)^2}$$

To see how this applies to regression, think of the data (x_i, y_i), $i = 1, 2, \ldots, n$, as two vectors

$$\mathbf{x} = \begin{bmatrix} x_1 \\ x_2 \\ \vdots \\ x_n \end{bmatrix} \text{ and } \mathbf{y} = \begin{bmatrix} y_1 \\ y_2 \\ \vdots \\ y_n \end{bmatrix}$$

in n-dimensional space. If the points (x_i, y_i) are not collinear, then vector $\mathbf{y}$ does not lie in the plane spanned by the vectors $\mathbf{l}$ and $\mathbf{x}$. That is, $\mathbf{y}$ is not equal to $b_0\mathbf{l} + b_1\mathbf{x}$ for any b_0 and b_1. The SSE is the square of the Euclidean distance between the vector $\mathbf{y}$ and the plane $b_0\mathbf{l} + b_1\mathbf{x}$.

These two articles give more on this geometric interpretation:

"The Geometry of Linear Regression" by Richard Parris in *Consortium*, n. 58 (Summer 1996), pages 8–9, or http://math.exeter.edu/rparris/documents.html.

"The 'Naturalness' of Squaring in Linear Regression," by Dan Teague, at http://courses.ncssm.edu/math/TALKS.

Properties of the Least Squares Regression Line

The boxed information on page 124 of the student text gives a concise summary of the important facts about residuals from a least squares regression line. In addition, it provides formulas and a procedure by which a student can calculate the equation of a least squares regression line.

The second property of the least squares regression line is equivalent to saying that the standard deviation of the residuals is as small as possible. Equivalently, the sum of the squares of the deviations of the values of y from their predicted value $\hat{y}$ is as small as possible. Or, finally, the SSE is as small as possible.

Proof of the Regression Formula

Many multivariate calculus books include a proof that the procedure given in the text does indeed give the equation of the line that minimizes the sum of the squared errors. A readable one may be found in William G. McCallum et al., *Multivariable Calculus*, 3rd ed. (New York: Wiley, 2002), page 714.

For a linear algebra proof, see David C. Lay, *Linear Algebra and Its Applications*, 2nd ed. (Reading, MA: Addison-Wesley, 2000), pages 404–416.

For a noncalculus-based approach, see Dan Kalman, *Elementary Mathematical Models* (Washington, D.C.: Mathematical Association of America, 1997), Chapter 8.

Practice

P7. **a.** and **b.**

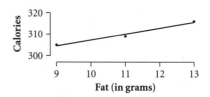

b. The equation is $\hat{y} = 279.75 + 2.75x$. The slope and y-intercept are found using the table below.

$$b_1 = \frac{22}{8} = 2.75$$

$$b_0 = 310 - 2.75(11) = 279.75$$

c. The slope of 2.75 means that for every additional gram of fat, these pizzas tend to have 2.75 more calories. The y-intercept means 5 ounces of pizza with no fat would tend to have 279.75 calories, which may be reasonable.

Lesson 3.2, P7b

Pizza	x	y	$x - \bar{x}$	$y - \bar{y}$	$(x - \bar{x}) \cdot (y - \bar{y})$	$(x - \bar{x})^2$
1	9	305	−2	−5	10	4
2	11	309	0	−1	0	0
3	13	316	2	6	12	4
Sum	33	930	0	0	22	8
Mean	11	310				

d. The point of averages is $(11, 310)$, which satisfies the equation

$$279.75 + 2.75(11) = 310.$$

e. The residuals are

$$305 - [279.75 + 2.75(9)] = 0.5$$

$$309 - [279.75 + 2.75(11)] = -1.0$$

$$316 - [279.75 + 2.75(13)] = 0.5$$

The sum is 0. (When computing, the sum of the residuals typically won't be exactly zero because the coefficients usually must be rounded.)

P8. The scatterplot is shown in P2 on page 106 of the student text. The equation of the least squares regression line is

% on time = $97.0 - 5.08$ *mishandled baggage*

In order, the residuals are 6.6099, -2.9260, 7.7093, -0.2896, 0.6501, -1.1108, 1.1770, -5.6494, 3.8536, and -10.0241.

Technology Note for the TI-83

Some graphing calculators automatically calculate residuals and store them for the user. The list RESID is updated and stored every time a regression is done on any two of its lists.

The TI-83 has the capability of performing a number of regressions and providing information on the residuals of any regression. In order to access these capabilities:

Make sure that Diagnostics is turned on: Go to 2nd [Catalog]; arrow down to and highlight DiagnosticOn; press ENTER twice.

Load your data sets into L1 and L2—it is customary to load the values of the explanatory variable in L1 and the response variable in L2. Press STAT CALC and select 8:LinReg(a+bx). Type in L1, L2 so that your command is LinReg(a+bx) L1, L2. Then press ENTER.

The values of a, b, r² and r will be displayed.

If you add the name of an equation for graphing in the regression command, that is, LinReg(a+bx) L1, L2, Y1, then the regression equation will be pasted into the location Y1 for easy graphing.

In addition, the TI-83 calculates the set of residual values each time a regression is called for. It stores the residuals in a list, RESID, which can be accessed from 2nd [LIST] under the NAMES menu.

Lesson Notes: Reading Computer Output

Complete regression analyses are supplied even though students will not learn to interpret most of the details of these analyses until later. Students should learn to pick out the needed computations from the entire analysis. Note how the software packages use the variable names supplied by the user.

Discussion

D7. **a.** $\hat{y} = -298.55 + 4.46145x$. The SSE is 75.3018.

b. Minitab gives the equation of the regression line as well as giving the coefficients in a table. There are also a few differences in the analysis of variance section, but basically the same information is presented.

See page 96 for information about least squares output for Fathom.

Practice

P9. Yes, the regression equation of $\hat{y} = 279.75 + 2.75x$ and the mean of the response variable, 310, are the same as we computed by hand. The SSE is $0.5^2 + 1^2 + (-0.5)^2 = 1.5$ and is found in the Analysis of Variance table in row "Error," column "Sum of Squares."

Exercises

E10. **a.** The slope is about $(67 - 37)/12$, or 2.5 inches/year. On the average, boys grow about 2.5 inches per year from the ages of 2 to 14. Answers will vary, but using this slope and the point $(3, 39)$, the equation is approximately *height* = $31.5 + 2.5$ *age*. The y-intercept of 31.5 would mean that an average newborn is 31.5 inches long. Because this is clearly too long, this extrapolation is not valid.

b. The equation is *height* = $31.6 + 2.43$ *age*. The equations for boys and girls are quite similar. Boys have a slightly larger slope. The least squares equation for boys is *height* = $31.6 + 2.47$ *age*, which is even closer to the equation for girls than the estimated equation for boys from part a. If your students would like to examine this situation more closely, here are the data for boys:

Age	Median Height of Boys (in inches)
2	35.8
3	39.1
4	41.4
5	44.2
6	46.8
7	49.6
8	51.7
9	54.1
10	56.3
11	58.0
12	60.8
13	63.7
14	66.6

E11–E13 are straightforward practice based on the pizza data.

E11. **a.** The calorie prediction for a pizza with 10.5 grams of fat is about 320 calories. The calorie prediction for a pizza with 15 grams of fat is about 360 calories.

b. The slope of the line is approximately $\frac{(360 - 320)}{(15 - 10.5)} = 8.9$. The equation is approximately $\hat{y} = 226.5 + 8.9x$.

c. The equation is $calories = 226.74 + 8.97\ fat$, but answers will vary somewhat depending on rounding. The slope and y-intercept are found using the table below.

$$b_1 = \frac{389.7}{43.43} \approx 8.97$$

$$b_0 = 332 - 8.97(11.7) \approx 227,$$
so $calories = 227 + 8.97\ fat$

d. $calories = 226.74 + 8.974\ fat$

e. The slope is very close to the value given by nutritionists for calories per gram of fat.

E12. **a.** $-14.37 =$ Pizza Hut's Pan
$-12.45 =$ Little Caesars' Pizza! Pizza!
$-7.47 =$ Little Caesars' Pan! Pan!
$-2.50 =$ Pizza Hut's Hand Tossed
$5.61 =$ Pizza Hut's Stuffed
$11.68 =$ Domino's Deep Dish
$19.50 =$ Domino's Hand Tossed

b. The number of calories is relatively low for a pizza with that number of grams of fat.

c. Positive; both points are above the regression line. The pizzas must get their calories from someplace, and apparently it is not fat. This indicates that the calories come from carbohydrates or protein.

E13. If your students are adept at making scatterplots, you may choose to provide them with copies of these two scatterplots. As this scatterplot and the one on the next page show, neither of these relationships should be modeled by a line. The plot of *cost* versus *fat* shows curvature, with low-fat and high-fat pizza costing much more than other brands. The plot of *cost* versus *calories* shows no particular pattern at all; the picture is all variation with little trend.

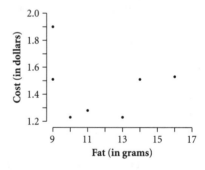

Lesson 3.2, E11c

	x	y	$x - \bar{x}$	$y - \bar{y}$	$(x - \bar{x}) \cdot (y - \bar{y})$	$(x - \bar{x})^2$
	9	305	−2.7	−27	72.9	7.29
	16	382	4.3	50	215.0	18.49
	14	338	2.3	6	13.8	5.29
	9	327	−2.7	−5	13.5	7.29
	10	309	−1.7	−23	39.1	2.89
	11	313	−0.7	−19	13.3	0.49
	13	349	1.3	17	22.1	1.69
Sum	82	2323	0	−1	389.7	43.43
Mean	11.7	332	0	0		

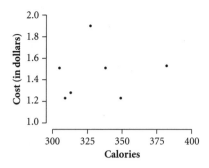

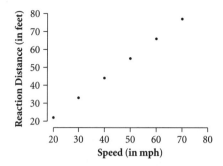

E14. This exercise illustrates computationally what the text presented visually—that the SSE depends on the slope and intercept of a fitted line and that some choices work better than others.

a. A line passing through the point (110, 1800) with slope 8.75 has equation $\hat{y} = 837.5 + 8.75x$.

The actual values, predictions, and residuals for the three points are shown in the table at the bottom of the page. The sum of squared errors (SSE) is 2812.5, much larger than the SSE for the least squares line.

Yes, the least squares line fits the data better than this line.

b. The slope is 8.75, and the equation is $\hat{y} = 875 + 8.75x$. For $x = 110$, $\hat{y} = 1837.5$. The residuals are 0, -37.5, and 0. The SSE is 1406.25 (half that of part a).

Even though it misses all the points, the least squares line fits the points better than the other lines in the sense that the sum of squared errors is minimized. The least squares line guards against a very bad prediction anywhere in the region covered by the predictor variable.

E15. **a.** The points in this scatterplot lie perfectly on a straight line.

b. The y-intercept should be 0 because if the car has zero speed, the reaction distance is 0.

c. The distance increases at the rate of 11 feet for every increase in 10 mph of the speed. Thus, the slope of the line is $\frac{11}{10} = 1.1$. This means that for every 1 mph increase in speed, the reaction distance is an additional 1.1 feet.

d. The equation of the line is $\hat{y} = 1.1x$, where y is reaction distance in feet and x is speed in miles per hour.

e. The predictions are $\hat{y} = 1.1(55) = 60.5$ ft and $\hat{y} = 1.1(75) = 82.5$ ft.

f. If the reaction time were longer, the reaction distances would be greater, with more than 11 feet between each successive value. Thus, the slope of the line would increase and the predicted distances would be longer than the corresponding predicted distances for the model given here. The equation would be $\hat{y} = 1.47x$.

Note: The formula for the reaction distance in feet for a given speed in miles per hour and reaction time in seconds is

$$\left(\frac{5280 \text{ ft/mi}}{3600 \text{ sec/hr}}\right)(\text{reaction time in sec})(\text{speed in mi/hr})$$

Lesson 3.2, E14a

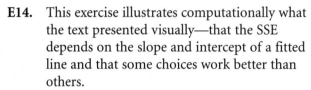

Predictor, x	Response, y	Prediction, $\hat{y}$	Error, $y - \hat{y}$
100	1750	1712.5	37.5
110	1800	1800	0
120	1925	1887.5	37.5

E16. **a.** $\hat{y} = 54.979 - 1.9455x$

b. 13; this college lies at the point (13, 52).

c. The fitted value is $\hat{y} = 54.979 - 1.9455x = 54.979 - 1.9455(13) = 29.6875$, which is equal to the value, 29.69, given in Display 3.34 in the student text. The residual is $y - \hat{y} = 52 - 29.69 = 22.31$, which again is the value given in the table.

E17. **a.** True; the ratio of price to gallons is the price per gallon, which is the same for all four purchasers. Another way to look at this is to observe that the price, y, increases at a constant rate for each additional gallon of gas purchased.

b. The relationship between *average speed x, time y,* and *distance* is $(speed)(time) = distance$, or $x \cdot y = 80$ in this scenario. Thus, plotting y (*time*) against x (*speed*) means plotting $y = \frac{80}{x}$, or $time = \frac{80}{speed}$, which will be a curve (it's a hyperbola) opening upward. Plotting $y^* = \frac{1}{y}$ against x results in a straight line because

$$80 = xy$$
$$\frac{1}{y} = \frac{1}{80}x$$
$$y^* = \frac{1}{80}x$$

which is a linear equation.

E18. **a.** The vertical slice shows the y-values for all x-values close to $x = 15$. The median is the value for which half of the y-values are larger and half smaller, so it is reasonable to use the median of the vertical slice as a prediction for an unknown y at $x = 15$, which is the midpoint of the slice.

b. The prediction errors should have about the same amount of variability as that in the boxplots themselves. The interquartile range for the box at $x = 15$ is about 20 percentage points, and the distribution is somewhat symmetric, so about half of the prediction errors should be no larger than about 10 percentage points.

E19. **a.** The vertical slices are shown here.

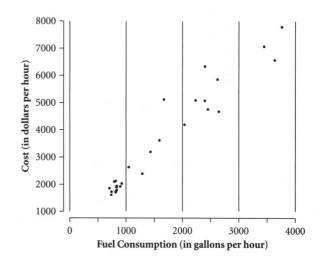

b. and **c.** The medians with a summarizing line are shown next.

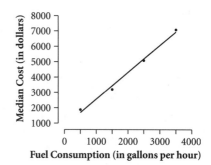

c. The equation of the line is approximately *cost* = 812.28 + 1.748 *fuel.*

d. Yes, the line is a reasonable summary because the medians are reasonable summaries of the centers of the vertical slices and these medians lie almost exactly on a straight line when viewed as a function of *fuel.*

E20. **a.** A horizontal line has the equation $y = a$, for some constant a. The three residuals are equal to

$$1750 - a$$
$$1800 - a$$
$$1925 - a$$

Their average is $1825 - a$. Thus, the mean of the residuals will be zero if and only if $a = 1825$, the mean of the responses. In that situation, the horizontal line does indeed pass through the point (110, 1825).

b. A straight line with slope b_1 has the form $y = b_0 + b_1x$. The residuals now have the form

$$1750 - b_0 - b_1(100)$$
$$1800 - b_0 - b_1(110)$$
$$1925 - b_0 - b_1(120)$$

Their average is $1825 - b_0 - b_1(110)$. Thus, the mean of the residuals will be zero if and only if

$$1825 - b_0 - b_1(110) = 0$$
$$b_0 + b_1(110) = 1825$$

or, equivalently, if an d only if the line passes through the point (110, 1825).

c. Generalizing the result of part b, the residual at the point (x_i, y_i) will be of the form

$$y_i - b_0 - b_1x_i$$

which when averaged over all values of i has mean

$$\bar{y} - b_0 - b_1\bar{x}$$

Thus, the mean residual will be zero if and only if

$$\bar{y} = b_0 + b_1\bar{x}$$

or, equivalently, the line passes through the point $(\bar{x}, \bar{y})$.

d. Because the regression line would not then be uniquely defined.

E21. This exercise is best done with a computer but may be done easily on a calculator if students "link" the data so only one student has to enter them.

a. The plot is shown here. This association shows a positive trend that is moderately strong. Even though one point lies relatively far from the pattern, fat content could be used as a reasonably good predictor of calories. The equation of the regression line is $\hat{y} = 253.078 + 6.47992x$.

The slope means that for every additional gram of fat, the pizzas tend to have 6.48 additional calories.

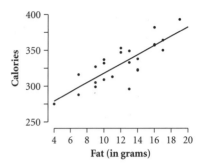

```
Dependent variable is:    Calories
No Selector
R squared = 67.8%    R squared (adjusted) = 66.3%
s = 16.92 with 24 - 2 = 22 degrees of freedom
```

Source	Sum of Squares	df	Mean Square	F-ratio
Regression	13240.6	1	13240.6	46.3
Residual	6297.21	22	286.237	

Variable	Coefficient	s.e. of Coeff	t-ratio	prob
Constant	253.078	12.10	20.9	≤0.0001
Fat	6.47992	0.9527	6.8	≤0.0001

b. The plot is shown next. There is a weak negative association between *fat* and *cost*. The equation of the regression line is $\hat{y} = 15.6819 - 3.27128x$.

The slope means that for every additional dollar in cost, the number of grams of fat tends to decrease by 3.27128. This hints at the possibility that low-fat pizzas cost more than others to make. One possible reason is that having a lot of toppings such as meat and vegetables adds to the cost. These generally have less fat than cheese, which is the primary ingredient of cheaper pizzas and contributes much of the fat.

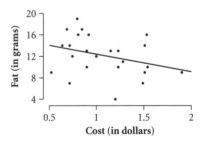

```
Dependent variable is:    Fat
No Selector
R squared = 10.4%    R squared (adjusted) = 6.3%
s = 3.584 with 24 - 2 = 22 degrees of freedom
```

Source	Sum of Squares	df	Mean Square	F-ratio
Regression	32.7074	1	32.7074	2.55
Residual	282.626	22	12.8466	

Variable	Coefficient	s.e. of Coeff	t-ratio	prob
Constant	15.6819	2.321	6.76	≤0.0001
Cost	-3.27128	2.050	-1.60	0.1248

c. The plot is shown here. There appears to be no association between *calories* and *cost.*

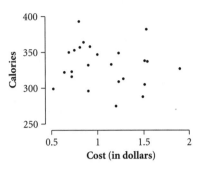

```
Dependent variable is:    Calories
No Selector
R squared = 1.5%    R squared (adjusted) = -3.0%
s = 29.58 with 24 - 2 = 22 degrees of freedom

Source      Sum of Squares  df  Mean Square  F-ratio
Regression  294.285          1    294.285     0.336
Residual    19243.5         22    874.707

Variable  Coefficient  s.e. of Coeff  t-ratio   prob
Constant  342.461       19.16          17.9     ≤0.0001
Cost       -9.81248     16.92          -0.580    0.5678
```

d. In the analysis of the pizza data, it appears that *calories* have a moderately strong positive association with *fat*—the two tend to rise or fall together. *Fat* appears to have a weak negative association with *cost,* perhaps because some of the low-fat pizzas are more costly to prepare. There appears to be no association between *cost* and *calories.*

E22. **a.** I – C; II – A; III – E; IV – B; V – D
      b. i – A; ii – E; iii – B; iv – D; v – C

Lesson 3.2, D7

With Fathom, students find the equation of the least squares line by creating a scatterplot and choosing **Least-Squares Line** from the Graph menu. They find the SSE by choosing **Show Squares** from the Graph menu. The output looks like this.

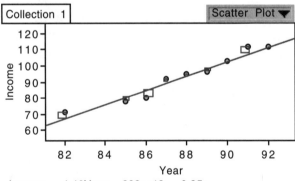

Income = 4.46Year - 299; r^2 = 0.95;
Sum of squares = 75.30

Alumni Giving Percentage Versus Student/Faculty Ratio

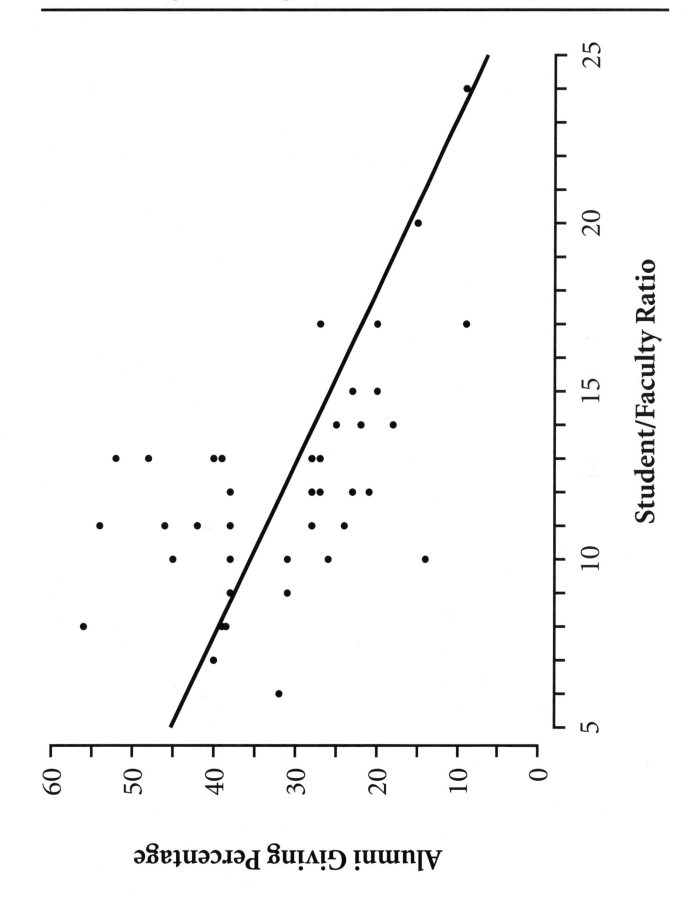

Operating Cost Versus Fuel Consumption Rate

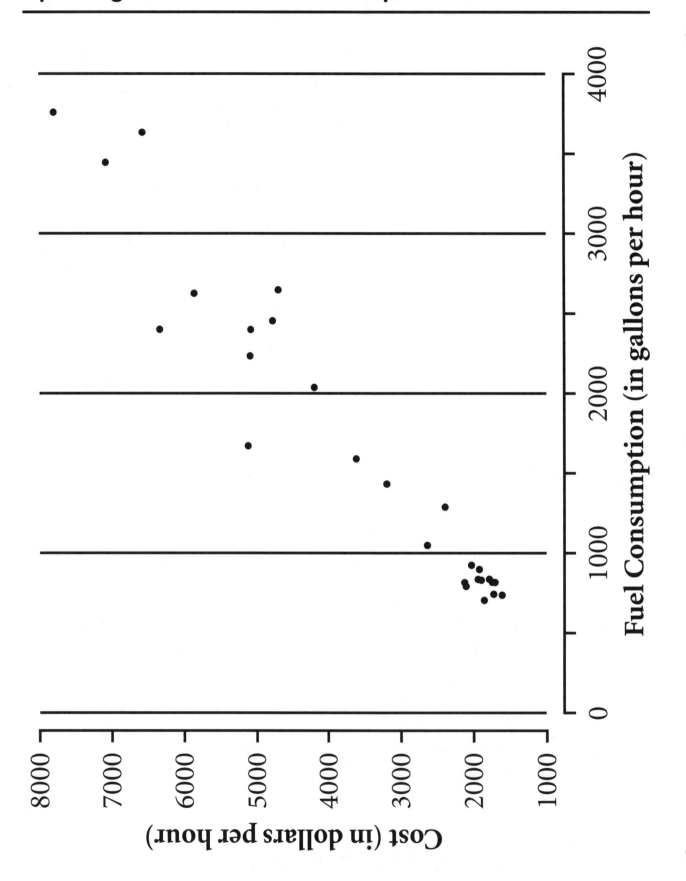

Statistics in Action Instructor's Guide
© 2004 Key Curriculum Press

3.3 Correlation: The Strength of a Linear Trend

Objectives

- to estimate correlation from a scatterplot
- to understand that correlation should not be computed from data that are not linear and that a high correlation does not mean that the data are linear
- to understand r as the average product of the z-scores
- to use the relationship between r and the slope of the regression line
- to be aware of possible lurking variables and not assume that correlation implies causation

The sections "Interpreting r^2" and "Regression Toward the Mean" are optional. The objectives for those sections are

- to interpret r^2 as the proportion of the variation in the values of y that can be explained by x
- to visualize the regression line as the line of the means of the values of y for fixed values of x
- to recognize the regression effect

Important Terms and Concepts

- correlation coefficient
- average product of z-scores
- lurking variable
- correlation versus causation

Optional Terms and Concepts

- r^2, the coefficient of variation, or $\frac{(\text{SST} - \text{SSE})}{\text{SST}}$
- regression line as the line of means
- regression toward the mean (the regression effect)

Lesson Planning

Class Time

Two days if neither of the optional sections ("Interpreting r^2" and "Regression Toward the Mean") is covered. Three days if the optional sections are covered.

Materials

For Activity 3.2, a measuring tape, a yardstick, or a meterstick for each pair of students

Suggested Assignments

Classwork		
Essential	**Recommended**	**Optional**
D8, D10, D11, D14, D15 P10–P12, P14–P16	Activity 3.2 D9, D12, D13, D16, D17 P13, P17	D18–D22 P18, P19

Homework		
Essential	**Recommended**	**Optional**
E23, E25–E27, E29, E30, E33, E37	E24, E31, E32	E28, E34–E36, E38, E39

Lesson Notes: The Strength of a Linear Trend

Once a linear trend is established (positive or negative) the strength of the association can be measured using the correlation coefficient. The correlation is a useful measure of strength only if the data are linear—clustered either loosely or tightly about a line.

Correlation

Francis Galton is credited with being the first to understand the idea of correlation (1888), which he called "co-relation." The correlation coefficient used in the text is called Pearson's correlation coefficient, after Karl Pearson, who introduced it in 1896. Other correlations not covered in this text include the rank correlation formulas of Charles Edward Spearman and Maurice G. Kendall. These give the correlation for paired observations that are ranks, such as the ranking of 10 gymnasts by Judge A paired with the ranking of the same 10 gymnasts by Judge B. If there are no ties in the ranks, Spearman's formula gives the same value as Pearson's.

What Happened to Normality?

The guiding features of analyzing data from Chapter 2 were

plot—shape—center—spread

In this section, they are interpreted for bivariate data as

scatterplot—shape—trend—strength

In Chapter 2, students were told that "normal" was the "ideal" shape—if a distribution is approximately normal, the mean and standard deviation generally are useful measures of center and variation. In this section, students are told that the ideal shape for a scatterplot is elliptical. With an elliptically shaped cloud of points, the regression line and the correlation are generally useful measures of center and variation. What happened to normality?

Look at Display 3.48 (page 148 of the student text) of a younger sister's height plotted against her older sister's height. The two "marginal" distributions, the separate distributions of the heights of the older sisters and the heights of the younger sisters, are approximately normal. Their "joint" distribution, the scatterplot, is an elliptical cloud that is more dense toward the middle than toward the edges. It is called a *bivariate normal distribution*. One characteristic of bivariate normal distributions that will be important in Chapter 11, "Inference for Regression," is that if you slice the distribution at any fixed value of x, the "conditional" distribution of the y's corresponding to that x is normal. The following diagram shows a bivariate normal distribution plotted as a function of two variables, $f(x, y)$. In this case, the distributions of x and y both have mean 0 and standard deviation 1; the correlation is .6.

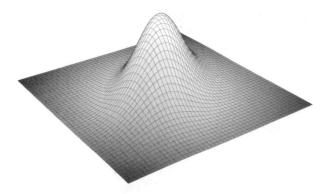

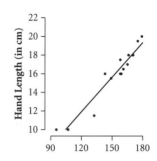

Activity 3.2 Was Leonardo Correct?

This activity is highly recommended. In order to orchestrate the sharing of data, you may wish to provide the blackline master provided at the end of this section and then have each student read his or her set of four values.

1. Student data sets will vary. Sample results from one group of children and teens are given in the following answers. These measurements are in centimeters.

2. If Leonardo is correct, the points should lie near the lines:

$$arm\ span = height$$

$$kneeling = \frac{3}{4}\ height$$

$$hand = \frac{1}{9}\ height$$

Looking at the plots here, these rules appear to be approximately correct. The lines are the least squares regression lines computed in Step 3.

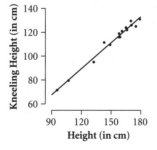

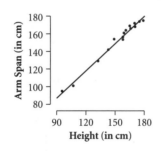

3. The least squares regression equation for predicting the arm span from the height is
arm span = −5.8128 + 1.03439 *height*; *r* = .99.

The least squares regression equation for predicting the kneeling height from the height is
kneeling = 2.1943 + 0.726933 *height*; *r* = .989.

The least squares regression equation for predicting the hand length from the height is
hand length = −2.9696 + 0.124118 *height*; *r* = .96.
In each case, the correlation is quite high, at least .96.

On many graphing calculators, for example the TI-83, you must perform the regression in order to calculate the correlation. You may need to instruct students to select **DiagnosticOn** from 2nd [CATALOG] in order for the calculator to display the correlation coefficient *r* and the coefficient of determination r^2.

4. For the first plot, the slope is 1.03. This means for every 1 cm increase in height, there tends to be a 1.03 cm increase in arm span. Leonardo predicted a 1 cm increase.

For the second plot, the slope is 0.73, which means that for every 1 cm increase in height, there tends to be a 0.73 cm increase in kneeling height. Leonardo predicted a 0.75 increase.

For the third plot, the slope is 0.12, which means that for every 1 cm increase in height, there tends to be a 0.12 cm increase in hand length. Leonardo predicted a $\frac{1}{9}$, or 0.11, increase.

In each case, the points are packed tightly about the regression line, so there is a strong correlation.

5. Leonardo's claims hold strongly. The slopes are about what he predicted, the *y*-intercepts are close to 0 in each case, and the correlations are high.

Discussion

D8.   **a.** .783   **b.** −.783   **c.** .999

        d. .885   **e.** −.572

D9. **a.** The second and third relationships are positive. The fourth relationship is negative because the more socks in a bag, the cheaper they tend to be per sock. The second relationship is the strongest, with $r = 1$. The first relationship is the weakest; r is almost 0.

b. For the first relationship, there should be no relationship between these two variables. That is, for any x students picked, the range of haircut costs will be about the same. This range will depend on local prices.

For the second relationship, y does vary with x, but for a fixed x, there will no variation in y. Each y will be exactly equal to πx.

For the third relationship, the more socks, generally, the more the price of the bag but with some variation because some brands of socks are more expensive than others. For a bag of, say, four socks, prices may range from $1.00 to $6.00.

For the fourth relationship, there will be some variation. Continuing with the example in the third relationship, the prices per sock for a bag of four socks would range from $0.25 to $1.50.

All else being equal, the larger the variation in y at each value of x, the lower the correlation.

Practice

P10. **a.** $-.5$ **b.** $.5$ **c.** $.95$
     d. 0 **e.** $-.95$

P11. $r = .885$

Lesson Notes: A Formula for the Correlation, *r*

You can use the spreadsheet capability of the TI-83 to speed the computation for the formula for the correlation on page 138 of the student text. Follow these steps:

1. Load the data into L1 and L2.

2. Run 2-VarSTATS L1, L2 from the STAT CALC menu.

3. Open the list screen from the STAT EDIT menu.

4. Highlight the name of the list L3. At the bottom of the screen, complete L3=(L1−x̄)/Sx. Press ENTER. Note that x̄, Sx, ȳ, Sy, and n are found on the VARS Statistics menu. 2-VarSTATS L1, L2 must be run first to update these values for our data set.

5. Repeat for L4, completing L4=(L2−ȳ)/Sy. Press ENTER.

6. Then let L5=L3*L4. Press ENTER.

7. Then r=sum(L5)/(n−1), where sum is found on the LIST [MATH] menu, item 5.

Discussion

D10. **a.** For Northwest,
$$\frac{x - \bar{x}}{s_x} = \frac{5.62 - 6.039}{1.14} = -0.36562$$
$$\frac{y - \bar{y}}{s_y} = \frac{75.0 - 66.26}{7.94} = 1.10076$$
$$\left(\frac{x - \bar{x}}{s_x}\right)\left(\frac{y - \bar{y}}{s_y}\right) = (-0.36562)(1.10076)$$
$$= -0.40246$$

b. United, in the lower right corner of Quadrant IV, has the largest $z_x \cdot z_y$ in absolute value.

c. TWA, near $(\bar{x}, \bar{y})$, has the smallest value of $|z_x \cdot z_y|$. (A point will make a small contribution if it is either near $(\bar{x}, \bar{y})$ or near one of the lines $x = \bar{x}$ or $y = \bar{y}$.)

D11. **a.** The correlation measures the strength of a linear association by measuring how tightly packed the data points are about a straight line. Its size is affected most strikingly by points far away from $(\bar{x}, \bar{y})$ and not near the new coordinate axes, $x = \bar{x}$ and $y = \bar{y}$.

b. Correlation is a unitless quantity because it is the average product of z-scores, which have no units. For example, the unit for mishandled bags is *bags per 1000 passengers*. When computing the z-scores, the units cancel out. For Northwest, this would be
$$\frac{x - \bar{x}}{s_x} = \frac{5.62 \text{ bags}/1000 - 6.039 \text{ bags}/1000}{1.146 \text{ bags}/1000}$$
$$= -0.36562$$

c. No. Because it is based on a symmetric calculation, $z_x \cdot z_y = z_y \cdot z_x$, r does not depend on which variable is chosen as x and which as y.

D12. This problem isn't as much work as it looks. Notice that for the first four tables, the means are all 0 and the standard deviations are all 1, so they have already been standardized. You can find the average product in your head. Table e has the same correlation as table a, table f has the same as table c, table g has the same as table b, and table h has the same as table c.

a. 1   b. .5   c. −.5
d. −1   e. 1   f. −.5
g. .5   h. −.5

D13. **a.** For well-behaved data, the correlation will be positive because most of the products $z_x \cdot z_y$ are positive. It is not necessarily the case that r is positive, however. The scatterplot here has more points in Quadrants I and III, but the correlation is negative, $r = -.237$.

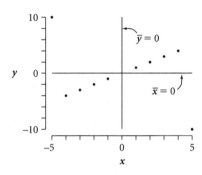

b. For well-behaved data, the correlation will be negative because most of the products $z_x \cdot z_y$ are negative. As in part a, it is not necessarily the case that r is negative.

c. The correlation probably will be near 0.

Practice

P12. Refer to the table below.

$$r = \frac{5.3068}{6} = .884$$

This is about the same value as in P11, except the calculator does less rounding and so is more accurate in the third decimal place.

All products are positive, resulting in a positive correlation. The second pizza contributes a large amount, making the correlation quite strong.

P13. **a.** Positive.
b. The point at the extreme upper right of the plot at about (5, 5) will make the largest positive contribution to the correlation because it is farthest away from the new origin $(\bar{x}, \bar{y})$ and from the new coordinate axes $(x = \bar{x})$ and $(y = \bar{y})$ and so has a large $z_x \cdot z_y$.
c. In Quadrants I and III; 20 have a positive product.
d. In Quadrants II and IV; 7 have a negative product.

Discussion

D14. Using the previous formula, an estimate of the slope is

$$b_1 = r \cdot \frac{s_{verbal}}{s_{math}} = .7 \cdot \frac{111}{113} \approx 0.688$$

To find the y-intercept, use the fact that the point (514, 505) is on the regression line:

$$verbal = b_1 \cdot math + b_0$$
$$505 = 0.688(514) + b_0$$
$$b_0 = 151.368$$

The equation is

$$verbal = 151.368 + 0.688 \ math$$

Lesson 3.3, P12

	Original Units		Standard Units (z-scores)			Product
	Fat (g)	Calories	$z_x = \dfrac{x - \bar{x}}{s_x}$	$z_y = \dfrac{y - \bar{y}}{s_y}$	$z_x \cdot z_y = \left(\dfrac{x - \bar{x}}{s_x}\right)\left(\dfrac{y - \bar{y}}{s_y}\right)$	
	9	305	−1.00743	−0.98535	0.99267	
	16	382	1.59480	1.83517	2.92671	
	14	338	0.85130	0.22344	0.19022	
	9	327	−1.00743	−0.17949	0.18082	
	10	309	−0.63569	−0.83883	0.53323	
	11	313	−0.26394	−0.69231	0.18273	
	13	349	0.47955	0.62637	0.30038	
Total	82	2323	0	0	5.3068	
Mean	11.71	331.9	0	0		
SD	2.69	27.3	1	1		

Practice

P14. **a.** The correlation is .650:

$$b_1 = r \cdot \frac{s_y}{s_x}$$

$$0.368 = r \cdot \frac{7}{12.37}$$

$$r = .650$$

b. The regression equation is
Exam 2 = 48.94 + 0.368 *Exam 1*.
The predicted *Exam 2* score is 78.38.

c. The regression equation is
Exam 1 = −14.1 + 1.149 *Exam 2*.

d.

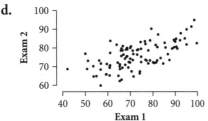

Lesson Notes: Correlation Does Not Imply Cause and Effect

Students will learn in Chapter 4 that to establish that one variable "causes" another, you must perform a randomized comparative experiment. Using observational data, such as the fact that smokers get more lung cancer than nonsmokers, does not establish that smoking causes lung cancer because other factors are not controlled, by randomization or otherwise.

For example, to establish that breathing cigarette smoke causes tumors in rats, you would have to randomly assign several treatments—no smoke and various amounts of smoke—to different rats and see whether the rats exposed to more smoke develop significantly more tumors. If they do and the rats were otherwise treated alike, you can say that cigarette smoke causes tumors in rats.

Causation is a tricky issue at this stage, not only because students haven't yet studied experimental design but also because of the various meanings of the word "cause." In some cases, there are known physical reasons that establish cause and effect, such as fire "causing" smoke. Scientists did not do a randomized comparative experiment to establish that fire "causes" smoke. In other cases, we can't determine a physical link but rely on statistical evidence, as we do when we say that receiving love and praise during childhood "causes" good behavior. In the best of all worlds, causation is established using both kinds of evidence: a probable physical link along with statistical evidence, preferably in the form of a randomized comparative experiment. For example, both kinds of evidence have been used to establish that cigarette smoking causes cancer. Often the statistical evidence leads scientists to look for a physical link. Once that link is established, we do not need more experiments.

Discussion

D15. It is possible that having planes arrive late would result in more bags not making their connecting flight and so end up mishandled. This would result in a negative correlation between percentage of on-time arrivals and number of mishandled bags. It is also possible that there is no direct link between the variables but that both are a result of the lurking variable of whether or not the airline is generally well run.

D16. At first glance, it would seem that the more highly rated the university, the lower its acceptance rate. One possible explanation is that few students apply to the most selective of these universities unless they are pretty sure they will be admitted. You would not say that one variable causes the other, rather that they are both associated with the most savvy students. Another possible lurking variable is that the very best students apply to more colleges because they are shopping for the college that will offer them the best deal. As a result, the more highly rated colleges must accept a high percentage of the students that apply because they know the students have applied many places and are likely to go elsewhere even if they are admitted.

D17. **a.** Some might say that a high percentage of males "causes" higher salaries because men are more favorably treated than women when it comes to salary. On the other hand, the lurking variable may be how quantitative the subject is. There tend to be far fewer graduates in quantitative subjects, and business and industry want to hire them also; therefore, these faculty positions are harder to fill. This may be the reason the people in those subjects (who tend to be male) are more highly paid.

b. Some people might say that a high number of hate groups "causes" a large number of people on death row because members of hate groups tend to commit murders. On the other hand, an obvious lurking variable here is the size of the state's population. Larger states have more of everything. In fact, in percentage terms, hate crimes account for a small proportion of those on death row. To determine whether more hate groups in a state results in more people on death row because of hate crimes, you might look at a scatterplot of the percentage of people on death row because of hate crimes against the percentage of people in the state who belong to hate groups.

c. Some people might say that a high rate of gun ownership "causes" lower rates of violent crime by making criminals reluctant to commit violent crime for fear the person will protect him- or herself with a gun. On the other hand, the explanation may be the lurking variable of how rural the state is. Rural areas have higher rates of gun ownership, presumably for hunting, and have lower reported crime.

Practice

P15. **a.** The size of the city's population.
b. You should divide each number by the population of the city to get the number of fast-food franchises per person and the proportion of the people who get stomach cancer.

P16. An obvious lurking variable is the age of the child. Parents tend to give higher allowances to older children, and vocabulary is larger for older children than for younger.

P17. A careless conclusion would be that people are too busy watching television to have babies. The lurking variable is how affluent the people in the country are. More affluent people tend to have more televisions and have fewer children.

Lesson Notes: Interpreting r^2

In the regression examples in this textbook, there is one predictor variable, x, and one response variable, y. But in many situations, there is more than one predictor variable. For example, in predicting the probability an entering student will graduate from a given college, the college may want to include such predictor variables as high school GPA, SAT scores,

and number of hours worked per week in the regression. This is called multiple regression.

The formula for r does not generalize to regression where there is more than one predictor variable, but the idea of r^2 as the proportion of variance accounted for by the regression does.

One of the reasons that statistical software gives the value of r^2, or R-squared, rather than the correlation r is that R-squared does generalize to multiple regression. The values for SSE and SST can still be computed, the former as the sum of the squared residuals from the fitted plane $\sum(y - \hat{y})^2$ and the latter still as the sum of the squares of the differences of the response value from its mean $\sum(y - \bar{y})^2$.

What Is R-sq(adjusted)?

Statistical software gives not only the value of r^2 (sometimes seen as R-squared or R-sq) but also a value for "R-squared(adjusted)," which is slightly smaller. Although introductory students should ignore this for now, it is actually the better value to use if your data are from a sample and you would like an approximately unbiased estimate of the r^2 for the entire population.

Discussion

D18. The mean number of calories is 331.86, so the fourth column is
$y - \hat{y} = 305 - 331.86 = -26.86$
which matches the value in the table. The regression equation is
calories $= 226.74 + 8.974$ *fat*
so the number of predicted calories $\hat{y}$ is
calories $= 226.74 + 8.974(9) = 307.506$
which is the same as in the table.
The final column should be
$305 - 307.506 = -2.51$
again the same as in the table.

D19. Rewrite the ratio as follows:
$$r^2 = \frac{SST - SSE}{SSE} = 1 - \frac{SSE}{SST}$$
Because SSE is less than or equal to SST and both are positive, the ratio $\frac{SSE}{SST}$ will always be between 0 and 1 inclusive. Thus, r^2 will always be between 0 and 1 inclusive. So r must always be between -1 and 1 inclusive.

D20. The number of "heating units" used by a house varies from year to year. A good predictor of how many units that will be is temperature. The investigator is saying that temperature accounts for 70%($r^2 = .7$) of the year-to-year variation.

Practice

P18. **a.** The formula relating these quantities is

$$r^2 = \frac{\text{SST} - \text{SSE}}{\text{SST}} = \frac{1050.76 - 469.22}{1050.76} \approx .5534$$

from which $r = -.744$. Note that the minus sign must be included because the slope of the regression line is negative (the scatterplot goes downhill).

b. The slope of -0.61 tells us that if one state has a graduation rate that is one percentage point higher than another, we expect its poverty rate to be lower by 0.61 percentage points.

c. No. Although it seems reasonable that it might be the case, the existence of a negative correlation alone does not allow us to say that a state can reduce its poverty rate by increasing graduation rates. There might be a lurking variable behind the negative correlation, such as the type of industry in the state. Some types may encourage people to stay in school to get needed training and also pay well enough to keep people above the poverty line.

d. x is in percentage of people, y is in percentage of families, b_1 is in percentage of families per percentage of people, and r has no units.

Lesson Notes: Regression Toward the Mean

Discussion

D21. The regression line is a "line of means" because it attempts to go through the mean value of the y's at each fixed value of x. That is, the regression line estimates the mean value of y for each fixed value of x.

D22. Two older sisters 1 inch apart in height will, on the average, have two younger sisters that are only 0.337 inches apart. For the line $y = x$, the interpretation would be that if one older sister is 1 inch taller than another, her younger sister also tends to be 1 inch taller than the younger sister of the other older sister. The latter interpretation is what most people would expect. But the element

of chance involved results in the "regression effect" that the younger sister is not as tall as expected.

Practice

P19. The plot should look similar to one of the two options shown here. The regression line is flatter than the line connecting the endpoints of the ellipse. This plot shows the regression effect as well. This time, it is the older sisters of the taller younger sisters who tend to be less tall than their younger sisters!

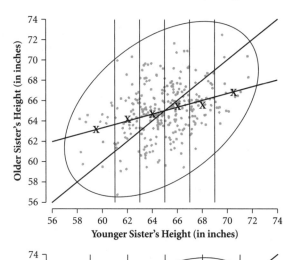

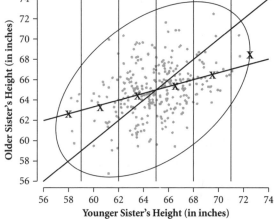

Exercises

E23. The correlations of the scatterplots are

a. .66	**b.** .25	**c.** $-.06$
d. .40	**e.** .85	**f.** .52
g. .90	**h.** .74	

E24. **a.** about $-.46$
b. about .65
c. about .53

E25. **a.** $r = .707$
b. $r = .707$

E26. A scatterplot is given here. We might expect that the more expensive cheese pizzas have more cheese and therefore more fat, but that doesn't appear to be the case. The correlation between *fat* and *cost* is very low and is negative. Students should compute the correlation using a table to get $r = -.179$. However, we should not make too much of this correlation for only seven pizzas, especially because there is one outlier in cost that is solely responsible for the negative value for r.

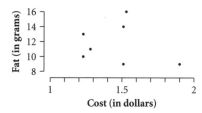

It is interesting that if you look at all of the pizzas (from Exercise 21 on page 134 of the student text), the correlation is moderately negative, $r = -.322$. (See the next scatterplot.) The negative association may be a result of low-fat cheese pizza containing other expensive ingredients in order to be tasty.

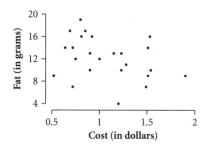

E27. Definitely not. The points on the scatterplot below all lie on the graph of $y = 2^x$, which is exponential, not linear. Yet the correlation is .894.

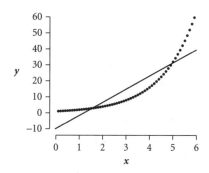

E28. **a.** (*calories, fat*) .95
(*calories, saturated fat*) .95
(*calories, sodium*) $-.5$
(*fat, saturated fat*) .95
(*fat, sodium*) $-.5$
(*saturated fat, sodium*) $-.5$

b. If you use more salt in your food, it will reduce the calories.

c. The lurking variable is whether the cheese is low-fat. Fat makes cheese taste good. In order to make up for this in low-fat cheese, manufacturers may add more salt.

E29. **a.** Not unless $s_x = s_y$. But even then, the units will be different. For example, for the group that measures in chirps per second and uses temperature for x, the units of the slope will be chirps per second per degree temperature. For the group that measures in chirps per minute, the units will be chirps per minute per degree temperature. So the slope for the second group should be 60 times that of the first group. For a group that measures in chirps per minute and uses chirps for x, the units of the slope will be degrees temperature per chirps per minute. Even if they use the same units, groups that interchange x and y will get different slopes (chirps per minute per degrees Centigrade, or degrees Centigrade per chirps per minute).

b. Yes. The correlation is the same no matter what the units or what you use for x and for y. That is because r is equal to the average product of z-scores, which have no units and $z_x \cdot z_y = z_y \cdot z_x$.

E30. **a.** An estimate of the slope is

$$b_1 = r \frac{s_y}{s_x} = -.5 \cdot \frac{.083}{4.3} \approx -0.00965$$

To find the y-intercept, use the fact that the point $(\bar{x}, \bar{y}) = (11.7, .827)$ is on the regression line:

$$y = \text{slope} \cdot x + y\text{-intercept}$$

$$.827 = -0.00965(11.7) + y\text{-intercept}$$

y-intercept $= 0.940$

The equation is $\hat{y} = -0.00965x + 0.940$.

b. An estimate of the slope is

$$b_1 = r \frac{s_y}{s_x} = -.5 \cdot \frac{4.3}{.083} \approx -25.90$$

To find the y-intercept, use the fact that the point $(\bar{x}, \bar{y}) = (.827, 11.7)$ is on the regression line:

$$y = \text{slope} \cdot x + y\text{-intercept}$$
$$11.7 = -25.90(.827) + y\text{-intercept}$$
$$y\text{-intercept} = 33.12$$

The equation is $\hat{y} = -25.90x + 33.12$.

E31. a. True. This is a direct result of the formula

$$b_1 = r\frac{s_y}{s_x}$$

If $s_x < s_y$, the factor on the right, s_y/s_x, will be greater than 1, which makes b_1 greater in absolute value than r.

b. The formula

$$1.6 = .8 \cdot \frac{s_y}{s_x}$$

can be true only if $s_x = 25$ and $s_y = 50$.

c. $\quad b_1 = r\frac{s_{estimated}}{s_{actual}}$

$$0.36 = r \cdot \frac{4.12}{0.93}$$
$$r = .081$$

d. $b_1 = r\frac{s_{actual}}{s_{estimated}}$

$$b_1 = .081 \cdot \frac{0.93}{4.12}$$
$$b_1 = 0.0183$$

E32. a. i. B $\qquad$ **ii.** C $\qquad$ **iii.** A

b. i.

ii.

E33. a. A large brain helps animals live smarter and therefore longer. The lurking variable is overall size of the animal. Larger animals tend to develop more slowly, from gestation to "childhood" through old age.

b. If we kept the price of cheeseburgers down, college would be more affordable. The lurking variable is inflation over the years—all costs have gone up over the years.

c. The Internet is good for business. The lurking variable is years. Stock prices generally go up due to inflation over the years. The Internet is new technology, and so the number of Internet sites also is increasing over the years.

E34. Examples will vary. Students are likely to think of examples where the cases are years and the two variables are increasing because of the lurking variable of time, which is linked to both inflation and population increases.

E35. Scoring exceptionally well, for example, on a test involves more than just studying the material. There is a certain amount of randomness involved, too—the teacher asked questions about what the student knew, the student was feeling well that day, the student was not distracted, and so on. It's unlikely that this combination of knowing the material and good luck will happen again on the next test for this same student. The student probably will get a lower, but still high, score on the next test even if he or she doesn't slack off. However, it would appear as if doing well the first time and getting praised prompted the student to relax and study less. On the second test, the student's place at the top of the class may be taken by another student who knew just as much for the first test but was also effected by randomness on the first test—perhaps unlucky in the questions the teacher chose or unlucky in another way at the time.

At the other end, a student who scores exceptionally poorly on the first test also has a bit of randomness involved—bad luck this time. Whether or not he or she is praised, the student scoring exceptionally poorly probably won't have all of the random factors go against him or her on the next test and the student's score will tend to be higher.

E36. This is an example of the regression effect. The explanation is similar to that of E35.

E37. a. $r^2 = \dfrac{SST - SSE}{SST}$

$= \dfrac{0.088740 - 0.016304}{0.088740} \approx .8163$

So $r = .903$. The value of r^2 above is equal to the "R-sq" in the regression analysis.

b. The largest residual occurs for the point $(55, 0.318)$. Its value is

$y - \hat{y} = 0.318 - [0.202 + 0.00306(55)]$

$= 0.318 - 0.3703$

$= -0.0523$

c. Yes. Hot weather causes people to want to eat something cold. But the correlation alone does not tell us that.

d. Degrees Fahrenheit, pints per person, pints per person per degree Fahrenheit, and no units.

e. "MS" was computed by dividing "SS" by "DF." It stands for "mean square."

E38. a. The scatterplot of *hat size* versus *circumference* appears here. An estimate for the correlation of about .9 is good. The correlation is actually .942.

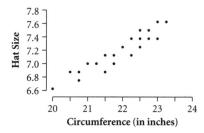

Circumference (in inches)

b. The table of standardized values used to calculate a correlation coefficient is provided below.

Circumference	Hat Size	z_x	z_y	$z_x \cdot z_y$
20.00	6.625	−2.04	−1.95	3.99
20.75	6.750	−1.21	−1.51	1.83
20.50	6.875	−1.49	−1.07	1.59
20.75	6.875	−1.21	−1.07	1.30
20.75	6.875	−1.21	−1.07	1.30
21.50	6.875	−0.38	−1.07	0.41
21.25	7.000	−0.66	−0.63	0.41
21.00	7.000	−0.94	−0.63	0.59
21.00	7.000	−0.94	−0.63	0.59
21.75	7.000	−0.11	−0.63	0.07
21.50	7.125	−0.38	−0.19	0.07

(continued)

Circumference	Hat Size	z_x	z_y	$z_x \cdot z_y$
21.75	7.125	−0.11	−0.19	0.02
21.50	7.125	−0.38	−0.19	0.07
22.25	7.125	0.45	−0.19	−0.08
22.00	7.250	0.17	0.25	0.04
22.50	7.250	0.72	0.25	0.18
22.25	7.375	0.45	0.70	0.31
22.25	7.373	0.45	0.70	0.31
22.50	7.375	0.72	0.70	0.50
22.75	7.375	1.00	0.70	0.70
23.00	7.375	1.28	0.70	0.89
22.75	7.500	1.00	1.14	1.14
22.50	7.500	0.72	1.14	0.82
23.00	7.625	1.28	1.58	2.02
23.00	7.625	1.28	1.58	2.02
23.25	7.625	1.55	1.58	2.45

Summing the last column and dividing by $n - 1 = 25$ gives $r = .942$.

c. The point contributing the largest amount to the correlation is $(20.0, 6.625)$, at the lower-left end of the scatterplot. The point contributing the smallest amount is $(21.75, 7.125)$, very close to the middle of the scatterplot near the point of means $(\bar{x}, \bar{y})$.

d. The scatterplot of *hat size* versus *major axis* appears here. An estimate of the correlation around .95 would be a good one. The correlation is actually .968.

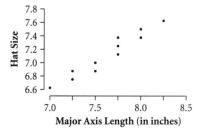

Major Axis Length (in inches)

e. The scatterplot is shown here. An estimate around .9 would be a good one. The correlation is actually .898.

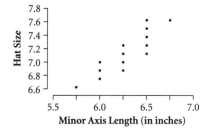

Minor Axis Length (in inches)

f. Either the circumference or the major axis appears to be a good predictor of a person's hat size. Some students may like circumference better because it has more "continuous" looking measurements spaced along the x-axis. High correlation with the response variable of interest is one thing to look for in a good predictor, but the final decision should never rest on correlation alone. Always look at a plot to see other features of the relationship being studied.

E39. **a.** A scatterplot matrix appears on page 111, and as a blackline master on page 113. Two pairs of variables are quite linear, both with negative relationships—the percentage of adults who have graduated from high school and the poverty rate, and the percentage of

Whites and the percentage of families headed by a single parent (with two different kinds of outliers, Hawaii and D.C.).

b. All correlations appear in this table. The strongest are the negative relationship between the percentage of adults who are high school graduates and the poverty rate, and the negative relationship between the percentage who are White and the percentage of families headed by a single parent.

	Metro	White	HS Grads	Poverty
White	−0.337			
HS Grads	−0.004	0.338		
Poverty	−0.061	−0.389	−0.744	
S Parent	0.260	−0.657	−0.220	0.549

c. Answers will vary.

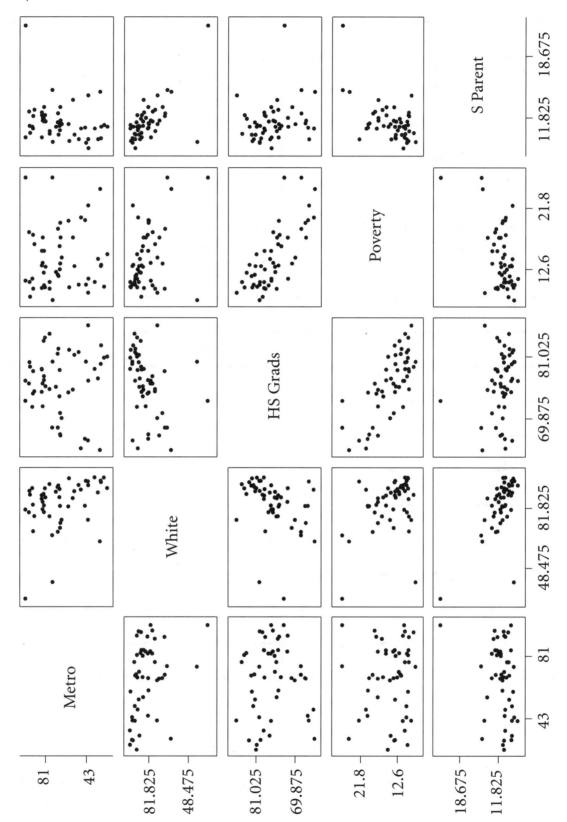

Activity 3.2 Was Leonardo Correct?

Height	Kneeling Height	Arm Span	Hand Length

Statistics in Action Instructor's Guide
© 2004 Key Curriculum Press

Relationships Between Poverty Rates and Four Variables

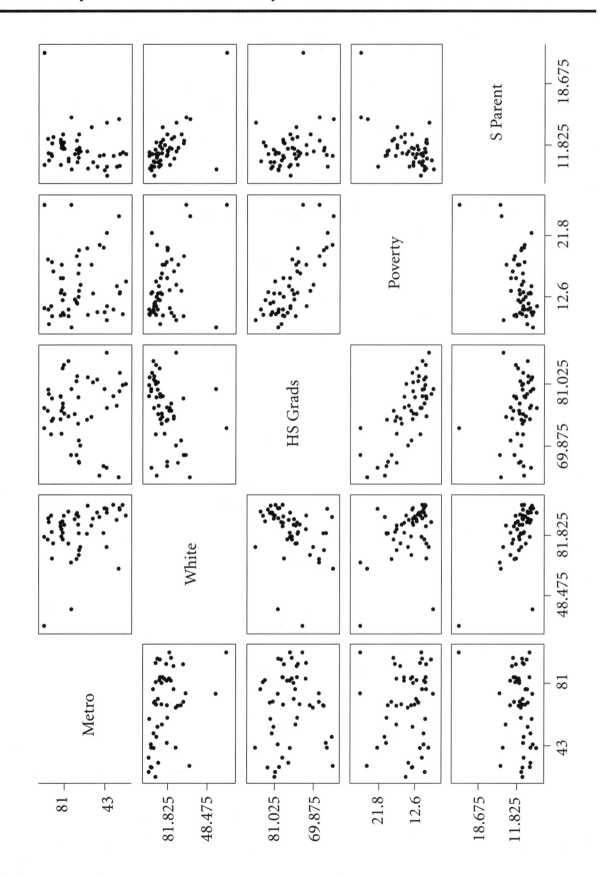

3.4 Diagnostics: Looking for Features That the Summaries Miss

Objectives

- to identify a potential influential point by examining a scatterplot
- to determine whether a point is influential by excluding it when computing the correlation and equation of the regression line
- to make and interpret a residual plot

Important Terms and Concepts

- influential point
- outlier
- predictor x

- predicted y, or $\hat{y}$
- residual plot

Lesson Planning

Class Time

One to two days

Materials

For Activity 3.3, a piece of paper for recording data

Suggested Assignments

Classwork		
Essential	**Recommended**	**Optional**
Activity 3.3	P20	
D23–D29		
P21–P23		

Homework		
Essential	**Recommended**	**Optional**
E40, E41, E43, E44, E46–E48	E42, E45, E51, E52	E49, E50

Lesson Notes: Influential Points and Outliers

You identify an influential point by "removing" the candidate from the data set and then recomputing the correlation and regression equation to see how much they change. If they change only a little, the point isn't influential. Students should not infer that a large change means that the point should be permanently discarded. Typically, a point should remain in the data set, but students should conclude that correlation and linear regression might not be suitable summary statistics for those data. If a point is an outlier, like all outliers, it should be carefully examined for a possible error in recording data.

Outliers and influential points are two separate ideas. In particular, some influential points may not be outliers. The example on animal longevity on page 156 in the student text covers both outliers and influential points.

Activity 3.3 Near and Far

You can have each student bring an index card or a piece of paper and have them list their six locations, their estimates, and their step count in columns. Answers will vary because students analyze their own data. For some students the far point may be very influential on the slope (in either direction), and for others it may not be. If the far point is far removed from the data, it will almost always have considerable influence on the correlation, even if it does not affect the slope.

1–3. A sample set of data from one student is shown next. He or she consistently underestimated distances.

Estimate (x)	Actual (y)
3	3
21	34
25	48
28	63
40	146
180	350

4–6. The scatterplots with and without the "far" point are shown here, along with the regression summaries and the correlations. The trend

appears linear in the first plot only because of the far point. In the second plot, the trend is a curve. Proportionally, the far point was not off by as much as some of the others, which show increasingly bad estimates with farther distance.

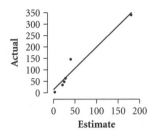

```
Dependent variable is:    Actual
No Selector
R squared = 94.6%    R squared (adjusted) = 93.2%
s = 32.40 with 6 - 2 = 4 degrees of freedom

Source      Sum of Squares   df   Mean Square   F-ratio
Regression  73163.2           1   73163.2       69.7
Residual    4198.14           4   1049.53

Variable  Coefficient  s.e. of Coeff  t-ratio  prob
Constant  13.6176      17.22          0.791    0.4733
Estimate  1.85958      0.2227         8.35     0.0011
```

$r = .972$

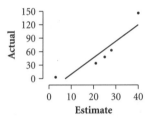

```
Dependent variable is:    Actual
No Selector
6 total cases of which 1 is missing
R squared = 84.8%    R squared (adjusted) = 79.7%
s = 24.14 with 5 - 2 = 3 degrees of freedom

Source      Sum of Squares   df   Mean Square   F-ratio
Regression  9718.15           1   9718.15       16.7
Residual    1748.65           3   582.885

Variable  Coefficient  s.e. of Coeff  t-ratio  prob
Constant  -27.0973     23.65          -1.15    0.3349
Estimate  3.67083      0.8990         4.08     0.0265
```

$r = .921$

7. Yes. Removing the far point decreased the correlation and almost doubled the slope. Although the far point doesn't follow the curved pattern of the other points, its distance from them results in a large $z_x \cdot z_y$ and so including it increases the correlation.

Lesson Notes: Why the Anscombe Data Sets Are Important

Discussion

D23. Plot I shows a positive linear trend that is moderately strong. Plot II shows points that lie along a curve. Plot III shows all points lying on a straight line except for the one point near the right end. (This point will have the effect of raising that end of the regression line fit through these points.) Plot IV has all but one of the points stacked up at the same value of *x*, although the outlier gives it a slight positive trend. (The regression line will go through the middle of the points on the left and through the isolated point on the right.)

a. A straight line is a good summary only for plot I. However, in all four plots the regression line has a slope of about 0.5 and an intercept of about 3.0. (See D24.)

b. The correlation is about .8 for plot I and should not be used to describe the others because it is a measure of the strength of a linear relationship.

D24. There is no way to tell which plot produced the given summary statistics. In fact, the summary statistics are essentially the same for all four plots. The moral? Draw a picture before you summarize data!

D25. a. Plots III and IV both have influential observations, but plot IV contains the more influential point. The influential point in plot IV is more isolated from the data and completely controls the slope of the regression line.

b. This influential point lies on the regression line through these data.

c. If the influential point (the isolated point) is removed from plot IV, all of the data points will stack up at the same value of x. Thus, a regression slope and correlation cannot be computed.

Practice

P20. Answers will vary because students analyze their own data. For some students the far point may be the only point of great influence; for others near points may be more influential on either the slope or the correlation.

P21. a. The scatterplot with the regression line is shown next. The data show no pattern except for the one outlier in the upper right.

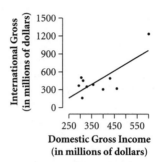

b. The regression summary is given here. The slope is positive, and the correlation appears to be fairly strong judging from the numerical summaries alone.

```
Dependent variable is:   International
No Selector
R squared = 57.4%    R squared (adjusted) = 52.1%
s = 201.6 with 10 - 2 = 8 degrees of freedom

Source       Sum of Squares  df  Mean Square  F-ratio
Regression   437912           1      437912     10.8
Residual     325226           8     40653.3

Variable   Coefficient  s.e. of Coeff  t-ratio   prob
Constant   -409.802       271.8         -1.51    0.1701
Domestic   2.28211        0.6953         3.28    0.0112
```

$$r = .758 \qquad \hat{y} = -409.80 + 2.28x$$

c. The plot and the numerical summary for the analysis without the influential point (*Titanic*) are shown here. Now both the slope and the correlation are very near zero. *Titanic* has a huge influence (as a big ship should).

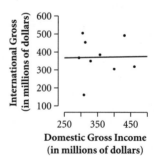

```
Dependent variable is:   International
No Selector
R squared = 0.0%    R squared (adjusted) = -14.2%
s = 114.2 with 9 - 2 = 7 degrees of freedom

Source       Sum of Squares  df  Mean Square  F-ratio
Regression   29.9510          1      29.9510    0.002
Residual     91262.0          7     13037.4

Variable   Coefficient  s.e. of Coeff  t-ratio   prob
Constant   359.734        238.1          1.51    0.1746
Domestic   0.031694       0.6613         0.048   0.9631
```

$$r = 0 \qquad \hat{y} = 359.73 + 0.03x$$

Lesson Notes: Residual Plots

Students can add a horizontal line to their hand-made residual plots where the *residual value* equals 0. This line will make it easier to visualize and evaluate where the model *overestimates* and *underestimates*. On a TI-83, the residual plot will display the "zero residual line" automatically.

Residual plot A in D28 presents a "good" residual plot, that is, one that displays random scatter and a fairly constant spread in the y's across all values of x.

The residual plots C and D in D28 are plots that show a pattern, whereas residual plot I in Display 3.65 is an example where the spread in y is not constant across all values of x. These residual plots show that a linear model is not the right model for the data.

Discussion

D26. Delta produces the residual on the extreme left of the plot, at point $(4, -2.93)$. Continental produces the seventh residual from the left and the second largest in absolute value at point $(6.21, 7.71)$.

D27. The residual plot shows nearly random scatter, with no obvious trends. This is the ideal shape for a residual plot, indicating that a straight line is a reasonable model for the trend in the original data.

D28. **a.** A–I; B–IV; C–II; D–III
b. The scatterplot shows the actual values of y and upward or downward trend but may obscure patterns in the residuals (or at least appear to diminish them a bit). The residual plots do not show the values of y or trend in the original data, but they do show the values of the residuals, and they make departures from linearity easier to see.

Practice

P22. **a.** A–IV; B–II; C–I; D–III
b. Curve with increasing slope: The residual plot will open upward, like a cup, as in plot II.

Curve with decreasing slope: The residual plot will open downward, like an inverted cup. No plot in this example shows this pattern.

Unequal variation in the responses: The residual plot has a fan shape, as in plot I.

Two linear patterns with different slopes: The residual plot will be V-shaped, as in plot III.

c. Plot D and residual plot III show a scatterplot that looks as though it should be modeled by two different straight lines. The V shape can be seen in the scatterplot, but it may be more obvious to many in the residual plot because the overall linear trend (tilt of the V) has been removed.

P23. **a.** The scatterplot with the regression line is shown next.

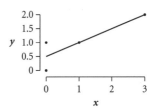

b. The table is as follows:

x	y	Predicted Value	Residual
0	0	0.5	-0.5
0	1	0.5	0.5
1	1	1	0
3	2	2	0

c. The residual plot is shown here.

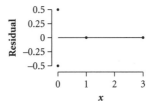

d. The residual plot straightens out the tilt in the scatterplot so that the residuals can be seen as deviations above and below zero rather than above and below a tilted line. The symmetry of the residuals in this example shows up better on the residual plot.

Discussion

D29. This question gives further information on plotting residuals versus x-values or predicted values, $\hat{y}$.

The only difference between the two residual plots is a matter of scaling. The second residual plot has essentially the same scale on the horizontal axis as the scatterplot, with x beginning at zero. Thus, it must be the one with residuals plotted versus x. The points on the first residual plot have horizontal scale values of 0.5, 1.0, and 1.5, which are the fitted values that are obtained when $\hat{y} = 0.5 + 0.5x$ and x is 0, 1, or 2, respectively. (See E52, page 170 of the student text, for more on this idea.)

Exercises

E40. **a.** The scatterplot appears here (with the regression line). A line is not a good model because the cloud of points is not elliptical.

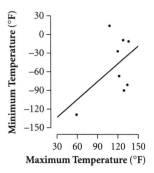

b. The equation is $\hat{y} = -161.17 + 0.95x$, and $r = .48$.

```
Dependent variable is:    Min
No Selector
R squared = 23.4%    R squared (adjusted) = 10.7%
s = 46.46 with 8 - 2 = 6 degrees of freedom

Source      Sum of Squares   df   Mean Square   F-ratio
Regression  3966.92          1    3966.92       1.84
Residual    12951.1          6    2158.51

Variable   Coefficient  s.e. of Coeff  t-ratio   prob
Constant   -161.169     83.63          -1.93     0.1023
Max        0.950159     0.7009         1.36      0.2240
```

c. With Antarctica removed, the correlation becomes negative, $r = -.46$ and the plot appears as shown here. (But a new potential influential point has appeared: Oceania.) Without a plot of the data, you might come to the following incorrect conclusion: In general, continents tend to be "warm" or "cold"; that is, continents with higher maximums also tend to have higher minimums. In fact, there is little relationship.

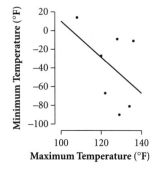

```
Dependent variable is:    Min
No Selector
8 total cases of which 1 is missing
R squared = 21.0%    R squared (adjusted) = 5.2%
s = 39.33 with 7 - 2 = 5 degrees of freedom

Source      Sum of Squares   df   Mean Square   F-ratio
Regression  2051.10          1    2051.10       1.33
Residual    7734.33          5    1546.87

Variable   Coefficient  s.e. of Coeff  t-ratio   prob
Constant   203.355      210.7          0.965     0.3789
Max        -1.93214     1.678          -1.15     0.3016
```

$$r = -.46 \qquad \hat{y} = 203.36 - 1.93x$$

E41. This scatterplot with regression line and regression summary is for the complete data set.

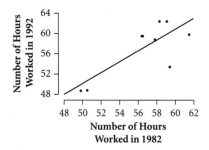

```
Dependent variable is:    Hrs92
No Selector
R squared = 61.9%    R squared (adjusted) = 56.5%
s = 3.545 with 9 - 2 = 7 degrees of freedom

Source      Sum of Squares   df   Mean Square   F-ratio
Regression  143.000          1    143.000       11.4
Residual    87.9798          7    12.5685

Variable   Coefficient  s.e. of Coeff  t-ratio   prob
Constant   -3.26936     17.92          -0.182    0.8604
Hrs82      1.06563      0.3159         3.37      0.0119
```

$$r = .79 \qquad \hat{y} = -3.27 + 1.07x$$

a. Upon removing radiology, the slope increases slightly because radiology is far below the right end of the regression line. The correlation increases considerably because radiology produces a large residual, which is now removed. The results are shown here.

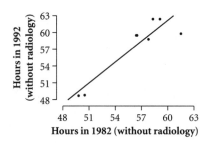

```
Dependent variable is:    Hrs92
No Selector
9 total cases of which 1 is missing
R squared = 83.9%   R squared (adjusted) = 81.2%
s = 2.408 with 8 - 2 = 6 degrees of freedom

Source      Sum of Squares   df   Mean Square   F-ratio
Regression  181.340          1    181.340       31.3
Residual    34.7892          6    5.79820

Variable   Coefficient   s.e. of Coeff   t-ratio   prob
Constant   -12.5140      12.55           -0.997    0.3571
Hrs82      1.24475       0.2226          5.59      0.0014
```

$$r = .92 \qquad \hat{y} = -12.51 + 1.24x$$

b. Removing psychiatry and pathology (but leaving radiology in the data set) removes the two points on the extreme left of the plot. Now, the left end of the regression line swings far upward, even to the point of producing a negative slope. Likewise, the correlation will become negative, but close to 0.

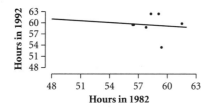

```
Dependent variable is:    Hrs92-PP
No Selector
9 total cases of which 2 are missing
R squared = 0.9%   R squared (adjusted) = -19.0%
s = 3.289 with 7 - 2 = 5 degrees of freedom

Source      Sum of Squares   df   Mean Square   F-ratio
Regression  0.468699         1    0.468699      0.043
Residual    54.0713          5    10.8143

Variable   Coefficient   s.e. of Coeff   t-ratio   prob
Constant   68.5590       44.01           1.56      0.1800
Hrs82-PP   -0.156756     0.7530          -0.208    0.8433
```

$$r = -.09 \qquad \hat{y} = 68.6 - 0.157x$$

c. Except for radiology, there is not much change in average number of hours worked over the decade from 1982 to 1992. There is a cluster of specialties averaging between 55 and 62 hours of work in both years and another smaller cluster of two specialties that average closer to 50 hours in both years. Within each group, there is no obvious trend.

E42. **a.** The scatterplot shows a positive and fairly strong linear trend except for one possibly influential point (obstetrics/gynecology) at the extreme right of the plot.

b. Obstetrics/gynecology is unusual in that it had the highest number of claims by far in

1985 but fell below the highest number in 1992. The point representing this specialty does not fit the pattern of the others. Possible explanations are that the claims against obstetrics/gynecology were excessive in 1985, or that this specialty got better between 1985 and 1992 or laws made it harder to sue.

c. The regression line is $\hat{y} = 0.42 + 0.88x$. Students' estimates may be different. The plot and regression summary are shown next. The slope is now quite close to 1, the y-intercept is close to 0, and the line fits the data very well. This indicates that the number of claims is very much the same for the two years.

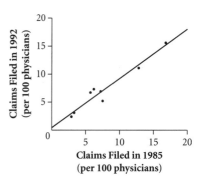

```
Dependent variable is:    Mal92
No Selector
9 total cases of which 1 is missing
R squared = 94.0%   R squared (adjusted) = 93.0%
s = 1.143 with 8 - 2 = 6 degrees of freedom

Source      Sum of Squares   df   Mean Square   F-ratio
Regression  122.075          1    122.075       93.5
Residual    7.83374          6    1.30562

Variable   Coefficient   s.e. of Coeff   t-ratio   prob
Constant   0.424410      0.8167          0.520     0.6219
Mal85      0.879883      0.0910          9.67      ≤0.0001
```

d. Yes, this is one possible reason that this specialty does not fit the pattern suggested by the others.

e. The fact that the rate for obstetrics/gynecology decreased much more than any other specialty resulted in a regression equation with a very small constant and a slope of only 0.58. This might suggest that the number of malpractice claims in 1992 was a little more than half what it was in 1985. That is not the case, as can be seen by the regression equation in part c where obstetrics/gynecology was omitted.

E43. **a.** The completed table is shown here.

Aircraft	Seats	Cost	Fitted	Residual
DC9-20	100	1750	1737.5	12.5
DC9-40	110	1800	1825.0	−25.0
DC9-50	120	1925	1912.5	12.5

b. The plot of the residuals versus x is given first followed by the plot of the residuals versus $\hat{y}$. The only difference between the two plots is the scaling on the horizontal axis.

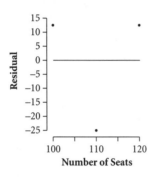

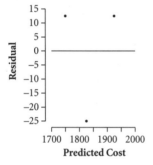

E44. **a.** The plot with the regression line and the regression summary are shown here. The equation of the line is $\hat{y} = -1.63 + 0.75x$.

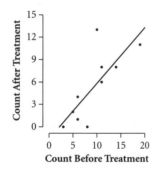

```
Dependent variable is:    y
No Selector
13 total cases of which 3 are missing
R squared = 58.4%    R squared (adjusted) = 53.2%
s = 3.177 with 10 - 2 = 8 degrees of freedom

Source       Sum of Squares    df    Mean Square    F-ratio
Regression   113.348            1    113.348         11.2
Residual     80.7516            8    10.0939

Variable   Coefficient   s.e. of Coeff   t-ratio   prob
Constant   -1.63057      2.299           -0.709    0.4984
x          0.745223      0.2224          3.35      0.0101
```

The completed table is as follows:

x	y	Fitted Values	Residual
11	6	6.567	−0.567
8	0	4.331	−4.331
5	2	2.096	−0.096
14	8	8.803	−0.803
19	11	12.529	−1.529
6	4	2.841	1.159
10	13	5.822	7.178
6	1	2.841	−1.841
11	8	6.567	1.433
3	0	0.605	−0.605

b. The residual plot shown here is a little unusual in that it shows more variability in the middle than at either end. But this is partly because there are more cases in the middle.

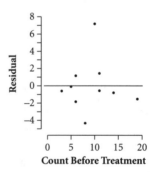

c. The disinfectant appears to be unusually effective for the person with the large negative residual, the point (8, 0) on the original scatterplot. It is seemingly ineffective for the person with the large positive residual, the point (10, 13) on the scatterplot.

E45. **a.** The pattern of the scatterplot is basically linear, so the slope is constant across the numbers of seats.

b. The spread in the flight lengths increases as the number of seats increases. The points fan out to the right.

c. This is a good bet only in the first case. It would be easier to predict flight length for planes with fewer numbers of seats because there is less variation in flight lengths for the smaller planes than for the larger.

d. The residual plot for this scatterplot also fans out (spread out more) as the number of seats increases. In fact, the fan shape may be seen better in the residual plot.

e. Planes that carry more passengers have more variation in their average flight lengths. This is because they tend to fly longer distances and there is a larger spread of numbers over which to vary. In general, larger numbers usually show a larger *absolute* variation than smaller ones. But the *relative* variation may be fairly constant. If you make a new variable defined as (*flight length*)/ (*number of seats*) and plot it versus *number of seats,* the fan shape disappears.

E46. **a.** The slope of the line is very close to 1, and the *y*-intercept is −3.57. This means that textbooks bought online tend to cost about $3.57 less than those bought at the college bookstore. (In fact, the mean cost of the college textbooks is $47.04, and the mean cost of the online textbooks is $45.03. Their difference is not $3.57 because the slope is not exactly equal to 1.)

b. The table for computing the residuals is shown here.

College	Online	Fitted	Residual
93.40	94.18	92.9281	1.2519
9.95	7.96	6.7092	1.2508
46.70	48.75	44.6786	4.0714
76.00	94.15	74.9508	19.1992
86.70	80.95	86.0058	−5.0558
7.95	6.36	4.6428	1.7171
24.00	16.80	21.2254	−4.4254
12.70	10.66	9.5505	1.1095
66.00	45.50	64.619	−19.119

The next residual plot shows that a line is a reasonable model for these data. The points are scattered randomly above and below 0, except that the points fan out to the right. This pattern indicates that the points lie farther from the regression line as the prices increase. It is easy to spot the two textbooks whose prices vary the most between the two types of bookstores. The calculus textbook is the one with residual about 19, meaning the online price is about $19 more than the price in the college bookstore. The art history textbook is the one with residual about −19, meaning the online price is about $19 less than the price in the college bookstore.

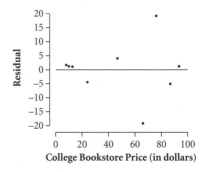

c. The plot with the line *y = x* is shown next. A point above the line represents a textbook that costs more at the online bookstore. A point below the line represents a point that costs less at the online bookstore. A point on the line represents a book that costs the same at both stores.

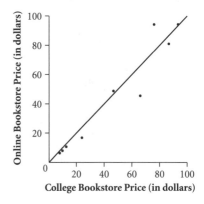

d. The boxplot is centered slightly above 0, indicating that most college bookstore prices tend to be slightly higher than the online prices. However, most of the differences are close to 0, so there is little difference in price. The median difference is about $2 more for the college bookstore. There are two outliers shown, which means that for two textbooks, the prices vary greatly, in one case being less expensive at the college bookstore and in the other case being less expensive at the online bookstore. The overall lesson is that with more expensive textbooks, it pays to shop around.

E47. No, for plot A. First, residual plots must center at zero on the vertical axis (the residuals must have a mean of zero). Second, the pictured pattern is impossible for residuals because the major linear trend shown here would already have been removed by fitting the regression line. The residuals show what is left over after any linear trend is removed from the data.

No, for plot B. These residuals do not have a mean of zero. Residual plots may, however, show a curved pattern that could come from a scatterplot that wrapped around a line. The plot shown here is an altered residual plot with the vertical scale slightly changed.

E48. The residuals are what are left over after a straight line has already modeled the linear trend. Thus, there cannot be a linear trend left in the residuals. A regression line fit through a residual plot will have a slope of zero.

E49. Scatterplots of the data, without and with the regression line, are shown here. Note that a linear model is not a good one for predicting life expectancy from GNP.

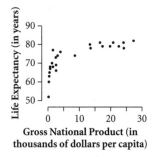

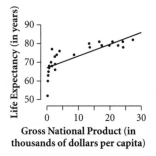

E50. Scatterplots of the original data, without and with the regression line, follow the commentary.

To estimate the recommended weight for a person whose height is 64 inches, add the fitted weight (given to be 145 pounds) to the residual of about 1.2 to get 146.2. The slope of the regression line must be about $(187 - 145)/(76 - 64) = 3.5$. For the second height, 65 inches, the fitted weight would be $145 + 3.5(1) = 148.5$. The residual is about 0.9 pounds. Thus, the recommended weight is about $148.5 + 0.9 = 149.4$ pounds. You could continue point by point to get the next plot, but a rough sketch can be obtained by making use of the linear patterns in the residuals (and hence in the original scatterplot). The points on the scatterplot must form a straight line up to a height of 71, where the weight must be about $145 + 7(3.5) - 1.5 = 168.0$.

The remainder of the points must form (approximately) another straight line up to a height of 76, where the weight must be about $145 + 12(3.5) + 2.2 = 189.2$.

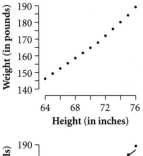

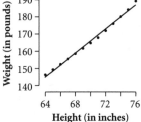

It is difficult to see the strong V shape of the residuals in a scatterplot drawn on the actual scale of the data.

E51. **a.** Here is what the residual plot for these data actually looks like.

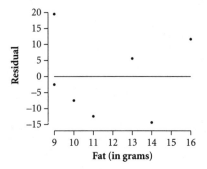

b. The largest positive residual belongs to Domino's Hand Tossed, which has more calories than would be predicted from a simple linear model. The largest negative residual belongs to Pizza Hut's Pan. None appear so far away that it would be called an exception, or outlier. In fact, you can check this by making a boxplot of the residuals, as shown here.

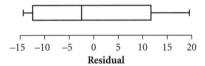

c. The regression summary for the complete data set shows a moderately strong positive trend with a slope of about 9 calories per gram of fat.

```
Dependent variable is:    Calories
No Selector
R squared = 78.3%    R squared (adjusted) = 73.9%
s = 13.94 with 7 - 2 = 5 degrees of freedom

Source       Sum of Squares   df   Mean Square   F-ratio
Regression   3497.17           1    3497.17       18.0
Residual      971.684          5     194.337

Variable   Coefficient   s.e. of Coeff   t-ratio    prob
Constant   226.737        25.33           8.95      0.0003
Fat          8.97368        2.115          4.24      0.0082
```

The most influential data point might be the one with the largest residual (Domino's Hand Tossed). On the other hand, it might be the one farthest away from the main cloud of points on the *x*-axis (Domino's Deep Dish). Removing Domino's Hand Tossed yields the following analysis.

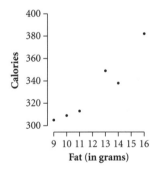

```
Dependent variable is:    Calories
No Selector
7 total cases of which 1 is missing
R squared = 90.6%    R squared (adjusted) = 88.2%
s = 10.23 with 6 - 2 = 4 degrees of freedom

Source       Sum of Squares   df   Mean Square   F-ratio
Regression   4022.74           1    4022.74       38.4
Residual      418.593          4     104.648

Variable   Coefficient   s.e. of Coeff   t-ratio    prob
Constant   201.919        21.50           9.39      0.0007
Fat         10.7464         1.733          6.20      0.0034
```

The slope is still around 10 calories per gram, but the correlation has risen considerably. The following analysis occurs when Domino's Deep Dish is removed.

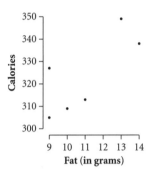

```
Dependent variable is:    Calories
No Selector
7 total cases of which 1 is missing
R squared = 57.2%    R squared (adjusted) = 46.5%
s = 12.82 with 6 - 2 = 4 degrees of freedom

Source       Sum of Squares   df   Mean Square   F-ratio
Regression   878.227           1    878.227       5.34
Residual      657.273          4     164.318

Variable   Coefficient   s.e. of Coeff   t-ratio    prob
Constant   254.000        30.51           8.32      0.0011
Fat          6.31818        2.733          2.31      0.0819
```

The slope decreases significantly, and so does the correlation. Therefore, which data point is more influential? When Domino's Hand Tossed with the large residual is removed, the slope goes from 8.97 to 10.7 and r^2 goes from 78.3% to 90.6%. Without Domino's Deep Dish, the large gap on the *x*-axis is removed, the slope goes from 8.97 to 6.3, and r^2 goes from 78.3% to 57.2%. It appears that the right-hand point (Domino's Deep Dish) has the greater influence on the regression line and correlation coefficient!

E52. The fitted value $\hat{y}$ is a linear transformation of *x*; that is, $\hat{y} = a + bx$. Thus, using $\hat{y}$ rather than *x* on the horizontal axis does not change the relative distance of the values from each other—it just translates and stretches the horizontal axis.

Consider this example for a regression line $\hat{y} = 1 + 2x$ with values of $x = 0, 1, 3, 4, 6, 6$. Then the values of $\hat{y}$ are 1, 3, 7, 9, 13, 13. These two sets of points are plotted on horizontal scales in the next plot. Note that the relative spacing of the points is exactly the same on each scale.

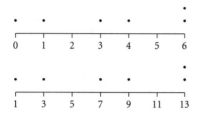

If the regression line has a negative slope, then the larger y's correspond to the small x's and one residual plot will be the mirror image of the other.

3.5 Shape-Changing Transformations

Objectives

- to understand that a linear transformation preserves the shape of a scatterplot
- to determine that removing the curvature from the shape of a scatterplot requires a nonlinear transformation
- to use power transformations and understand that the log-log transformation is the most useful "power" transformation
- to use a log transformation to straighten data that follow an exponential pattern

Important Terms and Concepts

- power transformations
- log-log transformations
- log transformations
- exponential growth and decay

Lesson Planning

Class Time

Three to four days

Materials

For Activity 3.4, a copy of the blackline master "Areas of Equilateral Triangles," page 140 (Display 3.80 in the student text) for each student
For Activity 3.5, a paper cup and 200 pennies for each student (or each pair of students)

Suggested Assignments

Classwork		
Essential	**Recommended**	**Optional**
Activity 3.4, Activity 3.5 D30–D33, D35, D37, D40–D42 P24–P26, P28, P30–P34	D34, D36, D38, D39, D43, D44 P27, P29	

Homework		
Essential	**Recommended**	**Optional**
E53, E54, E56, E58, E60, E62	E59, E61	E55, E57, E63

Lesson Notes: Activity 3.4 Finding Areas of Equilateral Triangles

Activity 3.4 is essential and will be referred to later in the book.

1–2. The results of one student's investigation of the triangles are shown here.

Triangle	Side	Area
1	6	15
2	9.5	36
3	13	75.5
4	11	55.5
5	4.5	7
6	14	80.5
7	20.5	180
8	9	33.5

3–4. The plot of *area* versus *side* shows curvature, which is easier to see when a straight line is laid on the plot.

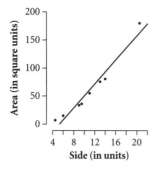

5. a. Dividing each area by 2 does not change the shape; it merely rescales the *y*-axis.

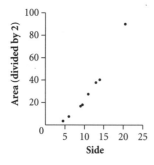

b. Taking the square root of the areas removes most of the curvature. Now a straight line fits the plot reasonably well.

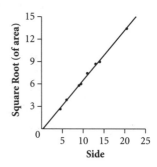

c. Squaring each area increases the curvature; this transformation seems to be moving things in the wrong direction.

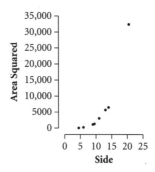

d. Squaring each side straightens things out.

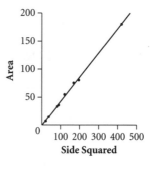

6. The equation of the regression line for the square root of the area versus the side is

$$\sqrt{area} = -0.21 + 0.67 \, side$$

The equation of the regression line for the area versus the side squared is

$$area = -0.75 + 0.43(side)^2$$

The true geometric relationship is given by

$$area = \left(\frac{1}{2}\right)\sin\left(\frac{\pi}{3}\right)(side)^2$$

$$area = \left(\frac{1}{2}\right)(0.866)(side)^2 = (0.433)(side)^2$$

So the approximate relationship found by measuring and fitting a line is close to the truth!

7. The area of an equilateral triangle is approximately 0.43 times the square of the length of a side, or the square root of the area is approximately 0.66 times the length of a side. The constant terms in the regression lines should be zero but did not turn out that way because of the variation in the sample data. You could force a regression line through zero in these cases and see what happens to the slope.

8. Because area is a square measure and length of a side is a linear measure, one can be expressed as a linear function of the other by either squaring the side or taking the square root of the area.

Lesson Notes: Power Transformations

Power transformations are appropriate when your data follow a power model of the form $y = ax^b$. However, a power transformation (as well as any other transformation) should only be employed when it is consistent with the physical situation in the problem. Unfortunately, some students will keep trying transformations until they get a so-called "good" fit regardless of its appropriateness. A correlation r close to ± 1 does not imply a "good" fit automatically. For example, in the triangle activity, the correlation for (*side, area*) was .96, but a linear model is not consistent with what we know about the sides and areas of triangles.

Many graphing calculators have spread sheet capabilities that make the transformation of data quite easy. For example, on a TI-83, you can load the x-data in list L1, the y-data in list L2, and then define L3=(L2)². A linear regression can then be done on (x, y) and (x, y²) and appropriate comparisons made.

Discussion

D30. Perhaps it is the cross-sectional area that is growing at a constant rate across time. This area would be proportional to the square of the diameter.

D31. There is less variation in the diameters at the left end of the scatterplot than at the right end. Thus, you would be able to get a more precise prediction of the diameter for 10-year-old trees than you would for 40-year-old trees. This should seem intuitively reasonable; older trees would naturally have more variability in size than younger trees. (The same is true of children.)

Practice

P24. a. i.

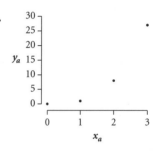

ii. The x-scale must be expanded. A cubic power transformation will straighten this relationship.

iii.

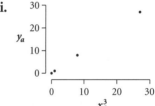

b. i.

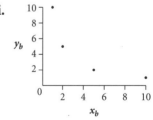

ii. The x-scale must be shrunk a bit. A reciprocal transformation (power of -1) will do the trick.

iii.

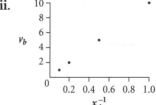

c. i.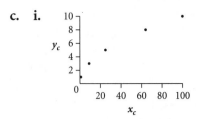

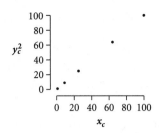

ii. Again, the *x*-scale must shrink. This time a square root transformation (power of 0.5) will straighten the points.

iii.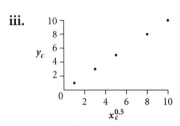

P25. For the points in part a in P24, the *y*-scale must be shrunk. The cube root transformation will straighten them (which is equivalent to raising *x* to the third power).

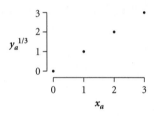

For the points in part b in P24, the *y*-scale must be shrunk again. The same reciprocal transformation (power of −1) will work.

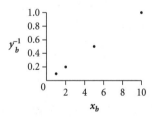

For the points in part c in P24, the *y*-scale must be expanded. A square transformation (power of 2) will straighten the points (which is equivalent to taking the square root of *x*). The exponents in P25 are the reciprocals of the exponents in P24.

P26. a. The area is proportional to the square of the radius ($y = \pi x^2$), so *y* would have to be raised to the power $\frac{1}{2}$ (square root).

b. The volume is proportional to the cube of a side ($y = x^3$), so *y* would have to be raised to the power of $\frac{1}{3}$ (cube root).

c. The volume is proportional to the square of the diameter ($y = 8\pi\left(\frac{x}{2}\right)^2$ or $y = 2\pi x^2$), so *y* would have to be raised to the power $\frac{1}{2}$ (square root).

P27. The following plots show the diameter plotted against the square root of age and the residuals from the regression line. The regression analysis is also provided. This transformation results in a scatterplot with less of a fan shape than the one for *diameter*^{2} versus *age*. If you want to predict diameters along the full range of ages, this transformation will allow more even precision in the predictions.

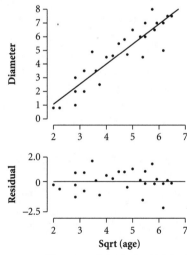

Diameter = 1.47 · Sqrt (*age*) − 1.86; r^2 = .83

```
Dependent variable is:    Diameter
No Selector
R squared = 83.2%    R squared (adjusted) = 82.5%
s = 0.9121 with 27 - 2 = 25 degrees of freedom

Source      Sum of Squares   df   Mean Square   F-ratio
Regression  102.855           1   102.855       124
Residual    20.7969          25   0.831876

Variable  Coefficient  s.e. of Coeff  t-ratio   prob
Constant  -1.85727     0.6175         -3.01     0.0059
√Age      1.46516      0.1318         11.1      ≤0.0001
```

Lesson Notes: Power Functions and Log-Log Transformations

The basic rules of logarithms and powers are shown in this table.

Logarithms	Powers
$\log_b(mn) = \log_b(m) + \log_b(n)$	$a^{m+n} = a^m \cdot a^n$
$\log_b(m^n) = n \log_b(m)$	$(a^m)^n = a^{mn}$
$\log_b(b^m) = m$	$a^{\log_a(m)} = m$

To solve $\log(area) = -0.484 + 2.10 \cdot \log(side)$, do the inverse operation and use the rules in the table as shown at the bottom of this page.

Some software packages will show the regression as $\log(area) = \ldots$. Graphing calculators generally do not. That is, if a student is doing a regression on $(\log x, \log y)$, the calculator will return the coefficients of $y = a + bx$. It is up to the student to realize that they must use the appropriate meaning to those calculated coefficients, that is, $\log y = a + b \log x$.

Discussion

D32. The cube root transformation pulls down the extreme y's too much and bends the curve the other way.

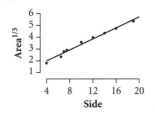

D33. Here is the base 10 analysis followed by the base e analysis. Notice that the x- and y-scales differ but the slopes of the regression lines are equal.

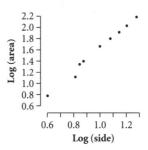

```
Dependent variable is:    LogArea
No Selector
R squared = 98.8%    R squared (adjusted) = 98.7%
s = 0.0530 with 9 - 2 = 7 degrees of freedom

Source      Sum of Squares   df   Mean Square   F-ratio
Regression  1.66412           1   1.66412       594
Residual    0.019627          7   0.002804

Variable  Coefficient  s.e. of Coeff  t-ratio   prob
Constant  -0.483512    0.0865         -5.59     0.0008
LogSide   2.10035      0.0862         24.4      ≤0.0001
```

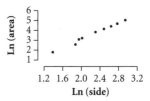

```
Dependent variable is:    LnArea
No Selector
R squared = 98.8%    R squared (adjusted) = 98.7%
s = 0.1219 with 9 - 2 = 7 degrees of freedom

Source      Sum of Squares   df   Mean Square   F-ratio
Regression  8.82299           1   8.82299       594
Residual    0.104059          7   0.014866

Variable  Coefficient  s.e. of Coeff  t-ratio   prob
Constant  -1.11333     0.1992         -5.59     0.0008
LnSide    2.10035      0.0862         24.4      ≤0.0001
```

Practice

P28. a. The plot of the data suggests that you must expand the y-scale or shrink the x-scale, so the power transformation on x will have to be a power less than 1. Students may suggest a square root transformation on y because it has been successful in the past.

Lesson 3.5, Lesson Notes

$$10^{\log(area)} = 10^{-0.484 + 2.10\,\log(side)}$$

$area = 10^{-0.484} \cdot 10^{2.10\,\log(side)}$ using the 1st and 3rd power rules

$area = 0.328 \cdot 10^{\log(side)2.10}$ using the 2nd log rule and calculating $10^{-0.484}$

$area = 0.328 \cdot (side)^{2.10}$ using the 3rd log rule

b. The log-log transformation yields a nearly linear plot, as shown here.

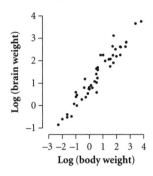

c. The regression equation is
$\log(brain) = 0.908 + 0.76 \log(body)$
or $brain = 8.08(body)^{0.76}$.

The slope of the line, 0.76, agrees with the insight that the *x*-scale must be transformed by a power less than 1.

```
The regression equation is
logBrain = 0.908 + 0.760 logBody
Predictor    Coef    Stdev  t-ratio       p
Constant   0.90754  0.04967   18.27   0.000
logBody    0.76020  0.03162   24.04   0.000
s = 0.3156  R-sq = 92.6%  R-sq(adj) = 92.5%

Analysis of Variance
SOURCE      DF      SS      MS       F       p
Regression   1  57.577  57.577  577.96   0.000
Error       46   4.583   0.100
Total       47  62.159
```

Lesson Notes: Exponential Functions and Log Transformations

Discussion

D34. Some of the flight lengths are in the low hundreds, whereas others are in the mid-thousands. This table shows the flight lengths paired with their base 10 logs. Notice that the 5063 is transformed to 3.7, whereas the 500 is transformed to 2.7. Logs really bring in the tails!

Flight Length	Log(flight length)
2882	3.45969
5063	3.70441
3321	3.52127
1363	3.1345
2451	3.38934
1493	3.17406
1963	3.29292
2379	3.37639

(continued)

Flight Length	Log(flight length)
1126	3.05154
3253	3.51228
2995	3.4764
2331	3.36754
1167	3.06707
2135	3.3294
782	2.89321
742	2.8704
1101	3.04179
702	2.84634
798	2.902
602	2.7796
345	2.53782
442	2.64542
570	2.75587
487	2.68753
468	2.67025
500	2.69897
413	2.61595

D35. Because there is a decreasing linear trend in the first half of the residuals and an increasing linear trend in the last half, perhaps a better model for these data would be two straight lines, one for smaller planes and one for larger planes. This analysis is shown in E57.

D36. It seems reasonable that, in general, larger planes go faster and also have longer average flight lengths. In fact, the larger planes tend to be deployed on longer flights intentionally; that is a management decision. There is a tendency for greater speed to "cause" longer flight lengths, but this is a result of human decisions that weigh other factors into the equation, such as the size of the plane.

Practice

P29. The table here shows the data with the log transformation on *y*.

x	y	Log y
2	1000	3
1	100	2
0	10	1
−1	1	0

The plot does indeed show a straight line.

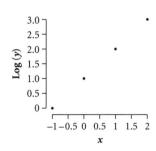

The equation of this line is $\log y = 1 + x$, so the slope is 1 and the y-intercept is 1.

P30. The tables and plots are shown here.

a.

x_a	y_a	Log y_a
6	1000	3
4	100	2
2	10	1
0	1	0

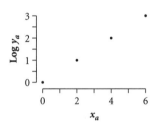

The equation of the line is $\log y_a = 0 + 0.5x_a$, so the slope is 0.5 and the y-intercept is 0.

b.

x_b	y_b	Log y_b
5	0.0001	-4.0
6	0.01	-2.0
2	100	2.0

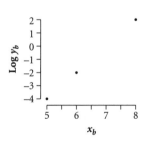

The equation of the line is
$\log y_b = -14 + 2x_b$, so the slope is 2
and the y-intercept is -14.

P31. If $\log y = c + dx$, then by rules of logarithms, $y = (10^c)(10)^{dx} = (10^c)(10^d)^x = ab^x$, where $a = 10^c$ and $b = 10^d$.

For P29, $y = 10(10)^x$.
For P30, part a, $y = 1(10^{.5})^x \approx 3.16^x$.
For P30, part b, $y = 10^{-14}(10^2)^x = 10^{-14} \cdot 100^x$.

P32. The equation of the line on the transformed scale is
$\log(\text{flight length}) = 0.293 + .006(\text{speed})$,
which yields $\text{flight length} = 1.96(1.01)^{\text{speed}}$.

Lesson Notes: Exponential Growth and Decay

At the bottom of this page is another example of how to solve a log equation for $\hat{y}$. *Note:* $e^{-25.61}$ is a constant.

Notice that in the computation, $e^{0.015} = 1.015$. Whenever you are computing e^x, where x is close to 0, it always will be the case that $e^x \approx 1 + x$. As another example, in E61a, students will find that $e^{-0.024} \approx 1 + (-0.024) = 0.976$.

Discussion

D37. The residuals indicate a lot of scatter around the trend line for the years up to 1850 and then a trend that increases faster than the model would indicate, up to about 1920, followed by an increase slower than the model would indicate. This same pattern can be seen in the original scatterplot if you look closely.

D38. In 1803, the Louisiana Purchase doubled the size of the United States but added relatively few people. Thus, the population density dropped dramatically below what any model would have predicted. Similarly, the drop in density from 1840 to 1850 may be accounted for by the addition of much of the Southwest to the United States.

Lesson 3.5, Lesson Notes

$$\ln y = -25.61 + 0.0151x$$
$$e^{\ln(y)} = e^{-25.61+0.0151x} \quad \text{raise both sides}$$
$$y = e^{-25.61}(e^{0.015})^x \quad \text{using the 1st and 3rd power rules}$$
$$y = e^{-25.61}(1.015)^x \quad \text{calculating } e^{0.015}$$

D39. a. The overall trend is curved upward in the original data, so the correlation coefficient is not a useful measure of the strength of the relationship.

b. These are time series data, with one observation per time period. In time series data, each observation is highly correlated with the preceding observation (things cannot change very much from one time period to the next), so it is not surprising to see points closely clustered about the linear trend in the transformed data. Of much more interest is the nonlinear component of the overall trend and the fluctuations around this trend, as revealed in the residuals.

D40. From the equation $\hat{y} = e^{-25.61}(1.015)^x$, you can see that the growth rate is estimated to be 1.5% per year. For a 10-year period, think of going from $x = 0$ to $x = 10$. If at year 0 the population is $\hat{y} = a$, at year 10 it will be $\hat{y} = a(1.015)^{10} = a(1.161)$ for a 16% gain. Make sure students observe that the 10-year growth rate is not $(10)(1.5\%) = 15\%$; it is greater than that.

Practice

P33. The Florida population shows a definite non-linear trend that could represent exponential growth.

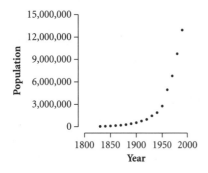

a. The log transformation transforms the pattern to a linear one that can be summarized by a straight line.

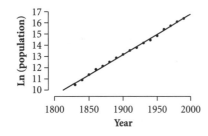

b. The equation of the line is

$$\ln(pop) = -55.525 + 0.0361 \, year$$

so that

$$pop = e^{-55.525}(e^{0.0361})^{year} = e^{-55.525}(1.037)^{year}$$

for a growth rate of 3.7% per year, which is a high rate of growth.

c. The residual plot shows a pattern. Florida grew less rapidly than the model predicts up to about 1845, then grew more rapidly than predicted, then less, then more. There was a big jump in the growth between 1950 and 1960.

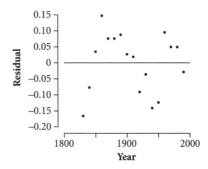

Lesson Notes: Exponential Decay

Activity 3.5 Copper Flippers

Activity 3.5 is essential, and the data will be used later in the book. This activity can be done in pairs—one to toss the coins and count and one to record.

1–3. The data from one student's results are shown here.

Toss	Heads
1	91
2	59
3	27
4	9
5	7
6	4

4. A scatterplot from the sample student results is shown in Display 3.101 on page 188 of the student text. The pattern appears to be exponential, not linear.

5. See D43.

Have students save their data to use in later chapters. The following discussion questions further analyze the data from this activity.

Discussion

D41. a. Yes, it appears negative exponential or exponential decay.

b. Any one "copper flipper," chosen at random, has a certain probability of death in a given time period. If this probability remains relatively constant across time periods, then the number of copper flippers "dying" in a time period will be a fixed proportion of the number "alive" at the beginning of the time period. In this example, approximately half of the copper flippers "die" in any one time period.

c. Yes; that number starts at 200 and ends near 0.

D42. On the scatterplot, it looks as though the transformed points lie very close to a straight line. The residual plot reveals, however, that there is a regular oscillation around that line, as is often the case with time series data. The exponential decay model is still very good, however, and about the best we can do with these data.

D43. a. $\hat{y} = (e^{5.21})(e^{-0.66x}) = (183.1)(0.52)^x$

b. In the situation of exponential decay, the 0.52 is $1 - $ *the rate of decay*. Therefore, the rate of "death" for the copper flippers is estimated to be .48, or 48%. About half die in each time period.

D44. If the chance of "living" was .6, then the rate of decay would be .4 and the line would drop less steeply.

Practice

P34. a. This plot shows the data for Dying Dice.

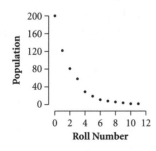

b. The transformed data show a nice linear trend. (See graph in next column.)

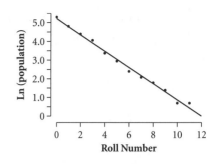

c. The equation of the line in part b is

$$\widehat{\ln y} = 5.22 - 0.435x$$

or

$$\widehat{\ln(pop)} = 5.22 - 0.435\ roll\ number$$

Because $e^{-0.435} = 0.647$, the rate of dying is estimated to be about .35, or 35%, per time period. This rate is close to the theoretical probability of dying, set up to be 1/3.

d. The residual plot shows some curvature, indicating a death rate of a little more than .35 in the early stages and a little less than .35 in the later stages. It would not be unusual to see this kind of pattern in data on real animals.

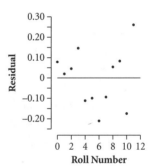

Exercises

E53. The plot of the square root of *flight length* versus *speed* still retains obvious curvature—this transformation is less satisfactory than the log transformation.

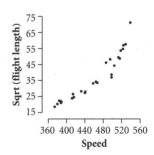

E54. The plots of the data and the regression analysis are shown next.

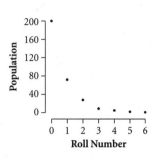

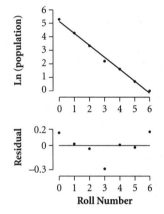

The equation of the regression line is $\widehat{\ln y} = 5.142 - 0.885x$.

Because $e^{-0.885} = 0.413$, the estimated rate of decay is $1 - 0.413 = .587$.

The curved residual plot shows that the rate of decay is greater than the estimated value during the first and last time periods and less than the estimated value over the middle time periods.

E55. The plot of the data shows curvature. Although the log-log transformation helps, it does not remove the curvature. (Neither will any other power transformation.) The residual plots clearly show that the data actually divide into two groups, and the trends in the residuals are linear in each group. So a good way to model these data is to split them into two groups (perhaps the first six years in one group and the last eight years in another). The younger group has a weight gain per centimeter of height that is lower than the overall average, whereas the older group has a weight gain per centimeter of height that is higher than the average.

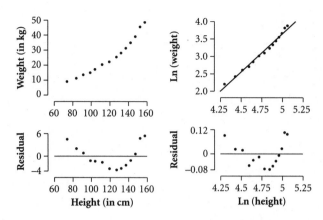

E56. a. i. From the plot, this looks to be a good fitting line.

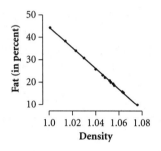

ii. The regression equation is $\hat{y} = 505.254 - 460.678x$ and the analysis is as follows.

```
Dependent variable is:    % Fat
No Selector
R squared = 99.9%    R squared (adjusted) = 99.9%
s = 0.2443 with 15 - 2 = 13 degrees of freedom

Source      Sum of Squares   df   Mean Square   F-ratio
Regression  1206.48           1      1206.48      20223
Residual    0.775560         13      0.059658

Variable   Coefficient   s.e. of Coeff   t-ratio    prob
Constant   505.254       3.386               149   ≤0.0001
Density    -460.678      3.239              -142   ≤0.0001
```

iii. The r^2 value of .999 seems to confirm that this is a good fitting model.

iv. The residual plot uncovers some problems; perhaps we could do better!

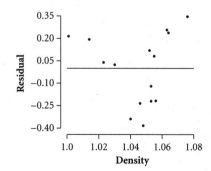

b. i. As the percentage of fat increases, the body density decreases. Perhaps the positive association between the reciprocal of density and the percentage of fat would be easier to model. The pertinent plots and the regression analysis are shown here.

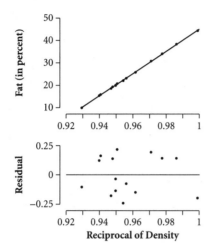

```
Dependent variable is:    % Fat
No Selector
R squared = 100.0%    R squared (adjusted) = 100.0%
s = 0.1690 with 15 - 2 = 13 degrees of freedom

Source       Sum of Squares   df   Mean Square   F-ratio
Regression   1206.88          1    1206.88       42246
Residual     0.371389         13   0.028568

Variable    Coefficient   s.e. of Coeff   t-ratio    prob
Constant    -450.632      2.309           -195       ≤0.0001
1/Density   495.654       2.412           206        ≤0.0001
```

The residuals here show less pattern; the picture is more like one of random scatter, suggesting that this is a better model.

The regression line has the equation

$$\% \text{ body fat} = -450.63 + 495.65(1/density)$$

which is very close to the Siri equation.

ii. The correlation is close to one for both models, but the second proves to be a better fitting model than the first. Moral: Never use correlation as the only criterion for choosing a model.

iii. *Percent body fat* as a function of log(*density*) works almost as well as Siri's model.

E57. When plotted against flight length, the airplanes separate nicely into the same two groups on all the variables that relate to size (seats, cargo space, and cost per hour). The A300–600 and the B757–200 sit on the boundary line between the two groups and

could go with either in the final analysis. See the scatterplot matrix in the answer to E7.

E58. The data show a curved pattern of growth over time, which could perhaps be modeled as exponential growth.

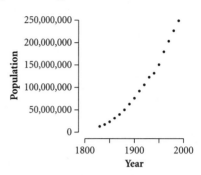

a. The next plot shows the actual growth figures for each decade. The growth is not constant—it is very low in the 1940s and very high in the 1960s. In recent decades, growth has been decreasing. These fluctuations make it difficult to come up with a good model for growth across the decades.

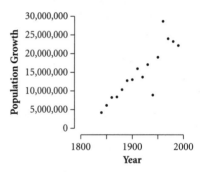

b. Taking the log of the population overcompensates for the curve in the original data; the growth is not really exponential growth. A better transformation is the square root of the population. The plot of these data along with the regression analysis and residual plot is presented next. The residuals still have some pattern, as is expected for time series data, but it is not very pronounced.

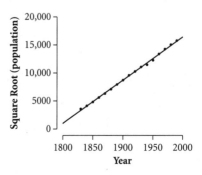

Dependent variable is: √Ppn

No Selector
18 total cases of which 1 is missing
R squared = 99.8%   R squared (adjusted) = 99.8%
s = 155.9 with 17 - 2 = 15 degrees of freedom

Source	Sum of Squares	df	Mean Square	F-ratio
Regression	242248177	1	242248177	9967
Residual	364582	15	24305.4	

Variable	Coefficient	s.e. of Coeff	t-ratio	prob
Constant	-137683	1475	-93.4	≤0.0001
Year	77.0549	0.7718	99.8	≤0.0001

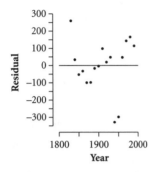

b. The log-log transformation works quite well here and gives a plot that seems appropriate for a regression line. The residual plot looks rather like random scatter and further supports this choice of a statistical model.

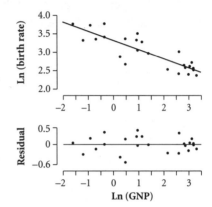

Dependent variable is: LnBrR
No Selector
R squared = 73.4%   R squared (adjusted) = 72.3%
s = 0.2428 with 25 - 2 = 23 degrees of freedom

Source	Sum of Squares	df	Mean Square	F-ratio
Regression	3.74798	1	3.74798	63.6
Residual	1.35612	23	0.058962	

Variable	Coefficient	s.e. of Coeff	t-ratio	prob
Constant	3.32229	0.0638	52.1	≤0.0001
LnGNP	-0.247740	0.0311	-7.97	≤0.0001

The regression equation is

$$\ln(\text{birth rate}) = 3.32 - 0.25 \ln(GNP)$$

or

$$\text{birth rate} = e^{3.32}(GNP)^{-0.25}$$

It is easier to interpret the terms of the model on the log-log scale than on the original scale. Ln(*birth rate*) decreases, on the average, 0.25 units for every 1 unit increase in ln(*GNP*).

c. The pattern in the immigration data is quite cyclical, which is another common time series pattern. No simple power transformation will straighten this out. There is more than one "bend" in the data; power transformations only work well for a single bend.

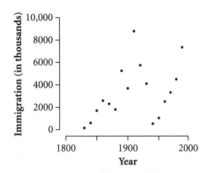

E59. **a.** The scatterplot of these data show a marked decrease in the birth rate as the GNP increases. The relationship is nonlinear but does not look like exponential decay.

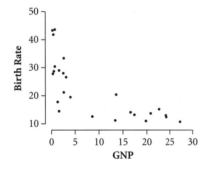

E60. **a.** It appears that *brain oxygen* versus *body mass* could be modeled by exponential decay, but a quick check will show that such a transformation does little to straighten the plot. The log-log transformation does well, once again.

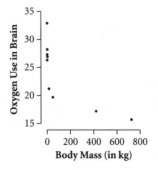

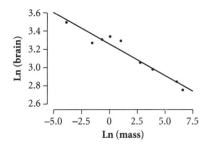

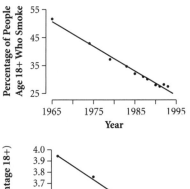

The equation of this regression line is

$$\ln(brain\ oxygen) = 3.26 - 0.07\ln(body\ mass)$$

which implies that $\ln(brain\ oxygen)$ decreases, on the average, by 0.07 units for every 1 unit increase in $\ln(body\ mass)$.

b. Using the log-log transformation, the relationship between *lung oxygen consumption* and *body mass* has a similar linear trend except for a couple of stray points.

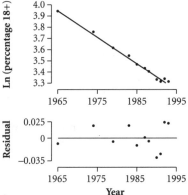

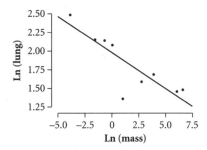

The equation of this line is

$$\ln(lung\ oxygen) = 1.976 - 0.0951\ln(body\ mass)$$

which implies that the $\ln(lung\ oxygen)$ decreases, on the average, by 0.0951 units for every 1 unit increase in $\ln(body\ mass)$.

c. If this theory is true and oxygen consumption is directly proportional to the relative size of the organ, then the lung oxygen consumption should decrease less rapidly than the brain oxygen consumption. But the data show that the lung oxygen consumption decreases *more* rapidly than that of the brain. There must be another explanation as to why the brain seems to use more oxygen, relative to its size, than does other organs.

E61. a. The decreasing trend has a slight curvature, especially toward the later years, so perhaps a log transformation (exponential decay) will work. This would make the interpretation of the results quite easy.

```
Dependent variable is:    Ln 18+
No Selector
R squared = 99.1%   R squared (adjusted) = 99.0%
s = 0.0200 with 11 - 2 = 9 degrees of freedom

Source       Sum of Squares   df   Mean Square   F-ratio
Regression   0.413237         1    0.413237      1032
Residual     0.003603         9    0.000400

Variable   Coefficient   s.e. of Coeff   t-ratio   prob
Constant   50.3191       1.457           34.5      ≤0.0001
Year       -0.023596     0.0007          -32.1     ≤0.0001
```

The exponential decay model fits well and shows that the rate of decrease in smoking is about 2.4% per year because $e^{-0.024} = 0.976$. (Remember, this rate of decrease is a percent of a percent because the original measurements are percentages.)

b. An exponential decay model works almost as well for the 18–24 age group, but there are a few points with larger residuals. The results of the regression analysis are shown here.

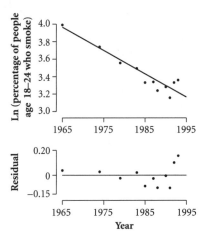

```
Dependent variable is:    Ln 18-24
No Selector
R squared = 88.9%    R squared (adjusted) = 87.7%
s = 0.0856 with 11 - 2 = 9 degrees of freedom

Source       Sum of Squares   df   Mean Square   F-ratio
Regression   0.529338          1   0.529338      72.3
Residual     0.065883          9   0.007320

Variable   Coefficient   s.e. of Coeff   t-ratio   prob
Constant   56.4305       6.232           9.06      ≤0.0001
Year       -0.026709     0.0031          -8.50     ≤0.0001
```

The exponential decay model shows that the rate of decrease in smoking in this age group is about 2.7% per year, because $e^{-0.027} = 0.973$—a slightly higher rate than the one for the population as a whole.

c. The pattern of decrease for the 65 and older category is much more linear; in fact, the log transformation will make things worse instead of better.

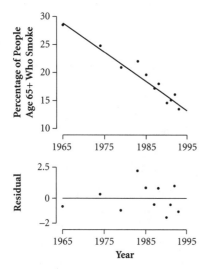

```
Dependent variable is:    65+
No Selector
R squared = 94.0%    R squared (adjusted) = 93.3%
s = 1.195 with 11 - 2 = 9 degrees of freedom

Source       Sum of Squares   df   Mean Square   F-ratio
Regression   201.331           1   201.331       141
Residual     12.8451           9   1.42723

Variable   Coefficient   s.e. of Coeff   t-ratio   prob
Constant   1052.60       87.02           12.1      ≤0.0001
Year       -0.520835     0.0439          -11.9     ≤0.0001
```

This nearly constant (linear) rate of decrease amounts to about half a percentage point per year.

E62. **a.** See plots in next column. There is definitely an increase in CO_2 over the years, and it appears to be exponential growth. But note that the log transformation is not much help here.

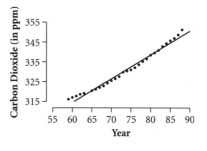

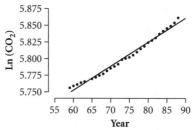

b. The fitted line appears in the first plot in part a. The residual plot from the original data shows that CO_2 increased at a rate lower than the overall average during the first part of the time period and at a higher rate than the overall average during the last part.

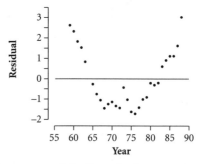

c. The two straight lines in the pattern of the residuals suggest that a better way to model these data might be to use two straight lines with different slopes, one line covering the period from 1959 to about 1970 and the other from about 1975 to 1988.

d. The first group results in the following plot and regression analysis. The average rate of increase over the time period is about 0.79 ppm per year.

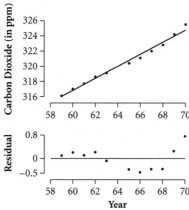

Dependent variable is: 1:CO2
No Selector
12 total cases of which 1 is missing
R squared = 98.5%   R squared (adjusted) = 98.4%
s = 0.3884 with 11 - 2 = 9 degrees of freedom

Source	Sum of Squares	df	Mean Square	F-ratio
Regression	90.1711	1	90.1711	598
Residual	1.35802	9	0.150891	

Variable	Coefficient	s.e. of Coeff	t-ratio	prob
Constant	269.106	2.102	128	≤0.0001
Year	0.794841	0.0325	24.4	≤0.0001

The second group results in the following plot and regression analysis. The average rate of increase over this time period has increased to about 1.52 ppm per year.

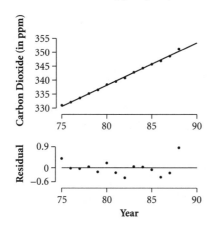

Dependent variable is: 2:CO2
No Selector
R squared = 99.7%   R squared (adjusted) = 99.7%
s = 0.3449 with 14 - 2 = 12 degrees of freedom

Source	Sum of Squares	df	Mean Square	F-ratio
Regression	524.401	1	524.401	4407
Residual	1.42787	12	0.118989	

Variable	Coefficient	s.e. of Coeff	t-ratio	prob
Constant	216.735	1.866	116	≤0.0001
Year	1.51824	0.0229	66.4	≤0.0001

Once again, notice that the residual plots (especially the first one) have an oscillating pattern typical of time series data.

E63. The plot of average SAT score versus the percentage taking the test shows a decreasing trend with a curvature. A log-log transformation straightens this out nicely, and the regression analysis of ln(SAT $score$) versus ln($percentage$ $taking$ SAT) provides a good model for prediction.

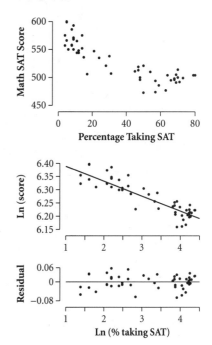

Dependent variable is: LnScore
No Selector
R squared = 80.7%   R squared (adjusted) = 80.3%
s = 0.0290 with 51 - 2 = 49 degrees of freedom

Source	Sum of Squares	df	Mean Square	F-ratio
Regression	0.172268	1	0.172268	205
Residual	0.041161	49	0.000840	

Variable	Coefficient	s.e. of Coeff	t-ratio	prob
Constant	6.45854	0.0138	467	≤0.0001
L%Tg	-0.059535	0.0042	-14.3	≤0.0001

Areas of Equilateral Triangles

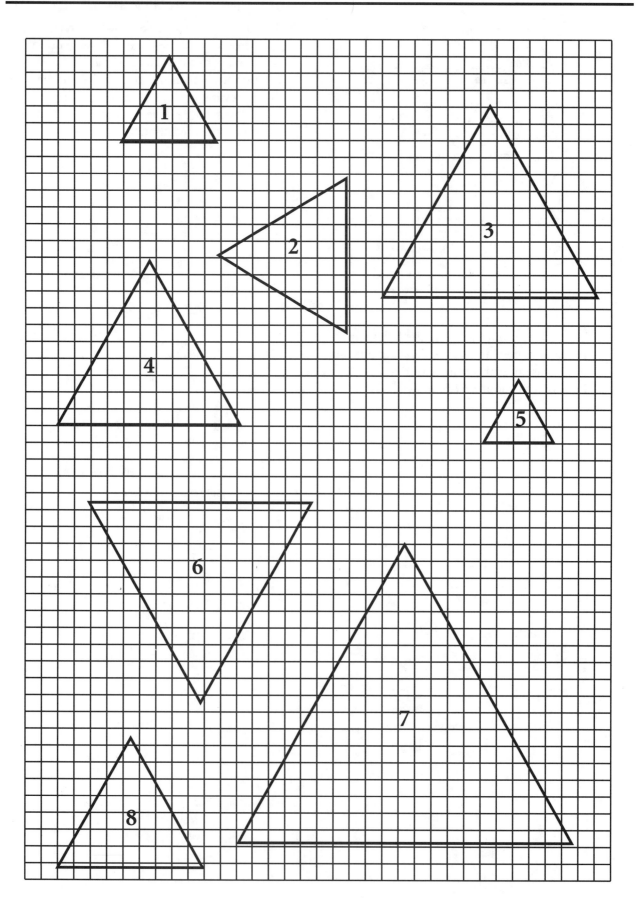

Review

Review Exercises

E64. **a.** This scatterplot shows no obvious association between temperature and number of distressed O-rings. Although the highest number of distressed O-rings was at the lowest temperature, the second highest number was at the highest temperature.

b. It is difficult to look at the scatterplot of the complete set of data, shown next, and not see that any risk is almost entirely at lower temperatures. The correlations are $r = -.263$ for the incomplete set of data but $r = -.567$ after all points are included, which is only moderately strong at any rate.

This is a tragic example of scientists and engineers not asking the right question: Do I have all of the data?

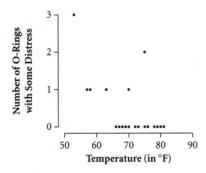

Background information: After each launch, the two rocket motors on the sides of the *Challenger* were recovered and inspected. Each rocket motor was made in four pieces, which were fit together with O-rings to seal the small spaces between them. The O-rings were 37.5 feet in diameter and 0.28 inches thick.

The Rogers Commission, which was appointed by President Reagan to find the cause of the accident, noted that the flights with zero incidents were left off the plot because it was felt that these flights did not contribute any information about the temperature effect. The Commission concluded that "A careful analysis of the

flight history of O-ring performance would have revealed the correlation of O-ring damage in low temperature" [*Report of the Presidential Commission on the Space Shuttle Challenger Accident* (Washington, D.C. 1986), page 148.].

E65. **a.** If Leonardo is correct, the data should lie near the lines:

$$arm\ span = height$$

$$kneeling = \frac{3}{4}\ height$$

$$hand = \frac{1}{9}\ height$$

Looking at the next plots, these rules appear to be approximately correct.

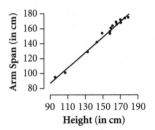

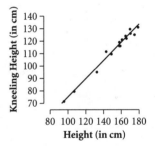

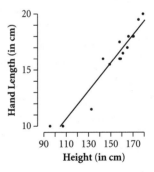

The least squares regression equation for predicting the arm span from the height is $\hat{y} = -5.81 + 1.03x$.

The least squares regression equation for predicting the kneeling height from the height is $\hat{y} = 2.19 + 0.73x$.

The least squares regression equation for predicting the hand length from the height is $\hat{y} = -2.97 + 0.12x$.

b. For the first plot, the slope is 1.03. This means for every 1 cm increase in *height*, there tends to be a 1.03 cm increase in *arm span*. Leonardo predicted a 1 cm increase.

For the second plot, the slope is 0.73, which means that for every 1 cm increase in *height*, there tends to be a 0.73 cm increase in *kneeling height*. Leonardo predicted a 0.75 cm increase.

For the third plot, the slope is 0.12, which means that for every 1 cm increase in *height*, there tends to be a 0.12 cm increase in *hand length*. Leonardo predicted a $\frac{1}{9} = 0.11$ cm increase.

Leonardo's claims hold reasonably well. The slopes are about what he predicted, and the *y*-intercepts are close to 0 in each case.

c. In each case, the points are packed tightly about the regression line and so there is a very strong correlation. The correlations are

arm span and *height*: .992 (strongest)

kneeling height and *height*: .989

hand length and *height*: .961 (weakest)

E66. **a.** Yes, the student who scored 52 on the first exam and 83 on the second lies away from the general pattern. This student scored much higher on the second exam than would have been expected. This point will be influential because the value of *x* is extreme on the low side and the point lies away from the regression line. The point sticks out on the residual plot. There is a pattern in the rest of the points; they have a positive correlation.

b. The slope should increase, and the correlation should increase. In fact, the slope increases from 0.430 to 0.540, and the correlation increases from .756 to .814.

c. The residual plot appears next. The residuals now appear scattered, without any obvious pattern, so a linear model fits the points well when point (52, 83) is removed.

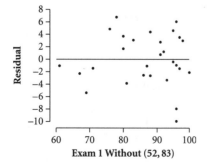

Exam 1 Without (52, 83)

d. Yes, there is regression to the mean in any elliptical cloud of points whenever the correlation is not perfect. For example, the student who scored lowest on Exam 1 did much better on Exam 2. The highest scorer on Exam 1 was not the highest scorer on Exam 2. A line fit through this cloud of points would have slope less than 1.

E67. **a.** Use the formula

$$b_1 = r \frac{s_y}{s_x}$$

to obtain

$$r = .51\left(\frac{11.6}{7.0}\right) \approx .845$$

b. Using the fact that $(\bar{x}, \bar{y})$ is on the regression line,

$$\hat{y} = \bar{y} + b_1(x - \bar{x})$$
$$= 87.8 + 0.51(x - 82.3)$$
$$= 45.83 + 0.51x$$

E68. **a.** Each value should be matched with itself.

b. Match each value with itself, except match 0.5 (or −0.5) with 0: (−1.5, −1.5) (−0.5, −0.5) (0, 0), (0, 0.5), (0.5, 0), (1.5, 1.5) for a correlation of .950.

c. (−1.5, 0) (−0.5, 0.5) (0, 1.5), (0, −1.5), (0.5, −0.5), (1.5, 0) has a correlation of −.1.

d. Match the biggest with the smallest, the next biggest with the next smallest, etc.: (−1.5, 1.5) (−0.5, 0.5) (0, 0), (0, 0), (0.5, −0.5), (1.5, −1.5).

E69. Students should not have to actually compute the correlations to answer these questions.

a. Zero correlations occur between A and B, B and E, B and F, C and D, and E and F. The correlation between D and E is .02. The pairs with zero correlation all have scatterplots that are symmetric around a center vertical line or center horizontal line or both.

b. A and E, D and F, and A and C

c. A and D, A and F, B and C, and C and F

d. Student responses may include the following: The scatterplot of A and B shows that there can be a pattern in the points (a shape) even though the correlation is zero. The fact that the scatterplots of A and D and of A and F have about the same correlation again shows that the correlation does not tell anything about their quite different shapes.

For your information, the complete correlation matrix is shown here.

	A	B	C	D	E
B	0				
C	.447	.258			
D	.224	.129	0		
E	.875	0	.091	.018	
F	.258	0	.289	.577	0

E70. **a.** True. Both measure how closely the points cluster about the "center" of the data. For univariate data, that center is the mean; for bivariate data, it is the regression line.

b. True. Refer to E69 for examples.

c. False. For example, picture an elliptical cloud of points with major axis along the y-axis. The correlation will be zero, but there will be a wide variation in the values of y for any given x.

d. True. Intuitively, a positive slope means that as x increases, y tends to increase. This is equivalent to a positive correlation. Similar statements can be made for a negative slope and a zero slope. Alternatively, the fact that this statement is true can be seen from the relationship

$$b_1 = r\,\frac{s_y}{s_x}$$

Because the standard deviations are always positive, b_1 and r must have the same sign.

E71. **a.** The correlation is quite high, at about $-.86$.

b. There are two clusters of points—one of states with a small percentage of students taking the SAT and one of states with more than 50% taking the SAT. The second cluster has almost no correlation and would have a relatively flat regression line, whereas the first cluster has a strong negative relationship. Combining these two clusters results in summary statistics that do not adequately describe either one of them.

c. A residual plot would be U-shaped with points above zero on the left, below zero in the middle, and above zero again on the right. The actual residual plot is shown in the next column.

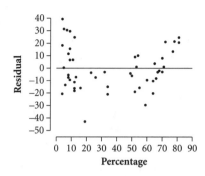

E72. **a.** Public universities that have the highest in-state tuition also tend to be the universities with the highest out-of-state tuition, and public universities that have the lowest in-state tuition also tend to be the universities with the lowest out-of-state tuition. This relationship is quite strong.

b. No, the correlation does not change with a linear transformation of one or both variables. However, if you were to take logarithms of the tuition costs, the correlation would change.

c. The slope would not change with the first transformation. Consider the formula for the slope:

$$b_1 = r\,\frac{s_y}{s_x}$$

The correlation remains unchanged with the change of units. The standard deviations would each be $\frac{1}{1000}$ as large as previously, but the factor of $\frac{1}{1000}$ would be in both the numerator and denominator and so would cancel out. But if you were to take logarithms of the tuition costs, the slope would change because the proportion s_y/s_x would be different.

E73. **a.** Quadrant I: $+, +, +$; Quadrant II: $-, +, -$; Quadrant III: $-, -, +$: Quadrant IV: $+, -, -$

b. The points near the origin or near one of the new axes make the smallest contributions. The contributions are small because either z_x or z_y would be close to 0.

E74. You can compute the values of r using the formula

$$b_1 = r\,\frac{s_y}{s_x}$$

Solving for r, the formula becomes

$$r = b_1\,\frac{s_x}{s_y}$$

These correlations are A: .5; B: .3; C: .25. So from weakest to strongest, they are ordered C, B, A.

E75. **a.** No. It is possible for one bookstore to be a lot more expensive than the other. For example, suppose your local bookstore sold each book for $10 less than the online price. The correlation would be 1.

b. The main reason for the high correlation is that the bookstores pay approximately the same wholesale cost for a book. They then add on an amount to cover their overhead costs and to give them a profit. To have a cause-and-effect relationship, a change in one variable should trigger a change in the other variable. That is not necessarily the case with these prices; however, if the online bookstore lowers its prices, it might force local bookstores to do the same.

E76. For example, stocks that do the best in one quarter may not be the ones that do the best in the next quarter.

E77. This matrix gives the correlations between all pairs of variables in this exercise.

	Ave Long	Max Long	Gestation
Max Long	0.769		
Gestation	0.577	0.761	
Speed	-0.215	-0.237	0.018

a. In general, animals with longer maximum longevity have longer gestation periods. The trend is reasonably linear, with a moderate correlation. The plot shows heteroscedasticity, with the points fanning out as maximum longevity increases. The elephant is an outlier, although it follows the general linear trend.

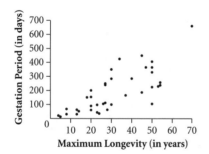

b. The pattern here is similar: The animals with longer average longevity have longer gestation periods. However, the relationship is not as strong as in part a, so maximum longevity is the better predictor of gestation period. There are two outliers, the elephant and the hippopotamus.

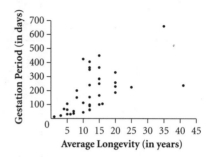

c. The three relatively slow animals (elephant, hippopotamus, and grizzly bear) in the lower-right corner give these data a slight negative correlation of −.215. However, the rest of the animals show a positive trend, with longer average longevity associated with greater speed. The lurking variable is the size of the animal. Larger animals tend to live longer and be faster (unless they get very big, like an elephant).

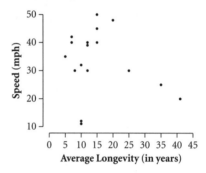

d. The next plot has two outliers (the elephant and the hippopotamus), which follow the general linear trend but are so far away from the others that you would have a lot of white space within any ellipse that contained them. Another animal that lies away from the general pattern is the beaver, which typically lives only 5 years but has been known to live to 50 years. Because the points don't form an elliptical cloud, the use of correlation and regression should be done with caution.

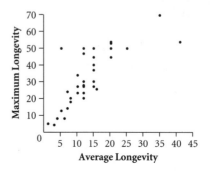

E78. **a.** The next scatterplot shows a very strong linear relationship between the expenditures for police officers and the number of police officers per state. This makes sense. There is one outlier and influential point, California, which has by far the largest population of any state listed. The correlation is .974, and the equation of the regression line is

$$expPolice = -271 + 58.4(number\ of\ police)$$

So for every additional thousand police officers, costs tend to go up by $58,400,000, or $58,400 each.

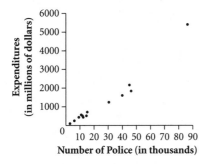

b. The scatterplot again shows a very strong linear relationship, with California as an outlier and influential point. The larger the population of the state, the more police officers. This time the correlation is .984, and the equation of the regression line is

$$number\ of\ police = -0.0008 + 2.92\ population$$

That is, for every increase of 1 million in the population, the number of police officers tends to go up by 2920. Remarkably, the *y*-intercept is exactly what you would expect it to be, at about 0: No population, no police officers.

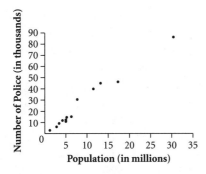

c. The scatterplot shows that there is a moderate positive but possibly curved relationship. For this scatterplot, it is not appropriate to compute the correlation or equation of the regression line. But, in general, the larger the number of police, the higher the rate of violent crime. (Note that this is the rate per 100,000 people in the state, not the number of violent crimes.) Almost equivalently, the larger the population of a state, the higher the violent crime rate. It is not at all obvious why this should be the case. Why would larger states (more police = more population) tend to have higher *rates* of violent crime? (Because of the strong relationship between the number of police officers per state and the population, a scatterplot of the crime rate versus the number of police officers per 100,000 population looks about the same.)

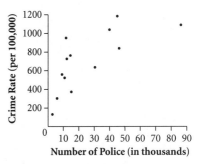

A log transformation of the number of police straightens these data quite well, as shown here in the scatterplot and residual plots.

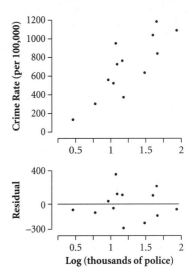

E79. a. A linear model works fairly well, as shown here in the scatterplot and residual plot. There is some heteroscedasticity, however, so the residuals for houses with a large number of square feet are larger. The equation is *price* = −25.2 + 75.6 *area,* and the correlation is .899.

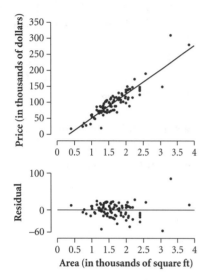

Separating the houses into new houses and old houses, the corresponding regression equations are *price* = −48.4 + 96.0 *area* and *price* = −16.6 + 66.6 *area.* These equations are very different, so you should not use one equation for both groupings. New houses cost quite a bit more per square foot. You can see the two relationships in this plot.

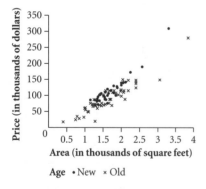

b. The two largest houses clearly are influential points, as could be the third largest house and the smallest house in the lower-left corner. If the two largest are removed from the data set, the correlation drops to .867 and the regression line changes to *price* = −10.3 + 65.7 *area.* This is quite a change in the

model—the price is now increasing $10,000 less per increase of 1,000 square feet.

c. Using the equation from part a, the price for an old house of 1,000 square feet would be *price* = −16.6 + 66.6 *area* = −16.6 + 66.6(1) = 50, or $50,000. The price for a house of 2,000 square feet would be *price* = −16.6 + 66.6 *area* = −16.6 + 66.6(2) = 116.6, or $116,600. You should have more confidence in the first prediction because the spread in the prices is less for the smaller houses than for the larger houses.

d. As seen in the boxplots shown here, the number of bathrooms is strongly related to the selling price. A lurking variable here is the number of square feet in the house, which is very strongly related to both the price and the number of bathrooms. A regression line is not appropriate here mostly because of the skewness in the prices for houses with three bathrooms and because you can do something better. You can compute the mean (or perhaps the median) price of a house with one bathroom, with two bathrooms, and with three bathrooms: $40,320; $99,290; and $201,400. This process is equivalent to regression but does not require a linear relationship.

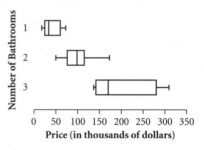

E80. a. The next scatterplot shows that *expenditures per pupil* (*expPP*) and *average teacher salary* (*teaSal*) are highly correlated: *r* = .832. The equation of the regression line is *expPP* = −1607 + 217 *teaSal.* In other words, for every increase of $1000 in the average teacher's salary, the per-pupil expenditure tends to increase by $217. In this case, there is a cause-and-effect relationship because if teachers are paid more, on average, the cost per pupil has to go up unless class sizes are increased proportionally.

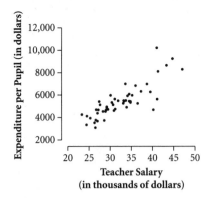

b. This next scatterplot has per capita expenditure on schools plotted against the average teacher salary. Again, you would expect a positive relationship, but $r = .661$ and so it is not as strong as in part a. It is reasonable that this is the case because the average teacher salary and the expense per student are directly related, whereas the average teacher salary and the expense per person in the state are related only by the fact that the more people there are, the more students there tend to be. But this relationship is not perfect, as you can see in the scatterplot matrix at the bottom of this page.

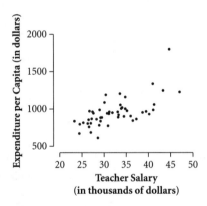

c. A scatterplot matrix and the correlations among the education variables are shown below and on page 148, respectively. No variable is highly correlated with the percentage of dropouts.

E81. **a.** There is almost no relationship between *rating* and *price*. The "best buy" would be one of the five points in the lower-right corner of the plot. But none of them sticks out as a clear best choice.

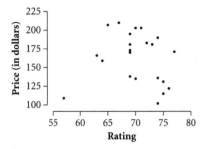

b. The point in the lower left corner has strong influence. The equations with that point and without it are

$$price = 220 - 0.81 \ rating$$
$$price = 424 - 3.66 \ rating$$

They are dramatically different; the first one reflects a negative relationship with small slope, and the second reflects a negative relationship with a steep slope.

E82. **a.** The plot over time appears here. It shows that the number of stores is increasing over time and that the rate of increase is increasing. There were two unusually large jumps in the number of stores: 1987 to 1988 and 1995 to 1996.

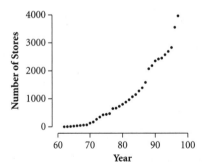

Lesson 3.3, E80c

```
Pearson Product-Moment Correlation

No Selector

            Dropout%   PPExp    PCExp    TeaSal   Enrollment   Teachers
Dropout%     1.000
PPExp        0.010     1.000
PCExp       -0.138     0.800    1.000
TeaSal       0.152     0.832    0.661    1.000
Enrollment   0.272     0.030   -0.001    0.286    1.000
Teachers     0.242     0.109    0.039    0.302    0.976        1.000
```

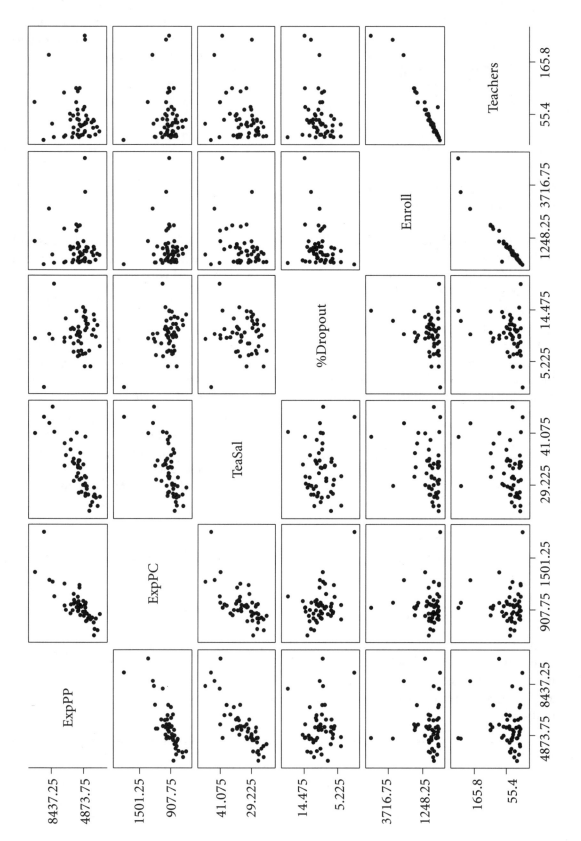

b. Because this pattern looks something like exponential growth, you might first try taking the log of the number of stores. But that results in a plot that is concave downward, so a log transformation is too strong. Perhaps, then, this is a power relationship, and a log-log transformation would be appropriate. Because the power equation is of the form $y = ax^b$ and contains the origin, you want to translate the data so they go near $(0, 0)$. You can do that by subtracting 61 from each year and then taking the logs of both the number of stores and your translated data. The resulting scatterplot, which is shown next, is reasonably linear.

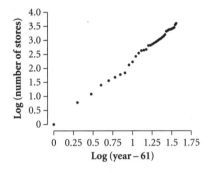

The regression equation is log(*number of stores*) = $-0.0220 + 2.29 \log(year - 61)$.

E83. The scatterplot of the original data appears here.

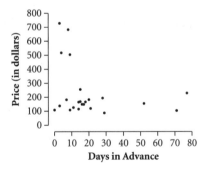

Because you would expect the price to go up as it gets nearer to flight time, a reciprocal transformation of the price (or 1/*price*)

might linearize data such as these. Actually, this transformation does a good job. The plot and residual plot are shown here.

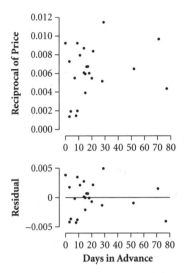

The regression equation is $\frac{1}{price} = 0.00541 + 0.000039$ days. If you solve for *price*, you get

$$price = \frac{1}{(0.00541 + 0.000039 \ days)}$$

That is, the number of days affects the price very little according to this model. (As students will learn later, the slope of the regression equation is not significantly different from 0.)

You get a linear relationship with some negative trend by plotting $(\ln(days), \ln(price))$. First, substitute $\frac{1}{2}$ day for 0 days before taking logs. This regression equation is $\ln(price) = 5.65 - 0.166 \ln(days)$. The plot and residual plot are shown next. If you solve the equation for the price, you get $price = 284.29 \ days^{-0.166}$. Notice that for the range, 10 days to 30 days, when most of the purchases were made, the range of prices is only from \$161.64 to \$193.98. Once again, *days* accounts for little of the variation in *price*. (And, again, the slope of the regression line is not statistically significant.)

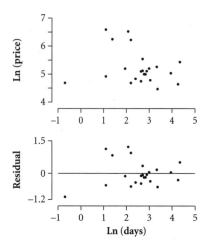

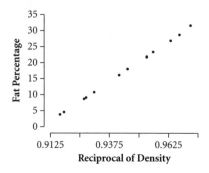

which is similar to Siri's model but not nearly as close as the equation for women. Thus, the model fits better for women than for men.

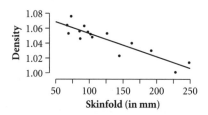

Here's the reason no transformation will give us a good model of predicting *price* from *day*: Five of the passengers paid a lot more for their tickets than did the other passengers, and they bought them 3, 4, 8, 9, and 9 days before the flight. (See the previous scatterplot.) But other passengers bought their tickets even closer to flight time and paid just about the same as passengers who bought their tickets months before. If the five passengers who paid extremely high prices are left out, the relationship is reasonably linear but flat. The correlation between *days* and *price* for the remaining passengers is .034, or practically nonexistent. Thus, the best model is to say that there is no relationship between the day these passengers bought their tickets and the price they paid, with the exception of five passengers who bought their tickets within 9 days of the flight and who paid more than double any other passenger.

E84. **a.** For women, the regression equation was % *body fat* = −450.6 + 495.6(1/*density*), almost identical to Siri's model. (See E56). The relationship is very strong and linear, with correlation almost equal to 1 and no pattern in the residual plot.

Using the same variables for men, the relationship is again extraordinarily linear (see the next scatterplot), with a correlation near 1. But this time the regression equation is % *body fat* = − 454 + 499(1/*density*),

b. For women, this scatterplot of *density* against *skinfold* is quite linear and does not require re-expression. Thus, a reasonable model is the regression equation, *density* = 1.08 − 0.000311 *skinfold*.

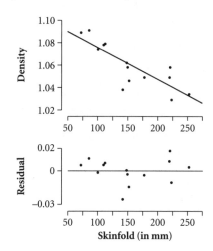

For men, the relationship is less strong and has some curvature (see the scatterplot shown here); however, the linear model is an adequate one. The residual plot shows some heteroscedasticity. So the model would be *density* = −0.000295 *skinfold* + 1.105.

4

SAMPLE SURVEYS AND EXPERIMENTS

Overview

Increasingly, statisticians have been calling for greater emphasis on the design of surveys and experiments and on the link between design and analysis in the introductory course. This call was reflected in the free response section of the 1997 AP Statistics exam: Two of the six questions—the fish and the ovens—could not be answered satisfactorily without basic knowledge of design principles. This chapter provides a good overview of design, which until recently was largely ignored by most introductory courses in statistics.

The most important lesson of this chapter is that chance-based data production beats all other methods on two paramount criteria: (1) protecting against bias and (2) validating the probability models required for statistical inference. The first half of the chapter (Sections 4.1 and 4.2) deals with samples and surveys. The last half (Sections 4.3 and 4.4) deals with comparative studies, especially true experiments, for which the conditions to be studied are actively assigned rather than passively observed, as they are in observational studies. The first section (4.1 and 4.3) of each half presents an overview of potential problems and pitfalls, illustrated by seemingly reasonable but faulty plans for gathering data. The second section (4.2 and 4.4) provides a systematic introduction to the most important design principles and offers familiar plans for data production based on these principles.

Goals

The overall goal of Chapter 4 is for students to learn good data collection strategies—how to design a survey by randomly selecting participants and how to design a sound experiment by randomly assigning treatments to subjects— that will allow generalization or inference from a sample to a population in order to draw conclusions from observed patterns.

Specific goals for students include being able

- to understand that population parameters can be estimated by looking at a properly chosen sample from that population
- to learn the basic terminology of sampling and sample surveys
- to learn how to recognize common sources of bias from methods of selecting the sample and from the method of getting the response
- to learn the characteristics of the most common types of sampling, including simple random sample, stratified random sample, cluster sample, and systematic sample with random start
- to understand that cause and effect can be established only with a randomized controlled experiment, not with an observational study
- to understand why each characteristic of a well-designed experiment (randomization of treatments to subjects, replication, and control or comparison group) is crucial
- to learn the common experimental designs (completely randomized, randomized block)
- to understand within-treatment variability versus between-treatment variability, and how blocked designs can minimize the former

Time Required

Traditional Schedule			Block	4 x 4 Block
Section 4.1				
2 days	Day 1	Overview of sampling, Activity 4.1	1.5 days	1 long, 1 short
	Day 2	Sampling bias, response bias, other sources of bias, summary, exercises		
Section 4.2				
2 days	Day 1	Overview, simple random samples, Activity 4.2	1.5 days	1 long, 1 short
	Day 2	Stratified random sampling and other sampling methods, summary, exercises		
Section 4.3				
3–4 days	Day 1	Overview and Kelly's hamsters	2 days	2 long, 1 short
	Day 2	Confounding, factors and levels		
	Day 3	Importance of randomizing, Activity 4.3, control groups		
	Day 4	Blind, double-blind, units and replication, summary, exercises		
Section 4.4				
3–4 days	Day 1	Difference between and variability within treatments, Activity 4.4	2 days	2 long, 1 short
	Day 2	Experimental designs, Activity 4.5, blocking		
	Day 3	More on blocking, Activity 4.6		
	Day 4	Summary, exercises		
Review				
1 day			1 day	1 long

Materials

Section 4.1: For Activity 4.1, a deck of cards and a blank copy of Display 4.3 for each group of students

Section 4.2: For Activity 4.2, a method of producing random digits, such as a table or a calculator; a copy of Display 4.4 (Random Rectangles) for each student

Section 4.3: For Activity 4.3, a coin for each student and a box with small equal-sized slips of paper; written on each slip of paper is the name of a student in the class

Section 4.4: For Activities 4.4 and 4.6, a launch ramp and launcher for each team and a supply of gummy bears. Each team will also need a coin, a tape measure or yardstick, and four textbooks. (See Displays 4.11 and 4.12 on pages 250–251 in the student edition for assembly instructions.)
For Activity 4.5, a stopwatch or watch with a second hand.

Suggested Assignments

Classwork			
Section	**Essential**	**Recommended**	**Optional**
4.1	D2–D8 P1–P3	Activity 4.1 D1, D9, D10 P4	
4.2	Activity 4.2 D11, D12, D14, D15, D17, D19, D20, D22, D23 P5–P7, P10	D13, D16, D18, D21 P8	P9
4.3	D24–D30, D32, D34 P11–P13, P16, P18, P19, P21	Activity 4.3 D31, D33 P14, P15, P20	P17
4.4	Activity 4.5 D35–D46, D49, D50 P22–P24, P26, P27	Activity 4.4, Activity 4.6 D35, D47, D48 P25	D51 P28

Homework			
Section	**Essential**	**Recommended**	**Optional**
4.1	E1, E3, E5, E6, E8	E4, E7, E9, E10, E12	E2, E11
4.2	E13–E16	E17, E18	E19, E20
4.3	E21, E23, E25, E26	E22, E24	
4.4	E27, E29, E31	E28, E30	
Review	E32, E36, E40, E41, E45, E47, E48	E33–E35, E37–E39, E43, E44, E46, E49	E42

4.1 Why Take Samples, and How Not To

Objectives

- to learn the basic terminology of sampling and sample surveys
- to learn reasons for using samples
- to learn to recognize common instances of sample selection bias and response bias

Important Terms and Concepts

- *population:* population size, sample, census, (sampling) units
- sample survey
- biased sampling methods versus unrepresentative samples

- *sample selection bias:* voluntary response bias, convenience sampling, judgment samples, and size bias
- sampling frame
- *response bias:* nonresponse bias, questionnaire bias

Lesson Planning

Class Time

Two days

Materials

For Activity 4.1, a deck of cards and a blank copy of Display 4.3 for each group of students

Suggested Assignments

Classwork		
Essential	**Recommended**	**Optional**
D2–D8	Activity 4.1	
P1–P3	D1, D9, D10	
	P4	

Homework		
Essential	**Recommended**	**Optional**
E1, E3, E5, E6, E8	E4, E7, E9, E10, E12	E2, E11

Lesson Notes: Census Versus Sample

This section is part cautionary tale and part catalog of common sampling pathologies. A good reference for students to read about Nielsen ratings can be found at http://www.nielsenmedia.com/whatratingsmean/.

Discussion

D1. **a.** Census. Each new car is inspected. This procedure is used because every customer expects their new car to be perfect.

b. Sampling. Counting the chocolate chips in a cookie is destructive, and counting all the chips in every cookie is time consuming.

c. Sampling. Theoretically, elections in the United States are a census of voters, but because not everyone who is eligible actually votes, elections are in practice a nonrandom and probably nonrepresentative sample.

d. Sampling. Not every movie theater owner reports ticket sales every weekend.

e. Sampling. There are thousands of teachers in the Los Angeles area. It would be too time consuming and expensive to do in-depth interviews with all of them.

D2. For either a sample or a census, get a list of the members from the American Statistical Association. To do a census, contact each of the 17,000 members. To do a sample of size 170, for example, you could take every hundredth member on the list and contact him or her.

D3. **a.** The population is all the households in your community. The unit is an individual household.

b. Sampling would be quicker, cheaper, and easier to carry out than a census.

c. Getting a response from each household chosen for the sample. Some may never respond.

Lesson Notes: Bias

Activity 4.1: Time in the Hospital

For this activity, each group of students will need a deck of cards. There is a blackline master of an empty grid at the end of this section that you can give to your students. This grid will speed the data collection process.

Before students start this activity, be sure they understand that the numbers on the playing cards represent the lengths of stay of 40 different patients. The order in which the patients arrive at the hospital is determined by shuffling the deck. Each patient is put into the first bed available. The goal is to estimate the average number of days a patient stays in the hospital.

This activity illustrates bias in the method of taking a sample. The method of sampling of choosing days at random results in longer stays being chosen more often than shorter stays. This results in an estimate of an average length of stay that is too long.

The bias is in the method, not in the result. A biased sampling method tends to result in a nonrepresentative sample, but not always. The dialogue between the student and the statistician in the student text on page 215 reinforces the difference between a biased sampling method and a nonrepresentative sample.

Part A

1. Students randomly select five cards. See Display 4.1 on page 213 for an example.

2. See Display 4.2 on page 213 for an example.

3. See Display 4.3 on page 214 for an example.

4. Suppose the day selected is 12.

5. For this example, on day 12, the average stay is $(3 + 1 + 7 + 7 + 5)/5 = 4.6$ days.

6. This figure shows a typical plot, based on a computer simulation of 100 trials of the activity. The distribution of these sample averages is centered at about 7 days with not much variability ($SD \approx 0.5$).

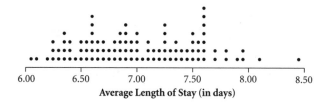

Average Length of Stay (in days)

7. The population average is 5.5, as shown at the bottom of this page.

8. The center of the plot lies well to the right of the population mean of 5.5, and in general, class estimates should be high. The sampling method is more likely to choose long stays than to choose short stays. If students do not see the bias, ask how many groups had a patient who stayed 1 day, 2 days, . . . , 10 days in their sample. They should begin to see the bias as longer stays become more prevalent.

9. The units are the individual patients. Each patient did not have an equal chance of being chosen. Patients with longer stays are more likely to be chosen. A stay of, say, 7 days had seven times the chance of being chosen as a stay of only 1 day.

Part B

1. Averages will vary.

2. The dot plot below shows averages for 100 random samples of size 5. This distribution is centered roughly at 5.4 days. The variability here is larger ($SD \approx 1.26$).

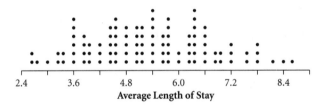

2.4	3.6	4.8	6.0	7.2	8.4

Average Length of Stay

3. Results will vary, but estimates should be about right.

4. The most important difference between this plot and the one for the size-biased method in Part A (step 6) is that the averages for the random samples (Part B) tend to cluster near the population average of 5.5, whereas those samples from the biased method tend to be too large. A second difference is that the averages from Part B (random samples) are spread out more than those from Part A, because you are likely to get both short and long stays in a random sample.

Discussion

D4. "Biased" is a property of the method of sampling. There is bias when a sampling method gives measurements that tend to be too small or tend to be too big. "Nonrepresentative" is a property of a specific sample. A sample is nonrepresentative when it does not resemble a miniature version of the population. A biased method can give a representative sample. On the other hand, a nonrepresentative sample can result from an unbiased method.

D5. All are possible. Use the results from the two sampling schemes in the hospital activity to illustrate the four cases.

Lesson Notes: Sampling Bias

Sample selection bias arises from the method used to select the sample and includes size bias, voluntary response bias, convenience sampling, judgment sampling, and problems with sampling frames. In all types of sampling selection bias, the method of taking the sample tends to result in numerical summaries that are systematically too high or too low.

Discussion

D6. **a.** No, because your class—the spoonful—is probably not representative of all students—the whole pot. The students in a college-level statistics class are probably more likely to study two or more hours than the typical student. If, however, your class is required of all students, it could be "yes" and representative of all students.

b. No, because the ambassadors are not representative. They undoubtedly have a higher income than the average citizens of their countries.

c. Yes, because Gallup uses a chance device to choose the sample. If the intention had been to determine the percentage of *all*

Lesson 4.1, Part A7

$$\frac{(1 + 1 + 1 + 1 + 2 + 2 + 2 + 2 + \cdots + 10 + 10 + 10 + 10)}{40} = \frac{1(4) + 2(4) + \ldots 10(4)}{4 \cdot 10}$$

$$\frac{(1 + 2 + \cdots + 10)}{10} = \frac{[(10)(11)/2]}{10} = 5.5 \text{ days}$$

United States residents that favored cuts, then the sample might be *highly* biased because it was limited to a certain age group.

D7. Answers will vary, but students should realize that the frame does not represent the population well. Two groups that belong to the population but not to the frame are those likely to vote who have unlisted telephone numbers and those likely to vote who do not have a personal telephone. Those too young to vote or those who are not registered can be in the phone book but not in the population. Because a substantial number of eligible voters do not go to the polls, the frame (phone book) will list many nonvoters and unlikely voters. These people are not a part of the target population. With such a poor fit between frame and population, it is hard to say with confidence what sort of bias there might be.

Practice

P1. **a.** Size bias. Larger farms are more likely to be selected than smaller farms.

b. This is a judgment sample. In his attempt to get a diverse sample, the professor may have inadvertently selected too few valedictorians from the most typical high schools. He may also have missed some important groups. The students may also see this as a convenience sample because the professor only used high schools in Illinois.

c. Voluntary response bias. Teachers whose students did well are more likely to report. Overall, the teachers from the AP discussion list reported that 426 out of 535, or 80%, passed (got a 3 or better). When the official results were released, the pass rate was 62.1%.

d. Size bias. Longer strings are more likely to be selected.

Note: If you would like to do this activity with your students, refer to the instructions in "Stringing Students Along" in *Activity-Based Statistics*, Richard L. Scheaffer, Mrudulla Gnanadesikan, Ann Watkins, and Jeffrey A. Witmer (New York: Springer-Verlag, 1996).

e. Voluntary response bias. Responders tend to have stronger opinions than nonresponders. Even though Ann Landers received a very large number of responses, a large

sample offers no guarantees about bias. Voluntary response samples are so likely to be biased that you should not trust them.

P2. The estimate will be too high. The sample will catch almost all those who came to Boston to see the museum, but only a tiny fraction of those who came to Boston for other reasons because those in the latter group are not likely to go to the museum at all.

Lesson Notes: Response Bias

Response bias arises from the method of getting the response and includes nonresponse bias (referring to who in the sample replies or doesn't reply), questionnaire bias (how questions are asked), and incorrect response or measurement bias (whether someone provides false information, an incorrect response, or an inaccurate measurement). Nonresponse bias can occur when you obtain responses from only a portion of your intended sample. Questionnaire bias is related to the way in which questions are asked, such as a question that leads or persuades the respondent to answer "yes." Bias may occur when respondents are generally likely to answer a question untruthfully. Similarly, incorrect response bias can occur when respondents are asked to measure or recall something, such as the number of vegetables they eat per day.

Discussion

D8. Those graduates who have been successful are more likely to respond to surveys about the high quality of their education. They will probably be happier with their education than those who do not respond.

D9. The second question: 62% of Americans agreed with the statement that it is not the government's job to financially support television programming. On the other hand, when Americans were asked if they would be disappointed if Congress cut its funding for public television, 54% said yes.

D10. Nonresponse bias comes from the fact that some of the sampled units, perhaps in a well-designed random sample, could not be measured for one reason or another. Voluntary response bias comes from a poor design of the sampling plan. It is often possible to measure nonresponse bias by working a little harder to get some responses from those who initially formed the nonresponse group. It is usually impossible to measure the bias in a voluntary response survey.

Practice

P3. Question I is more likely to draw "yes" responses.

P4. This is incorrect response bias where people gave an answer that they thought made them look knowledgeable.

Lesson Notes: Summary

Sampling Bias	Response Bias
size bias	nonresponse
voluntary response sample	questionnaire bias
convenience sampling	incorrect response or measurement bias
judgment sampling	
inadequate frame	

Exercises

E1. **a.** Too high. Your polltakers will never get in touch with people who are away from home between 9:00 a.m. and 5:00 p.m., so these people will eventually be dropped from the sample. Because these are the people who are less likely to have children under the age of 13 at home (those with small children are more likely to stay home to take care of them), the sample will contain an artificially high percentage of those who do have children under the age of 13 at home.
b. At suppertime, adults are more likely to be at home.

E2. Here's a possible way to word the questions:

I. Should society have the right to protect itself by executing convicted murderers who are known sociopaths and likely to kill again if given the opportunity?

II. Given the established fact that innocent people have been falsely convicted and executed, do you favor life imprisonment without possibility of parole as an alternative to the death penalty?

E3. Sample selection bias. Students who take a statistics course are more likely to like math than students in general, unless it is a required class. The estimated response will tend to be too high in the first case and about right in the second case.

E4. There are tens of millions of adult males in the United States. It would be impossible to contact them all. Questionnaire bias is unlikely for a factual question like this. Assuming that a nonbiased sampling method is used, there still might be an incorrect response bias because some people might be reluctant to admit to smoking.

E5. From respondents 40 years old or older you would expect to get an estimate that is too high. 40-year-olds are older than average. As people get older, they tend to visit more and more states. (They can't visit fewer!) From the residents of Rhode Island you might get an estimate that is too high as well, as Rhode Island is a small state close to many other small states. Compare this result to what you might expect from asking people who live in Texas or Montana.

E6. The answer may depend on whether your statistics class consists primarily of students living with their parents or students who have established their own family. If the students are living with their parents, the estimate will be too high. There are two reasons. First, families with no children have no chance of being in the sample. Second, families with many children will be over-represented. In Activity 4.1, a person who stays 5 days is five times as likely to be chosen as a person who stays 1 day. Similarly, families with 5 children would be five times more likely to be represented in the sample than families with only 1 child.

If your class consists mainly of older students, they may be young enough to have formed their own family, but not old enough to have children and the estimate will be too low.

E7. There is no right answer here, and there is probably no really good answer. The main point is that it is hard to balance all four characteristics.

E8. **a.** No, this is a voluntary response sample, so people who responded probably felt strongly one way or the other.
b. Quite a bit less than 92%: The percentage is almost surely inflated by voluntary response bias.

E9. This convenience sample probably will be too optimistic about how well their candidate will do.

E10. Sampling Method II will give you an unbiased estimate of the average class size. The unit is the class, and you are taking a random sample from the classes. Sampling Method I is a size-biased method, and the estimate will be too high. Because there are more of them, students who are in larger classes will be more likely to be selected than students in smaller classes. In addition, more than one student might be selected from the same large class, thereby inflating the influence of that class size.

E11. Examples will vary.

E12. The ABC News poll. From the Gallup poll, 36% were in favor of U.S. air strikes. From the ABC poll, 65% were in favor. Note that the ABC News poll mentions the involvement of allies of the United States and also makes it sound as though the air strikes will hit only objects and not soldiers. Students might reasonably think that the Gallup poll will produce a higher favorable response, because it mentions why the United States would want to conduct air strikes, i.e., it justifies air strikes. It can be hard to predict in advance which direction the psychology of questionnaire bias will go.

Activity 4.1: Grid for Hospital Length of Stay

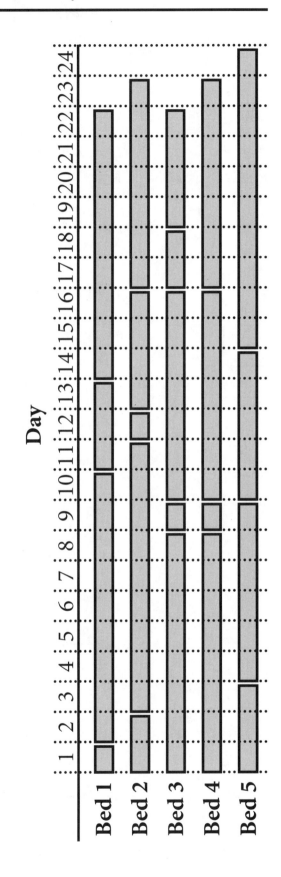

4.2 Randomizing: Playing It Safe by Taking Chances

Objectives

- to understand the two main reasons for relying on chance to choose samples
- to learn the definition of a simple random sample
- to recognize and implement several kinds of probability samples

Only references to simple random, stratified, and systematic sampling techniques appear on the AP Statistics syllabus. However, cluster and two-stage (multistage) sampling techniques are very useful tools that can help to broaden students' understanding of sampling methods. In addition, real-world sampling tends to use these more complicated but efficient methods.

Important Terms and Concepts

- simple random sample
- probability sample
- strata
- stratified random sample

- cluster sample
- two-stage sample and multistage sample
- systematic sample

Lesson Planning

Class Time

Two days

Materials

For Activity 4.2, a method of producing random digits, such as a table or a calculator, and a copy of Display 4.4 (Random Rectangles) for each student

Suggested Assignments

Classwork		
Essential	**Recommended**	**Optional**
Activity 4.2	D13, D16, D18, D21	P9
D11, D12, D14, D15, D17, D19, D20, D22, D23	P8	
P5–P7, P10		

Homework		
Essential	**Recommended**	**Optional**
E13–E16	E17, E18	E19, E20

Lesson Notes: Simple Random Samples

This second section presents a systematic overview of sound strategies for sampling and demonstrates how one can use these sampling strategies in practical applications. The two main reasons for choosing your sample by chance are that it is the only method guaranteed to be unbiased and it is randomization that makes inference possible.

Activity 4.2: Random Rectangles

The random samples of step 5 in Activity 4.2 will tend to be more representative than the samples from the size-biased judgment sampling method of step 1. On occasion, just by the luck of the draw, your class will get samples that are less representative. If this happens, you have a serendipitous opportunity to proselytize: "Although chance-based sampling methods give representative samples most of the time, there will be times when, just by chance, you get an unrepresentative sample. One of the great advantages of relying on chance is that you can use mathematical theory or simulations to calculate the probability of getting a 'bad' (unrepresentative) sample. No other sampling method can offer you protection anywhere near as good as that."

1–3. This plot shows the results from one class for the means of judgment samples of five rectangles.

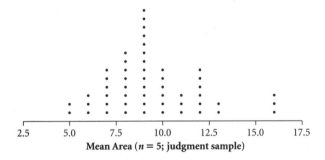

Mean Area ($n = 5$; judgment sample)

4. The mean area of the population of rectangles is 7.4, with a standard deviation of 5.2. The judgment sampling is biased toward the high side with mean, in this case, 9.4 and a standard deviation of 2.55.

5–7. The following plot shows the means of random samples of five rectangles. The sampling distribution for the judgment sample means is more spread out and not quite as normal looking as the one for random samples. The observed sampling distribution for the random samples centers approximately

where the theory says it should, and it looks quite normal. For this example, the mean is 6.9.

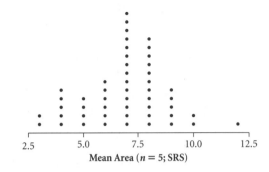

Mean Area ($n = 5$; SRS)

	N	MEAN	MEDIAN	TRMEAN	STDEV	SEMEAN
Judge	52	9.423	9.000	9.261	2.554	0.354
Random	50	6.900	7.000	6.886	1.876	0.265

8. In general, random sampling will give a better estimate of the population mean. The first method is size-biased, generally resulting in an estimate of the mean that is too large.

Discussion

D11. no; no; yes

D12. Suppose you have 32 students. Assign a two-digit number to each student: 01, 02, 03, . . . , 32. Then, go through the random digit table one pair of digits at a time until you find six of these assigned numbers. Ignore 00 and any pairs that give a number larger than 32. Also, ignore any duplicate pairs. The sample should be representative on some variables and unrepresentative on others.

D13. First, get a list of all instructors of English classes. Then go to each instructor and ask for a list of all students in all of their English classes. Finally, combine the lists, delete any repeating names, and use a random digit table to select the sample.

D14. Number the characters in the book. To be concrete, suppose there are exactly one million characters. Use a computer or random number table to choose 10,000 random numbers between 1 and 1,000,000. Each of these 10,000 numbers is the number of a character in your list—that character goes in the sample. Finding the characters in the SRS would take forever!

Practice

P5. **a.** No. The students at the end of the list have no chance of being chosen.

b. Each student has the same chance of being chosen, and if you think of the phone numbers as being assigned randomly before class, all possible groups of students have the same chance of being in the sample. However, an implicit assumption in simple random sampling is that the sample size is fixed in advance, and in this situation the sample size would be random. So, although this produces a random selection of students, it does not produce a simple random sample of a fixed sample size.

c. No. Although each student has the same chance of being chosen, not all possible groups of students have the same chance of being chosen. Two students sitting in different rows cannot both be in the sample.

d. Yes

e. No. Although each student has the same chance of being chosen, not all possible groups of students have the same chance of being chosen. A group of six girls cannot all be in the sample.

f. No. Although each student has the same chance of being chosen, not all possible groups of students have the same chance of being chosen. Two students with last names starting with different letters cannot both be in the sample.

Lesson Notes: Stratified Random Samples

Stratum is Latin for "layer." You may have seen the earth science meaning of stratification in a picture showing the layers of the earth's crust. Social scientists rely on the same image when they talk about socioeconomic or population strata, metaphorically dividing the population into layers by income or by age or by gender. In sampling, "stratification" borrows from the social science meaning of *strata* as groups of similar sampling units.

Some important reasons for stratification are *convenience*, *coverage*, and *precision*. Sometimes it is more convenient and less expensive to select

members of the sample by choosing randomly from well-defined strata, such as choosing a sample of voters from separate Democratic and Republican registration lists. Further, by selecting randomly from each stratum, you are assured that each stratum will be represented in the sample. This qualification is important if you want to look at the results for each stratum separately. Finally, you can get a more precise estimate of the population parameter if strata can be constructed so that the variability within strata is less than the variability in the population as a whole and if, in addition, sample sizes are chosen so that they are proportional to the sizes of the population in each stratum. That is, you are more likely to be closer to the population parameter when you compute your estimate from such a stratified random sample than from a simple random sample. If the variability is greater in some strata than in others, an even more precise estimate of the population parameter can be obtained by allocating more of the sample to those strata with the larger variation.

Optional Activity

Suppose an instructor wants to interview a sample of five students from her class to estimate the mean number of hours students in that class study each week. She believes that how far a student sits from the front of the room is strongly associated with how many hours the student studies per week. The instructor is correct. Unknown to her, the actual number of hours studied each week by the 25 students in her class are

Back of the Room

0	5	3	6	1
4	7	9	7	10
8	12	9	13	6
15	13	7	14	14
19	18	16	23	19

Front of the Room

The instructor is considering three random sampling designs to select her sample of five students.

A. Simple: Select five students at random.

B. Stratified with columns as strata: Select one student at random from each vertical "column."

C. Stratified with rows as strata: Select one student at random from each horizontal "row."

Evaluate these three sampling designs. Begin by going through the following steps for each design:

1. Select a sample using that design.
2. Compute the sample mean.
3. Repeat until you have at least 30 sample means.
4. Make a dot plot of the sample means.

The population mean, for all 25 students, is 10.32 hours. Which design gives the smallest variability for the sample means? Explain.

Answer You can see from the simulation that stratified random sampling with rows as strata produces sample means with smaller variation than does either simple random sampling or stratified random sampling with columns as strata. That is because the rows are more homogeneous than the columns, and one observation within a row gives much information on the measurements in that row.

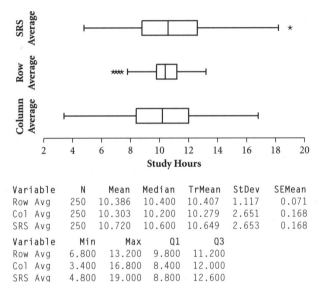

Variable	N	Mean	Median	TrMean	StDev	SEMean
Row Avg	250	10.386	10.400	10.407	1.117	0.071
Col Avg	250	10.303	10.200	10.279	2.651	0.168
SRS Avg	250	10.720	10.600	10.649	2.653	0.168

Variable	Min	Max	Q1	Q3
Row Avg	6.800	13.200	9.800	11.200
Col Avg	3.400	16.800	8.400	12.000
SRS Avg	4.800	19.000	8.800	12.600

The variation in sample means can be seen here because of the repeated sampling in the simulation. If, however, you were to conduct a survey like this in practice and were to do it only one time, you would need at least two observations in each row so that you could measure the variability within each stratum. Because each column has about the same amount of variation as the population as a whole, there is essentially no difference between simple random sampling and stratified random sampling by columns. Using the sample mean as an estimate of the population mean for the stratified samples is correct in this situation because the sample sizes (one per stratum) are proportional to the population sizes (five per stratum).

Discussion

D15. The main difference is that in a simple random sample, you select your sample randomly from the entire group. In a stratified random sample, you select your sample by separately sampling at random from subgroups of the population.

D16. Up to a point. If the rocks could be stratified into piles of rocks with no variation among the diameters of rocks in the same pile, then the mean diameter could be calculated exactly by taking one observation from each stratum. Achieving that degree of precision may require many strata and, hence, many observations. Generally, that degree of reduction in variation is either not possible or not practical.

D17. Strata should be as different from each other as possible. So one good point is that older students tend to have a different form of transportation than younger students—they often drive themselves to school. However, this stratification scheme may not be the best method. The best method might be to stratify students according to how far they live from school. That variable probably has the biggest effect on travel time.

D18. Ideally, you would want all of the students who study a lot in one stratum and all those who do not study much in another. This would, no doubt, be impossible to arrange, so the next best thing is to look for some variable highly related to study hours as the basis for stratification. Perhaps those taking science and math courses study more than others, or perhaps juniors study more than seniors. You could, then, stratify on the basis of academic program or year in school.

Lesson Notes: Other Methods of Sampling

Multistage samples extend the logic of two-stage samples. For example, a three-stage sample of chocolate chip cookies might start with an SRS of supermarkets, then take an SRS of bags of cookies from each supermarket, and finally take an SRS of cookies from each bag.

Discussion

D19. No. Not all possible groups have a chance of being in the sample.

D20. **a.** A cluster sample, with pages as clusters, is much more efficient, although the random mixing would not be as good as the SRS. In practice, the advantages far outweigh the disadvantages.

b. Take an SRS of pages. Then take an SRS of lines from each of those pages.

c. Start with the two-stage sample, as in part b, and add a third stage that involves taking an SRS of characters from each line in the second stage.

D21. We would expect earlier mortgages to be smaller amounts. A systematic sample with random start should give a good mix of mortgages of all dates and would be quick.

D22. In stratified random sampling, the population is divided into groups (strata) that are as different as possible but the individuals within a group are as alike as possible. Samples are then selected randomly and separately from each group (strata). Cluster sampling tends to be used when people are already in groups that cannot easily be separated; everyone in the sampled cluster is in the sample in single-stage cluster sampling.

D23. Agree on an ordering of the students in your class, perhaps by rows of seats or by names on the class roster, and number them. Divide 5 into the number of students to see how many possible systematic samples there are. For example, if there are 33 students in the class, you could think of six possible systematic samples, with a random start between numbers 1 and 6. But the 3 students at the end of the list have no chance of being sampled under this plan. There is no good solution. Suppose you think of starting between 1 and 7. If the random start is student number 6, then the sampled students are 6, 13, 20, 27, and 34. Because there is no number 34, start over again and turn 34 into number 1. But now numbers 1 and 2 have twice the probability of being selected as other students.

Practice

P6. Take 5% of 200, which is 10 people, and then calculate k (200/10 or 20). Then choose a random start between persons 1 and 20, and take every 20th person thereafter.

Take 20% of 200, which is 40 people, and find k: 200/40 or 5. Then choose a random start between persons 1 and 5, and take every 5th person thereafter.

P7. A sample of 1000 is every 17th name because 17,000/1,000 = 17. Choose a random number between 1 and 17 as your start and include that person in your sample, as well as every 17th person thereafter. For example, if your random number is 8, choose the 8th, 25th, 42nd person, and so on.

P8. One suggestion is to sample from auto registrations. Another is to take samples from parking lots (clusters of cars) and other open areas where cars are visible. The latter method might introduce bias. It is conceivable that an owner of one type of car (foreign or domestic) might be more likely to keep the car out of sight.

P9. **a.** This is closest to three-stage cluster sampling. First, one lot was chosen. (This is like choosing one cluster—a lot—from all possible lots.) Then three containers were chosen from that lot—again like cluster sampling. At the final stage, however, not all pills in the bottle were in the sample, only 10. We do not know whether the sampling was random at any of the three stages.

b. If an overall picture is needed, it would be better to use more lots, more containers, and possibly fewer pills per container.

P10. .65(84/100) + .35(59/75) ≈ .82

Exercises

E13. The frame misses all cases of heart disease that are not yet diagnosed and all those that are diagnosed but did not result in hospitalization in the last five years. If people who smoke are more likely to be hospitalized than others with heart disease, the estimate will be too big. If they are less likely—probably not the case because smokers tend to have multiple health problems—it will be too small.

E14. **a.** All the cookies must be numbered, which means buying all the bags in the store, numbering all the cookies, and choosing the SRS using random digits.

b. Use bags as clusters. Number the bags and choose an SRS of bags. Use all the cookies in those bags as the sample. A cluster sample is much more practical.

c. As in part b, number the bags and choose an SRS of bags. Then, take an SRS of cookies from each bag in the cluster sample. Which method you prefer depends on the patterns of variation and on how much time and money you have. If you have lots of time and not much money, use a cluster sample: Buy a small number of bags and count the chips in every cookie. If money is no object, but you do not have much time, you could use the two-stage sample: Buy more bags and count fewer cookies from each bag. This would give better estimates if chip contents vary a lot from bag to bag, but tend to be comparatively uniform from cookie to cookie within each bag.

E15. Although the times are changing, it is still true that haircut prices are higher for females than for males, so stratification by gender is likely to be the best strategy. In fact, samples of students have shown that females still pay quite a bit more than males for a haircut, and more males than females get their hair cut for free, usually by a family member. Stratification allows separate estimates of the mean for each gender, which may be more inform- ative than estimating a single overall mean. Stratification gives a more precise estimate of the overall mean if the two groups really do have different means.

E16. The first. It is just too unlikely to get all women in a random sample of size 25.

E17. Because there are only five farms and a large number of acres per farm, choosing a sample from the farms (cluster sampling) does not seem reasonable. Instead, consider the farms as the five strata and take a random sample of, say, 10 acres from each farm.

E18. To get 30 pages from 600, $k = 600/30 = 20$. So, take every 20th page, starting at a page chosen at random from those numbered 1 through 20.

E19. Sampling plans will vary. Stratification by age and by gender may be appropriate as attitudes toward movies probably differ by age and gender of the student. Using fresh- man, sophomore, junior, and senior as proxies for age and male and female for gender, there would be eight strata. Then take an SRS of size 6 from each stratum.

E20. Systematic sampling with random start from this line is quickest and easiest. Do systematic sampling with random start from each of the five lines (strata). With production line samples, it may be preferable to sample from the beginning, middle, and end of the production line because there may be greater variation in a product at these three points (stratified systematic sampling).

Activity 4.2: A Population of Rectangles

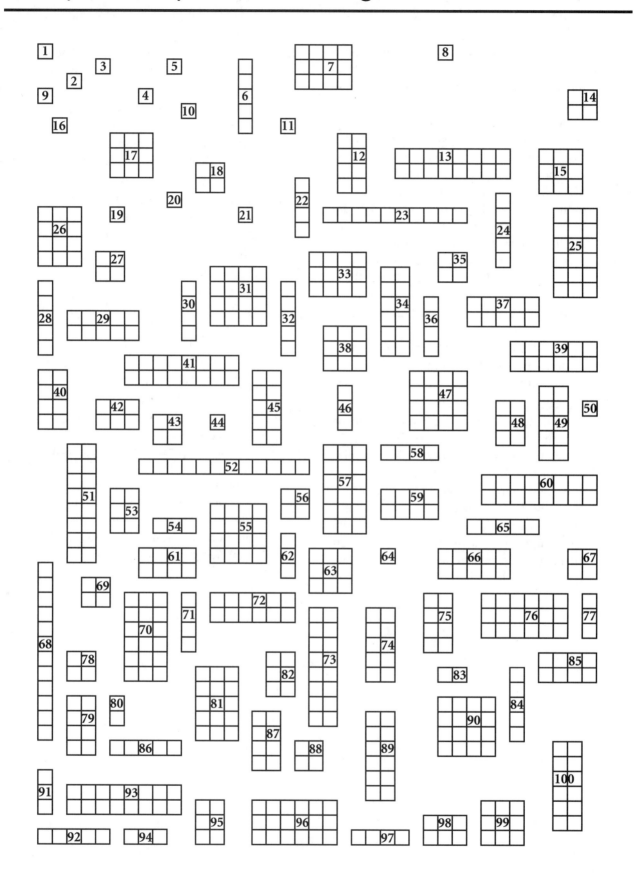

4.3 Experiments and Inference About Cause

Objectives

- to recognize cause and effect and that the only way to establish cause and effect is with a randomized experiment
- to learn the characteristics of a well-designed experiment
- to learn the difference between an experiment and an observational study
- to learn to recognize instances of confounding
- to learn that randomizing the assignment of treatments to subjects makes cause and effect statements possible by protecting against confounding

Important Terms and Concepts

- cause and effect
- explanatory variables
- lurking variable
- confounding
- experiments versus observational studies
- factors and levels
- control group or comparison group
- placebo
- placebo effect
- blind and double-blind experiments
- randomized comparative experiment
- experimental units
- replication
- randomizing treatments to subjects

Lesson Planning

Class Time

Three to four days

Materials

For Activity 4.3, a coin for each student and a box with small equal-sized slips of paper; written on each slip of paper is the name of a student in the class.

Suggested Assignments

Classwork		
Essential	**Recommended**	**Optional**
D24–D30, D32, D34 P11–P13, P16, P18, P19, P21	Activity 4.3 D31, D33 P14, P15, P20	P17

Homework		
Essential	**Recommended**	**Optional**
E21, E23, E25, E26	E22, E24	

Lesson Notes: A Real Experiment: Kelly's Hamsters

Like Section 4.1 on sampling, this first section on comparative studies (experiments and observational studies) is part cautionary tale and part catalog of common design mistakes. Students should connect causation only with well-designed, randomized experiments.

The goal of the hamster experiment is to establish causation by comparison of two or more treatments. The components of good experimental design are (1) defining the question, (2) defining the experimental units, (3) defining the treatments, (4) assigning treatments randomly to subjects, (5) defining the response variable, (6) developing a clearly written protocol on how the measurements are to be made, and (7) analyzing the results.

Discussion

D24. The figure below shows a stacked dot plot for comparing concentrations of the enzyme (Na^+K^+ ATP-ase) in the brains of Kelly's hamsters. The evidence supports Kelly's hypothesis that there tends to be more of the enzyme in the brains of hamsters raised in short days.

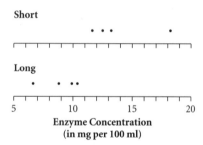

D25. Almost. If we are convinced that the two groups were treated exactly alike except for the length of their day, there are only two possible explanations for the difference: (1) the hamsters with the higher concentrations happened to get assigned to the short day group and (2) day length caused the enzyme concentrations to change. Because she randomly assigned the hamsters to the two treatments, it is unlikely that all the hamsters with high enzyme concentration were assigned to the short day group. (In fact, the probability of getting all the highest values in one group is only 1/35.) Thus, we would tend to favor (2) as the explanation.

Practice

P11. **a.** The population is the students who took the SAT; the response variable is the SAT score; and the treatments are taking the course or not.

b. No, because the students are not randomly assigned to the two treatments of taking the special course or not taking it.

c. No. Those who choose to take the special course might be unrepresentative due to selection bias. Those who take the course might tend to score higher anyway, either because of higher motivation to do everything possible to raise their score, or because students who expect scores high enough to try for the most selective colleges might be more likely to take the course.

P12. **a.** The lurking variable is the person's age. Older people are more likely to do both.

b. I causes II. Experiments have shown that drinking more milk, which is high in calcium, results in stronger bones. Of course, there are other causes of strong bones, such as heredity and exercise.

c. II causes I. People who go to school longer tend to earn more money. However, this statement is based on observational studies, not on randomized experiments, so occasionally the cause and effect relationship is questioned. Some people believe that family background is a lurking variable: People from more well-off families tend to go to school longer and to earn more money, but it isn't the schooling that caused the higher income, it was their family's support in getting established. However, most people believe that although family background certainly contributes, the number of years of schooling is another cause of higher income.

Lesson Notes: Confounding in Observational Studies

Two variables are confounded if their effects on the response variable cannot be separated. (All males get treatment A, all females get treatment B.) A lurking variable is one that lies in the background and is not being measured as a response or used in the design, but may affect the response variable anyway. (Those receiving treatment A may all be younger than those receiving treatment B, but age was not considered in the design.) A variable that is confounded with the treatments may or may not be a lurking variable. In an experiment, the researcher uses a random process to place the units in groups and imposes treatment(s) on units that are randomly placed in the treatment group(s); in an observational study, the units are placed in groups based on whether they exhibit the condition of interest.

Discussion

D26. **a.** No. It may be the other way around. The respiratory problems may have caused the thymus to enlarge.

b. For an experiment, randomly divide the children with respiratory problems into two groups: one that gets surgery and one that does not. Otherwise, treat them exactly alike. Record how many survived under each treatment.

D27. In an experiment, treatments are assigned to units. In an observational study, the conditions you want to compare come already attached to the units.

D28. **a.** The factors are type of lighting (brightness of the room) and type of music. For the type of lighting, the levels are low, medium, and high. For the type of music, the levels are pop, classical, and jazz.

b. Answers will vary. Possibilities are heart rate, blood pressure, or self-description of anxiety level.

Practice

P13.

| | | Motivation | |
		High	**Low**
Took Course?	**Yes**	Higher SAT	No evidence
	No	No evidence	Lower SAT

P14. **a.** Students should not believe this. Their explanations will vary but the actual explanation is in P15. The pipe- and cigar-smokers are a bit older on average.

b. Observational study

c. The factor is smoking behavior. The levels are nonsmoking, cigarette smoking, and pipe or cigar smoking. The response variable is the number of deaths per 1000 men per year.

P15. Older men have a higher death rate; the pipe- and cigar-smokers are older than the others. Here are the age-adjusted death rates per 1000 men: nonsmokers 20.3, cigarette-smokers 28.3, and pipe- and cigar-smokers 21.2. The new factor is the age. The discussion loosely follows Paul R. Rosenbaum's *Observational Studies* (New York: Springer-Verlag, 1995, page 60). (These data come from William G. Cochran, "The Effectiveness of Adjustment by Subclassification in Removing Bias in Observational Studies," *Biometrics* 24 (1968): 205–213. The original study was by Best and Walker.)

P16. **a.** This study is observational.

b. The factor is the legal age for driving. The levels are the age groups. The response variable is the highway death rate by state.

c. The "treatments," legal driving age, may be confounded with driver education, as states with higher age limits may generally be more restrictive about getting a driver's license and so also require driver's education courses. Also, if it is the case that the legal driving age tends to be lower in western states, the geography of the states would be confounded with age because western states with many miles of high-speed highways tend to have higher death rates than congested eastern states.

P17. The factors are brand of popcorn and type of popper, each having two levels (brand/generic and air/oil). Thus, there are four treatments (each combination of brand of popcorn and type of popper) to try in the experiment. Each treatment should be replicated as many times as is practical, with the trials done in a random order to minimize possible confounding of the explanatory variables with variables such as temperature of the room or of the ingredients, the amount of popcorn put in the popper (which should be exactly the same for all trials of the experiment), the length of time the popper is allowed to run, and the condition of the popper. (Was the popper already warm?)

Lesson Notes: The Importance of Randomizing

Activity 4.3: Randomization and Its Effect

The goal of random assignment of treatments to subjects is to have each group of subjects be as nearly alike as possible. Randomization tends to take care of balancing the groups on all variables, those that can be observed (such as gender) as well as those that cannot be observed (such as genetic conditions). Randomization protects against confounding by distributing any variables that might be confounded with the explanatory variables as evenly as possible among the treatment groups.

Note: Pick two leaders who are not alike, such as a male and a female student, to increase the probability that the students they pick are as unlike as possible.

1–2. The two groups will probably look different because each leader will usually choose his or her friends or people with whom they have something in common. For example, if one leader is a male and the other female, more than likely the male will pick more males and vice versa. Study habits within one group could be similar within the group and very different between the groups.

3–4. Randomly drawing the names of the groups from a hat should balance the groups nicely unless your class is small.

5. Assignment by a flip of a coin is also random, but it may not lead to equal group sizes. It is not essential that the group sizes be equal, but most experiments assign the same number of subjects to each treatment group.

6. As in step 4, the variables should be reasonably balanced across the groups.

7. The first method is not random and can lead to other variables confounded with the treatment. The other two methods are random and should balance the groups nicely. The drawback to method three is that there is no guarantee that the groups will have nearly equal sizes. It is possible that one group could have very few members and that, too, could lead to groups that differ on significant variables.

Method two is probably the best method in this example.

Lesson Notes: A Control or Comparison Group Is Vital

A control or comparison group is an essential component in a well-designed experiment. Generally, students easily understand issues of placebos, blinding, and double-blinding.

Discussion

D29. Experiments should be blind because of the placebo effect and because people are eager to please and appear knowledgeable. People do better, for example, when they know they are getting a drug rather than the placebo. People who participate in an experiment want to help it have a favorable outcome and have been known to try harder when getting a new treatment. The experiment should be double-blind for the same reasons. The person who evaluates the effects of the treatment should not know which treatment the person received so that their subconscious beliefs about which treatment is better will not shape his or her judgment and analysis, and so that they won't unintentionally convey expectations to the subjects.

D30. Assign subjects who suffer from depression at random to three groups, one to receive St. John's wort, one to receive an antidepressant drug, and one to receive a placebo. Treat the subjects exactly the same otherwise, including having the pills look exactly alike. After at least eight weeks, have a doctor evaluate the extent of the depression. The doctor should not know which treatment the person received. Students may suggest the good strategy of evaluating the extent of the depression both at the beginning and the end of the study and recording the degree to which it improved.

D31. *Note:* We encourage you to do this experiment with your class if you have the time. Instructions for making the bear launcher are given in Activity 4.4 in Section 4.4. Divide your class into teams. Each team will launch 10 times; the first five launches with a red bear and the second five launches with a green bear. Plotting the distance against launch number may show that the effect of practice is confounded with the color of the bear.

a. Green bears went farther. The display below shows the average distances for each team for both red bears and green bears, using the data in the student text. On the surface, it looks as though color has a real effect on launch distance.

Team	Red	Green	Difference
1	26.2	32.4	6.2
2	54.4	89.8	35.4
3	31.8	60.2	28.4
4	30.0	34.8	4.8
5	31.1	41.2	10.1
6	102.6	115.4	12.8

b. The greater distances traveled by the green bears is due to confounding of launch order with bear color. As students got more practice, they were able to launch the bear farther. This table shows how the variables are confounded.

		Practice Doing Launches	
		Less	**More**
Color of Bear	**Red**	Shorter distances	No evidence
	Green	No evidence	Longer distances

c. The plots in the following figures for the data in the student text show a clear time trend: Later launches tend to travel farther, because most people get better with practice. (If you do this experiment and your class gets results that do not show a time trend, it is worth spending a few minutes trying to figure out why. For example, several practice launches before starting to record data could minimize confounding of the launch order with bear color.)

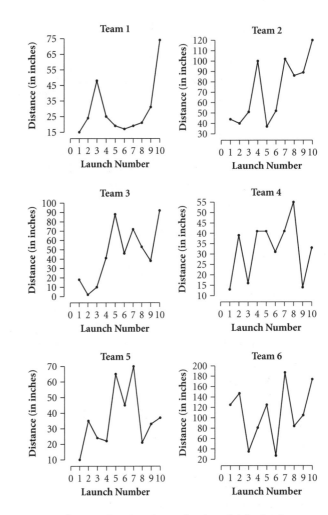

d. Randomize the order in which the bears of different colors are launched. For example, put five bears of each color in a box and mix them up. For each launch, draw out a bear without looking. Don't return that bear to the box. A more risky strategy is to use practice launches until the learning effect appears to go away.

Practice

P18. For his control group, Dr. Mayo used adults who died of nonrespiratory causes. He was right to use a control group, but he failed to isolate the effect of interest because when it comes to thymus size, adults and infants are not comparable. If Mayo had used infants who died of nonrespiratory causes as his control group, he would have seen that they all had large thymus glands and would not have concluded that the thymus was responsible for the breathing problems. The placebo effect could have been a factor because Dr. Mayo was a trusted physician. It was not possible for this study to be blind or double-blind because it was obvious to everyone which infants had had surgery.

P19. **a.** There are quite a few problems with this study. It is possible that students were pointing home not from some magnetic sense, but because they could feel how much "turning" they had done or because they knew the roads. It is also possible that they could tell direction because they knew the direction of the sun even though they were blindfolded.

b. The group that has the magnets.

c. Whether the students were assigned randomly to the treatments. Students may also mention that the study was not double-blind.

d. Answers will vary, but the second design is certainly better than the first.

e. Because the subjects could tell whether or not they had the magnet because of the magnet's attraction to the walls of the van, this study was not blind. It was not double-blind either because the experimenter who evaluated how well the students pointed home was the same person who chose which kind of bar they wore.

Lesson Notes: Experimental Units and Replication

Experimental units are the objects to which treatments are applied and upon which the response variable is measured. In a well-designed experiment, the treatments are randomly assigned to the experimental units. The experimental units used in an experiment are those that happen to be available; they are not usually sampled from a larger population of units. This implies that experimental results cannot be generalized to a wider set of units without repeating the experiment on different units. In contrast, in a sample survey any unit in the population may end up in a sample through a random selection process. This random sampling process allows generalization of results from the sample to the population. The goal of an experiment is to compare treatments, whereas the goal of a sample survey is to estimate population characteristics. Replication can mean either to repeat the same treatment on different units or to repeat the entire experiment. Here, we use the first meaning.

You may want to use the table at the bottom of the page as a visual aid when discussing the difference between a sample survey and an experiment. A blackline master of this table is provided at the end of this section.

We usually speak of "assigning treatments to experimental units" because the terminology came from agricultural field trials where you can't pick up a plot of land and move it to an area of fertilizer type A. But (to use a famous example) if you are

---

Lesson 4.3, Lesson Notes

Surveys vs. Experiments

	What You Examine	Ultimate Goal	Role of Randomization	How You Control Variation
Sample Survey	Population	Describe some characteristic of this population	Take a random sample from the population	Stratify
Experiment	Treatments	See whether different treatments cause different results	Assign treatments at random to available subjects	Block

feeding fish, you can either put the food into the tanks and then randomly drop one fish in each tank or you can put the fish into the tanks and randomly drop in the food. It doesn't matter which way you do it, as long as the fish and the food are randomized to each other.

Discussion

D32. The effectiveness of a method for teaching reading highly depends on the teacher and the classroom atmosphere. The reading scores of the children in the classroom are not independent. Typically, an entire classroom will do well, or poorly.

D33. As in the reading study, the best unit is probably a hospital. *Note:* This is actually a sampling problem (stratified) rather than an experiment, although the discussion of units still applies.

D34. For the same reason that you have more faith in a poll if there is a large sample size—as the sample size gets larger, the percentage of successes tends to approach that of the population. In an experiment, a large number of subjects tend to ensure that the ones in each treatment group are more representative of the whole.

Practice

P20. treatments: the two text books
units: the 10 classes
sample size: 10

P21. The experimental units are carnation plants, and the ones used for the experiment should be as nearly alike as possible. Randomly assign the new product to about half of a number of plants, and leave the others growing under standard conditions. There must be at least two plants in each group, and preferably many more. The plants

receiving the standard treatment can be used as a control; the goal is to see whether the new product is better than the standard treatment at producing large blooms. Putting the plants in their places before randomly assigning treatments helps ensure that the two treatments aren't confounded with variables such as the amounts of heat, light, water, and temperature the various plants receive.

Exercises

E21. observational

E22. Plants do not like being dug up. Unless all plants are dug up, the effects of changing the environment would be confounded with the effects of being dug up. The study is experimental.

E23. **a.** dormitories
b. 20
c. experimental

E24. **a.** the dishes of insects
b. 8
c. experimental

E25. A reason for using death *rate* instead of total number of deaths is that the sizes of the populations are different. There is a possibility that climate is confounded with age. Florida has a much higher proportion of older people than does Alaska because Florida is a state where a great number of people move after retiring.

E26. No, not unless the subjects are in random order to begin with. Suppose the subjects in poorest health are all at the end of the list. Then, all of those in poorest health probably are going to be assigned to the same treatment group, a serious confounding effect.

Surveys and Experiments Compared

Surveys vs. Experiments

	What You Examine	Ultimate Goal	Role of Randomization	How You Control Variation
Sample Survey	Population	Describe some characteristic of this population	Take a random sample from the population	Stratify
Experiment	Treatments	See whether different treatments cause different results	Assign treatments at random to available subjects	Block

Statistics in Action Instructor's Guide
© 2004 Key Curriculum Press

4.4 Designing Experiments to Reduce Variability

Objectives

- to distinguish between variability within treatments and differences between treatments
- to understand that it is desirable to reduce variability within treatments by strategies such as experimental protocols and blocking
- to learn the difference between a completely randomized design, randomized paired comparison design (matched pairs or repeated measures), and randomized block design
- to learn the advantages and disadvantages of the kinds of design, and how to use them in practice

Important Terms and Concepts

- within-treatment variability versus between-treatment differences
- random assignment
- completely randomized design
- randomized paired comparison design using matched pairs or repeated measures
- blocking and the randomized block design

Lesson Planning

Class Time

Three to four days

Materials

For Activities 4.4 and 4.6, a launch ramp and launcher for each team and a supply of gummy bears. Each team will also need a coin, a tape measure or yardstick, and four textbooks. (See Displays 4.11 and 4.12 on pages 250–251 in the student edition for assembly instructions.) For Activity 4.5, a stopwatch, or watch with a second hand.

Suggested Assignments

Classwork		
Essential	**Recommended**	**Optional**
Activity 4.5	Activity 4.4, Activity 4.6	D51
D35–D46, D49, D50	D47, D48	P28
P22–P24, P26, P27	P25	

Homework		
Essential	**Recommended**	**Optional**
E27, E29, E31	E28, E30	

Lesson Notes: Differences Between Treatments Versus Variability Within Treatments

Like Section 4.2 on sampling, this section on experiments presents a systematic overview of sound strategies for designing experiments, uses these strategies in practical applications, and addresses (as stratification did for sampling) the desire to reduce variability within experimental groups. In a well-designed experiment, you compare two or more treatments, block experimental units into similar groups to reduce what variation within treatments you can, randomize the assignment of treatments to subjects within each block to spread out evenly between treatments the variation that is left, and replicate the treatments on as many experimental units as practical. We will look at three experimental design strategies: the completely randomized design, the randomized paired comparison design, and the randomized block design.

A randomized block design is called "complete" when each block is assigned a complete set of treatments. Note that "randomized complete block design" means something very different from "completely randomized design." In this book there are no incomplete block designs.

Stratification in surveys and blocking in experiments have the same purpose—to produce homogeneous groups whose means differ.

To Establish Causation

What Must Be Done	Strategy
1. Observe a difference.	Have a control or comparison group.
	Minimize within-treatment variation by using blocking.
2. Rule out chance as the cause of the difference.	Have as many subjects assigned to each treatment as is practical.
	Perform a test of significance, as shown in Chapters 8–11.
3. Rule out confounding as the cause of the difference.	Assign treatments at random to subjects (within blocks, if used).

Activity 4.4: Bears in Space

Activity 4.4, Bears in Space, illustrates the problem of having too much variability among units that are given the same treatment (*within*-treatment variability). This variability obscures any difference caused by the treatments themselves (*between*-treatment variability). This activity is highly recommended but it is time-consuming. If you choose not to do it as a class activity, bring in one bear launcher and demonstrate how the experiment is done. Then give students the sample data found in step 5. (A blackline master of the table and plot can be found at the end of this section.) Then begin with D35.

1. *Form launch teams and construct your launcher.* Although one person can generate data, a team approach works much better. As few as two and as many as eight on a team will work.

2. *Randomize.* In this activity, each team uses only one of the launch angles. Randomizing is done by shuffling and drawing from slips of paper, but it is worth pointing out to students that in practice, using a table of random numbers works better. It is hard to mix the slips of paper well enough to give truly random results.

3. *Organize your team.* A sketch of the various roles follows, but there is a lot of room for flexibility, and you can leave it to the teams to divide the tasks themselves. Two people can be responsible for setting up each launch: placing books under the ramp, positioning the fulcrum, positioning the launcher on the ramp, and so on. These two people can also be responsible for holding the ramp and launcher in place. One person should be designated to load the gummy bear onto the launcher, and another does the actual launching. Students should use a coin instead of their fingers to release the spring, or you will end up with a class of students with sore fingers. Measuring is best done by two people, at either ends of the tape, and you may want to have two people independently record the data as protection against mistakes.

4. *Gather data.* Because launch distances are quite variable, with a standard deviation of at least 15″, it works best to make multiple launches and report averages.

5. *Summarize.* See the table below for some actual results of individual distances for six teams and their sets of 10 launches, along with some summary statistics. The plots below the table show the launch distances for the six teams.

Note: You will want to copy this information (the table and the plot) for your class if students have not done the experiment. See the blackline master at the end of this section.

	Flatter Launch: One Book			Steeper Launch: Four Books					
Launch	Team 1	Team 2	Team 3	Team 4	Team 5	Team 6	Median	Mean	SD
1	15	44	18	13	10	125	16.5	37.5	44.6
2	24	40	2	39	35	147	37.0	47.8	50.6
3	48	51	10	16	24	35	29.5	30.7	16.8
4	25	100	41	41	22	81	41.0	51.7	31.7
5	19	37	88	41	65	125	53.0	62.5	38.9
6	17	52	46	31	45	27	38.0	36.3	13.4
7	19	102	72	41	70	187	71.0	81.8	58.9
8	21	86	53	55	21	84	54.0	53.3	28.6
9	31	89	38	14	33	105	35.5	51.7	36.4
10	74	120	92	33	37	174	83.0	88.3	53.4
Median	22.5	69.0	43.5	36.0	34.0	115.0			
Mean	29.3	72.1	46.0	32.4	36.2	109.0			
SD	18.4	30.5	31.1	14.0	19.2	53.6			

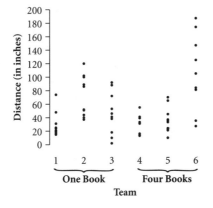

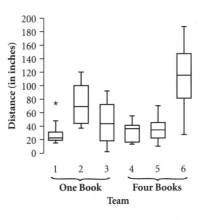

Discussion

D35. The main sources of within-treatment variability in distance are variability in the force of the launch and the effect of practice. Within-team variability can also be caused by changes in the position of the fulcrum, the bear, the launcher on the ramp, and the books under the ramp. The preceding plot shows side-by-side dot plots for the launch distances from the six teams. Teams 1 through 3 used one book and teams 4 through 6 used four books.

D36. It is standard practice in lab-based research to practice procedures until trends disappear and variation stabilizes. Doing several practice launches is the analog for Activity 4.4.

D37. The basic idea is to keep all the sources of variability listed in D35 as constant as possible. Thus, a sample protocol might include the following: The book(s) under the ramp should always touch the ramp at the same place. Mark the ramp at this spot to make sure.

Mark the position of the fulcrum on the launcher, and always reposition the fulcrum to its designated place before each launch.

Always position the launcher at the back of the ramp. Mark the location to make sure it is held constant.

The person who holds the launcher on the ramp should check the position of the books and ramp, then check the position of the fulcrum, and then place the launcher on the ramp, holding it steady.

Always position the bear the same way: Place the bear on the launcher on its back, on the stick rather than the rubber band, but touching the rubber band, and lying sideways, so that its long direction (head to foot) is perpendicular to the direction of the launcher.

The person doing the launching should try to keep the force of the launch constant from one launch to the next.

To eliminate time trends, each team should practice a set number of launches before beginning the experiment.

Lesson Notes: Between-Team Variability

Discussion

D38. Ordinarily, either the median or the mean will provide a reasonable summary. If the distances are strongly skewed toward extreme values or there are outliers, however, the median may be better.

D39. The figure below is a side-by-side dot plot of team medians. Sources of variability include those listed in D35, to the extent that these vary from one team to another. Typically, the single biggest source of variability is the technique of the person doing the launching. The variation between teams is smaller than the variation between launches for the same team. The reason for doing 10 launches and using the mean or median rather than doing only one launch should be apparent. If each team does only one launch, it might not be very representative of their launch distance.

For One Book:	For Four Books:
SD of the medians: 23.3	*SD* of the medians: 46.2
SD of the means: 21.6	*SD* of the means: 43.2

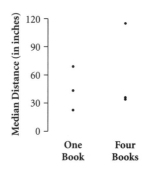

D40. Students may have ideas for improving the protocol to reduce differences between teams, but the best strategy (blocking) is to ask each team to do two sets of launches, one set with each ramp angle (which will be done in Activity 4.6). Some students may come up with this idea on their own. If they don't, we suggest that you not tell them. Subsequent questions and activities will give them additional chances to think about these issues.

Lesson Notes: Difference Between Treatments

Discussion

D41. See Lesson Notes (page 29) for the dot plots.

Variability from the launch angle: Find the overall average distance for each of the two launch angles, and compute the difference. For the sample data, the averages are 49.1 for the teams with one book and 59.2 for the teams with four books. The difference is 10.1.

Variability due to the particular team: Start with the team averages, and compute one standard deviation for each treatment. For the sample data, the standard deviation for teams 1 through 3, with one book, is 21.6. The standard deviation for teams 4 through 6, with four books, is 43.2.

Variability from launch to launch for the same team: Use the standard deviation or *IQR* for each team's set of 10 launches. For the sample data, the standard deviations for the six teams are 18.4, 30.5, 31.1, 14.0, 19.2, and 53.6.

It is difficult to say whether the largest variability is within the teams (the individual launches) or from team to team (the particular team). The smallest variability is between the two treatments (the launch angle).

There are formal methods (analysis of variance) for measuring components of variation, but at this early stage an informal sense based on simple summaries is enough.

D42. If results from your class are typical, then II will be the best answer. Variation between teams tends to be large in comparison to the effect of launch angle, as it is with the sample data. This means that it is often not possible to tell whether launch angle has an effect.

D43. The following figure shows a stacked dot plot, boxplot, and summary statistics of the launch distances, ignoring teams. There is a clear suggestion in the dot plot that the steeper angle leads to longer launches. However, ignoring teams gives up the essential information that team 6 alone accounts for the greater mean distance when four

books are used. The dot plots also show, however, that the data are fairly skewed for the steeper angle group, so perhaps using the medians and the *IQR* is better for comparisons. The boxplots show that the centers are roughly in the same place and that the *IQR*'s are nearly the same as well. It is hard to make a case for either launch angle using the boxplots. Ignoring teams gives up essential information.

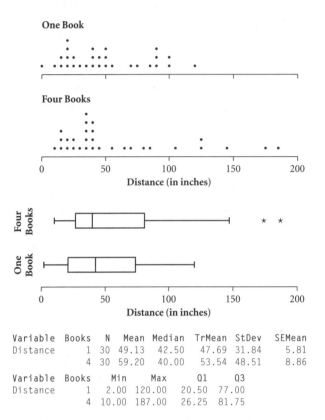

Variable	Books	N	Mean	Median	TrMean	StDev	SEMean
Distance	1	30	49.13	42.50	47.69	31.84	5.81
	4	30	59.20	40.00	53.54	48.51	8.86

Variable	Books	Min	Max	Q1	Q3
Distance	1	2.00	120.00	20.50	77.00
	4	10.00	187.00	26.25	81.75

Practice

P22. a. Students should list reasons why dorms that get the same soap still vary in the number of visits to the infirmary. Some possible reasons include the following: Some dorms have a less healthy atmosphere than others (e.g., they are too stuffy or contain contaminated drinking fountains), some dorms may be for athletes or others that tend to be healthier on average, or some dorms may have students who just happen to be sicker more often than usual.

b. To equalize variation between the treatments.

Lesson Notes: A Design for Every Purpose

Activity 4.5: Sit or Stand

Activity 4.5 goes quickly and illustrates how blocking can reduce variability. Emphasize that when blocking, you place similar units in the same block and then randomly assign treatments within each block. When at least two similar units receive each treatment, you can see how different treatments affect similar units. Part A, Completely Randomized Design, doesn't use blocking. Students are randomly assigned to the treatments of sitting or standing. Part B, Matched Pairs, assigns two students with similar heart rates to the same block. Then the treatments of sitting and standing are randomly assigned to the two students and the difference in their heart rates after treatment is computed. Part C, Repeated Measures, assigns one student to a block, with two measurements taken on that student. The treatments of sitting and standing are assigned in random order to the student, and the difference in the heart rates is computed.

If you aren't able to do this activity with your class, have your students use the sample data in Display 9.36 on page 549 while they answer the discussion questions on pages 254 and 255.

Part A

1. Pass around a box with slips of paper in it. Half should say "stand" and half should say "sit."

2. Have your students measure their pulse for 30 seconds and then double their measurement.

3. Have students record their heart rate in a class data record in either the column "Sit" or "Stand," depending on which treatment they were given. (See the blackline master at the end of this section for the class data record.) Here are the data for one class, from page 549 of the student text.

Part A: Completely Randomized

Sit	Stand	Stem-and-leaf of Heart Rates
70	66	N = 14
88	82	Leaf Unit = 1.0
82	86	Sit | Stand
88	102	
66	62	6 | 4 |
70	70	4 | 5 | 0
72	50	| 5 | 6
86	62	| 6 | 2 2
74	56	6 | 6 | 6
86	104	4 2 0 0 | 7 | 0
80	86	| 7 |
46	86	2 0 | 8 | 0 2
54	80	8 8 6 6 6 | 8 | 6 6 6
86	96	| 9 |
		| 9 | 6
		|10 | 2 4

Variable	N	Mean	Median	StDev	Min	Max	Q1	Q3
Sit	14	74.86	77.00	13.00	46.00	88.00	69.00	86.00
Stand	14	77.71	81.00	17.04	50.00	104.00	62.00	88.50

4. The side-by-side stemplot and summary statistics for the sample class are given in part 3. The means and medians are fairly close, and there is a great deal of variability, especially in the "stand" treatment group. Both are somewhat skewed left. From the data it is hard to tell whether the treatments made any difference.

Part B

1–4. Have your students form matched pairs by going through steps 1–4 as outlined in the student text on pages 253 and 254.

5. Have each pair record the two heart rates, as well as the difference in their heart rates, in a class data record. Be sure each pair subtracts in the order *Stand – Sit.* Here are the sample data for a class.

Part B: Matched Pairs

Pair Number	Sit	Stand	Difference	Stem-and-leaf of Difference
1	62	68	6	N = 14
2	74	78	4	Leaf Unit = 1.0
3	82	80	-2	
4	88	92	4	1 -2 4
5	82	58	-24	1 -1
6	66	96	30	5 -0 2446
7	64	72	8	(5) 0 24468
8	84	100	16	4 1 026
9	72	82	10	1 2
10	82	76	-6	1 3 0
11	80	92	12	
12	72	74	2	
13	64	60	-4	
14	62	58	-4	

Variable	N	Mean	Median	St Dev	Min	Max	Q1	Q3
MP Diff	14	3.71	4.00	12.38	-24.00	30.00	-4.00	10.50

6. The stemplot of the difference in heart rate for each pair and summary statistics for the differences are shown above. The mean of the differences should be zero if the treatment makes no difference. Here the mean and median are fairly close to zero, considering the high variability (*SD* 12.38, *IQR* 14.50). The observed mean difference of 3.71 could easily be due to variation between individuals and not due to a particular treatment.

Part C

1–3. Have your students go through steps 1–3 as outlined in the text on page 254.

4. Have each student record in a class data record his or her two heart rates plus the difference *Stand–Sit* in their heart rates. Here are the sample data for a class.

Part C: Repeated Measures

Subject	Sit	Stand	Difference
1	60	64	4
2	70	72	2
3	72	76	4
4	78	82	4
5	80	92	12
6	84	98	14
7	60	68	8
8	62	64	2
9	66	70	4
10	72	86	14
11	82	100	18
12	74	80	6
13	50	58	8
14	52	54	2
15	64	66	2
16	70	76	6
17	76	86	10
18	70	88	18
19	88	96	8
20	80	86	6
21	54	56	2
22	68	82	14
23	86	96	10
24	68	74	6
25	68	80	12
26	48	58	10
27	64	72	8
28	74	94	20

```
Stem-and-leaf of Diff
N = 28
Leaf Unit = 1.0
    5   0  22222
    9   0  4444
   13   0  6666
  (4)   0  8888
   11   1  000
    8   1  22
    6   1  444
    3   1
    3   1  88
    1   2  0
```

Variable	N	Mean	Median	StDev	Min	Max	Q1	Q3
RM Diff	28	8.357	8.000	5.279	2.000	20.000	4.000	12.000

5. The stemplot of the difference in heart rate for each student and summary statistics for the differences are shown above. Here the mean and median are larger than in part B (8.357 and 8.0, respectively), and the variability is smaller (*SD* 5.3, *IQR* 8). The observed mean difference of 8.357 and lower variability suggest the treatment really does make a difference.

Discussion

D44. The unwanted variability is the range in individual heart rate, which can be 30 or even 40 beats per minute within a class of students. For this experiment—to see whether standing people have a higher heart rate than sitting people—the repeated measures design is best, as it eliminates more of the unwanted variability than do the other two designs by looking at the *difference* between the sitting heart rate and the standing heart rate for each student.

D45. The completely randomized design is the least suitable because all of the individual variability remains. As an example where the completely randomized design is best, suppose you are a theater owner and you want to determine the effect of giving movie-goers a flier advertising popcorn when they buy their tickets. Your response variable

will be whether the ticket purchaser goes directly to buy popcorn or not. If you expect, say, 200 people at the movie where you are doing this experiment, you would have to use a completely randomized design, assigning each treatment randomly to the people as they enter. You can't use a matched pairs design because you can't examine the people beforehand in order to match them. You cannot use repeated measures because once a movie-goer gets one method, you cannot use the other method on them.

D46. The variability is the natural differences in heart rate between different individuals. By matching two students with approximately the same heart rate and taking the difference in their rates under the two treatments, the design in Part B made the fact that some students naturally have higher rates and some have slower rates largely irrelevant. By having the same student measure his or her heart rate under the two treatments, the Part C design accomplished even more by eliminating individual differences almost entirely.

Lesson Notes: Variation Within and Between

Discussion

D47. There is more variation within the rural twins, with standard deviation 19.00, than within the urban twins, with standard deviation 14.39, or within the differences with standard deviation 10.15. This is not a true experiment because the environment was not assigned randomly. From the data alone, because six of the seven differences are negative, it looks as though a rural environment results in faster lung clearing. However, there is the possibility of confounding. For example, suppose the "urban" twins were having health problems and moved to the city to be near medical care, or the "rural" twins were the more robust of the two and had moved to the country to participate more actively in outdoor activities.

D48. Identical twins were used because they are genetically identical and usually have the same childhood environment as well. Using identical twins in experiments minimizes the individual differences as much as possible without repeated measures on the same person.

Practice

P23. **a.** randomized paired comparison with repeated measures

b. randomized paired comparison with matched pairs

c. randomized paired comparison with matched pairs because there may be a residual effect of one or both of the drugs—that is, it does not clear out of the bloodstream in the time allowed between treatments

P24. randomized paired comparison with repeated measures

P25. **a.** There is a lot of variability in how well students memorize, so some sort of blocking seems desirable. Your students may suggest a randomized paired comparison design with repeated measures. First, find the seniors in the school who are willing to participate. Then randomly select half to go into a room that has the radio playing and the other half to go into a room that is quiet. The students would be given a familiar task to study, such as a list of new vocabulary words. Afterward, they would be tested on the meaning of the words. The number that they remember is the response variable. Then, the students would switch rooms and be given another new list of vocabulary words. If your students feel that this would take too much time, they might suggest matching students by GPA or, if that is impossible, a completely randomized design.

b. For this experiment, the treatments are soup with MSG and soup without MSG. The response variable is the amount of soup eaten by a customer who orders soup. Even though there is a lot of variation in how much soup people will eat, blocking seems difficult to do. (However, it might be possible to block by estimating a person's weight.) In this case a completely randomized design seems best. For each customer who orders soup that night, a treatment is randomly selected, perhaps by flipping a coin each time.

Lesson Notes: More on Blocking

Activity 4.6: Block Those Bears!

Activity 4.6 is meant to show students that a randomized block design can reduce the variability that resulted in Activity 4.4. Each team (block) is reused, so that it can provide two sets of five launches. This procedure makes it possible to isolate the effects of launch angle, by making launch angle a within-teams factor. In this experiment, the basic terms have the following interpretations:

Response: launch distance

Treatment: launch angle (flat or steep)

Block: a team (both treatments are carried out in each block)

Replication: each team measures five responses to each treatment

Design: randomized block design with the teams as blocks. For each team, one (randomly assigned) set of five launches is done with a steep angle, the other set of five with a flat angle. The randomization is done separately for each team. Each team can toss a coin to decide on the order of treatments.

1–3. After students have formed teams and assigned jobs, they might also want to do a few practice launches for each launch angle before they record their data.

4. Here are the results from one class. Each average distance in the table is the average of five launches.

Average Distance (in inches)

Team	One Book	Four Books	Difference
1	87	246	159
2	43	67	24
3	87	244	157
4	81	38	−42
5	49	103	54
6	44	64	20

It is reasonable to conclude that four books results in a longer launch than one book. (You might have students check to see whether their results match the theory from calculus that a 45-degree launch angle maximizes the horizontal distance.)

Note: The effectiveness of blocking depends on how similar the units are in each block and how different the blocks are from each other. Here, "similar" units are units that would tend to give similar values for the response if they were assigned to the same treatments. *The more similar the units in a block, the more effective blocking will be.*

From a statistical point of view, a block is just a group of similar units, but in practice, there are three rather different ways to generate blocks:

1. *Reuse* subjects or chunks of material (blocks) in each of several time slots (units).

2. *Subdivide* larger chunks (blocks) of material into sets of smaller pieces (units).

3. *Sort* units into groups (blocks).

In Activity 4.6, students created blocks by *reusing* teams. In the design in Part C of Activity 4.5, the blocks were determined by reusing the same individual. In the wheat example, Fisher created blocks by *subdividing* large pieces of land into smaller pieces. In the Part B design of Activity 4.5, your class was *sorted* into pairs based on initial heart rate.

Discussion

D49. This is a randomized block design or, more specifically, a randomized paired comparison design with repeated measures. The blocks are the teams.

D50. The unit is a set of five launches by a team.

D51. Instead of having the team do all five launches of one type and then all five launches of the other type, randomly decide how many books to use for each launch by drawing one of 10 slips of paper from a box. Five of the slips of paper would say "one book" and five would say "four books."

Practice

P26. In a completely randomized design, treatments are assigned randomly to the subjects. In a randomized block design, the subjects first are divided into blocks of subjects that are alike and then the treatments are assigned randomly *within each block.*

P27. Blocking is desirable because you can then look, within each block of like subjects, at the differences between the treatments. This method reduces the variability due to individual differences in the subjects. Students' examples of where you would want to block should involve situations where individual differences would be large compared to the difference between treatments. In general, you would not want to block in situations where it is impossible or inconvenient.

P28. **a.** Although there are more low scores on Exam 1 than on Exam 2, it is not easy to see whether the students are improving, because there is a lot of variability in both sets of scores and the scores overlap considerably.

b. Yes, most of the students got higher scores on Exam 2, some by a considerable amount. (The exceptions are many of the students with relatively high scores on Exam 1, who did a little less well on Exam 2.) It is easier to answer the question from the scatterplot because the change in score for a student is easily seen as the vertical distance from the point to the line $y = x$. If the student did better on Exam 2, they are above the line $y = x$, and if they did not improve, then they are on or below the line.

c. If there were two independent samples of students, you would have only the information in Display 4.16, where the variability among students overwhelms the variability between the exams. To reduce the considerable variability from student to student, have each student take both exams and compute the difference in the two scores. When blocks are used (each student is a block, taking both exams), you get the more conclusive information in Display 4.17.

Exercises

E27. The modified SAT study is a completely randomized experiment, where students are randomly assigned to two groups, one group for each treatment.

Units: high school students who want to take the special course

Factor and levels: the only factor is course-taking behavior, and the levels are the same as the treatments

Response: SAT score

Blocks: none

Treatments: course, or no course (control)

E28. *Block:* patient (more precisely, two weeks of a patient's time)

Treatments: low phenylalanine diet or regular diet

Unit: one week of a patient's time

Design: the design is a randomized paired comparison design with repeated measures

Response: dopamine level

E29. Treatments were assigned to units using a block design. In particular, the design was a randomized block with repeated measures on the same subject.

Response: rate of finger tapping

Unit: one day of a subject's time

Treatments: caffeine, theobromine, or placebo

Block: subject (more precisely, three days of a subject's time)

E30. The treatments were assigned completely at random in this completely randomized design.

Response: time (months) until baby walks unaided

Unit: infant

Treatments: four kinds of exercise/follow-up program

Blocks: none

E31. The treatments were assigned completely at random in this completely randomized design.

Response: quantity eaten (relative to body weight)

Unit: hornworm

Treatments: diet of regular food or diet of 80% cellulose

Blocks: none

Data from Activity 4.4

Launch	Flatter Launch: One Book			Steeper Launch: Four Books			Median	Mean	SD
	Team 1	Team 2	Team 3	Team 4	Team 5	Team 6			
1	15	44	18	13	10	125	16.5	37.5	44.6
2	24	40	2	39	35	147	37.0	47.8	50.6
3	48	51	10	16	24	35	29.5	30.7	16.8
4	25	100	41	41	22	81	41.0	51.7	31.7
5	19	37	88	41	65	125	53.0	62.5	38.9
6	17	52	46	31	45	27	38.0	36.3	13.4
7	19	102	72	41	70	187	71.0	81.8	58.9
8	21	86	53	55	21	84	54.0	53.3	28.6
9	31	89	38	14	33	105	35.5	51.7	36.4
10	74	120	92	33	37	174	83.0	88.3	53.4
Median	22.5	69.0	43.5	36.0	34.0	115.0			
Mean	29.3	72.1	46.0	32.4	36.2	109.0			
SD	18.4	30.5	31.1	14.0	19.2	53.6			

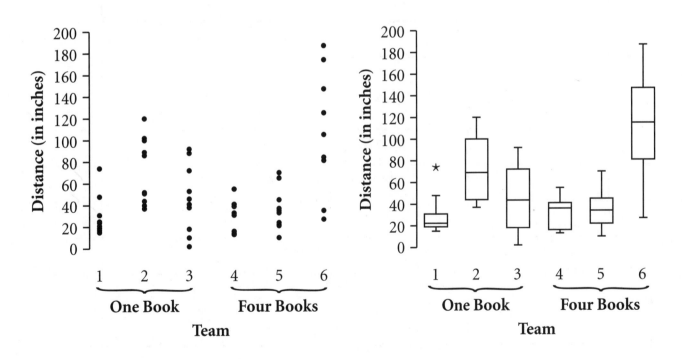

Activity 4.5 Data Sheet

Part A		Part B				Part C			
Sit	Stand	Pair Number	Sit	Stand	Difference	Subject	Sit	Stand	Difference

Statistics in Action Instructor's Guide
© 2004 Key Curriculum Press

Review

Homework	
Essential	E32, E36, E40, E41, E45, E47, E48
Recommended	E33–E35, E37–E39, E43, E44, E46, E49
Optional	E42

Review the concepts found in this chapter:

- Sample surveys and experiments have different purposes: estimating a parameter versus establishing causation.
- Randomization is the key to both data-gathering processes.
- Reduction in variability can be achieved by *stratification* for sampling and *blocking* for experiments.

Review Exercises

E32. **a.** Sample. The measurement process is destructive, and the size of the population makes a census too expensive.

b. Census. The population size is small, the information is easy to get, and the measurement process is not destructive.

c. Sample. The population is so large that a census would be too costly and time-consuming.

E33. **a.** The class is likely to be reasonably representative.

b. The class will not be representative: Its average age will be much lower than that of the population.

c. The class is likely to be reasonably representative.

d. Students who choose to take a statistics course as an elective are more likely to prefer science to English than students who do not take statistics. So in this case, it would not be reasonably representative. If your classmates took statistics because it is required for a variety of majors, they could be reasonably representative.

e. Blood pressure increases with age. The average blood pressure for the class will almost surely be much lower than for the population.

E34. **a.** Decrease, because take-home pay is less than gross earnings.

b. The worker might overstate his or her earnings, misclassify his or her occupation/title, or include overtime, for example.

E35. Yes; actors and actresses listed in the almanac are better known, and so better paid, than those who are not listed.

E36. Method I is size-biased and will tend to overestimate the true average. (States with fewer representatives are less likely to end up in the sample than are states with more representatives. In fact, a state's chance of being chosen is proportional to the number of representatives it has.) Method II is unbiased.

E37. The frame will not include most owners who bought their 1998 models used from either a private party or from dealers of other makes. It will include people who have sold their 1998 model. These owners may be the ones with the higher repair bills.

E38. This method is size-biased. Authors with more quotations are more likely to be chosen than authors with fewer quotations. (Authors with longer quotations also are more likely to be chosen.)

E39. Your net allows tiny fish to escape. Dragging it behind a boat will miss fish that are far below the surface.

E40. Maps will vary. The larger trees are more likely to be chosen. For example, suppose the lot is subdivided into six sections, with five big and five small trees on six plots. Each of the five big trees is on its own section, whereas the five small trees are all clustered on one section. If a section is selected at random, a big tree is more likely to be chosen.

E41. *New York Times* readers tend to have higher incomes and more years of education in comparison with the average New Yorker.

E42. For example, any survey that takes a lot of time to answer or that asks a sensitive question is likely to get nonresponse bias. In the case of the long survey, people with more time on their hands and people who just want to talk to someone are more likely to respond. In the case of the sensitive question, people who can give a socially acceptable response are more likely to respond.

E43. Stage 1: Choose an SRS of states.
Stage 2: Choose an SRS of congressional districts from each state chosen in stage 1.
Stage 3: Choose an SRS of precincts from each congressional district chosen in stage 2.
Stage 4: Choose an SRS of voters from each precinct chosen in stage 3.

E44. Stage 1: Choose an SRS of shelves.
Stage 2: Choose an SRS of books from each shelf chosen in stage 1.
Stage 3: Choose an SRS of pages from each book chosen in stage 2.
Stage 4: Choose an SRS of lines from each page chosen in stage 3.

E45. A design that uses no blocks would randomly divide the subjects into the four treatment groups. A block design that groups subjects might group them on the basis of how fast they threaded a needle in a pretest, or perhaps on the extent to which they can distinguish different colors. A block design that reuses subjects would give each of the four treatments to each subject, in a randomly selected order.

E46.   **a.** The blocks in the article by D. D. Reid, "Does Inheritance Matter in Disease?" are pairs of twins in the Danish Twin Register. The studies described are observational.
   b. The blocks in the article by Elisabeth Street and Mavis G. Carroll, "Preliminary Evaluation of a New Food Product," are men and women. They are asked to taste each of three products and rate them. This is an experiment.
   c. The blocks in the article by Louis J. Battan, "Cloud Seeding and Rainmaking," are pairs of areas that are close to each other and have similar physical geography (page 422). This is an experiment.

E47. One possible experiment is to have each person be a block. Each person is then presented the three kinds of cookies in a random order.

E48. Students should include the following points in their design: a description of the treatments, a rationale for any blocking, a description of the blocking scheme, a description of the random assignment of treatments to units *within* blocks, the protocol for the experiment such as making

it double-blind if possible, and the response variable to be measured and compared. (Have the students keep their notes so they can refer back to this example after Chapter 9.)

Sample response: The two treatments will be the two types of exercise bike. I will assign four bikes of each type to the eight units or spaces on the floor of the gym. Bikes nearer the door and bikes in front of the televisions may be more (or less) likely to be used than the other bikes. Thus, I will form four blocks of spaces with similar locations in the gym: 1 and 4, 2 and 3, 5 and 8, 6 and 7. Then *for each block,* I will flip a coin, and if it is heads, a bike of the first type goes into the even-numbered space and a bike of the second type into the odd-numbered space. If it is tails, a bike of the second type goes into the even-numbered space and a bike of the first type goes into the odd-numbered space. There is no reason to make this experiment blind or double-blind because we want the customers to observe the different choices and the number of hours of use is recorded automatically for each bike.

Note: After Chapter 9 is completed, a student could give a more complete answer to this question: I will use the number of hours each bike is used as the measure of attractiveness. So at the end of the experiment, preferably several months, I will compare the number of hours each type of bike is used. I will do this with a paired *t*-test, first looking at each block separately and subtracting the number of hours the second type of bike was used from the number of hours the first type of bike was used.

E49. Because the mailed portion of the census depends on the goodwill of the citizens to return the questionnaires, many people are left uncounted. Making an intensive effort to find those not counted and estimating the undercount for a sample of regions seems like a good way to improve the accuracy of the census count, at least for that segment of the population in the sample. The adjustment to the census count through sampling can correct many deficiencies of the mail campaign if the Census Bureau pays careful attention to the kinds of errors discussed below.

There are three large weaknesses in the sampling plan for adjustment. First, many of those not found by the mail campaign are also difficult to find in a follow-up survey of geographic regions, so the sampling will still underestimate some segments of the population. Second, the matching of records is subject to error. Many of the census forms are incomplete or filled out incorrectly by the respondents, sometimes intentionally, so that deciding whether or not a sampled household has already filled out a form is not always easy. In addition, a sampled block may show completed census forms for persons who are no longer in that block or may not even exist. (It is possible for a block to be over-counted.) Third, applying adjustments from a sampled region to other similar regions for which no sample data are taken is also error prone.

5

SAMPLING DISTRIBUTIONS

Overview

This chapter focuses on sampling distributions of various summary statistics. In later chapters, we will use sampling distributions as the basic building blocks for developing inferential procedures (tests of significance and confidence intervals). As in earlier chapters, we focus on the distributions of variables and the distribution's shape, center, and spread. A sampling distribution is the distribution of *potential values* for a sample statistic, so the distribution can be examined before the sample data are actually collected. In some cases, students will be able to find the probability that certain potential values will actually occur. Thus this chapter forms a bridge between data distributions and probability distributions, which are discussed formally beginning in Chapter 6. In addition, this chapter continues the foreshadowing of statistical inference by having students find "reasonably likely" outcomes versus "rare" outcomes.

Goals

The main goal of this chapter is to have students generate, understand, and use sampling distributions for common summary statistics.

Specific goals include having students learn

- to take random samples of a fixed size n from a population by using a table of random digits
- to use the four-step guide (model, sample and summary, repetition, and distribution) to construct sampling distributions
- to see that all summary statistics have sampling distributions and to explore a variety of these distributions
- to know the shape, mean, and standard error of the sampling distributions of the sample mean and the sample proportion—the two most commonly used summary statistics

- to understand the relationship between the sampling distribution of the sample mean and the sample total
- to use the idea of "a range of reasonably likely values" to make decisions based on sampling distributions
- to know the shape, mean, and standard error of the sampling distribution of a sum and a difference of sample values

Content Overview

Much of the work on sampling distributions is built around simulations. There are two reasons for this. First, designing and carrying out a simulation forces a student to understand what the sampling distribution represents. Otherwise, he or she may easily loose sight of the fact that, for example, every dot in a dot plot of a sampling distribution represents an entire sample. Second, simulations are powerful—students can investigate the properties of summary statistics for distributions that could not possibly be tackled by mathematical theory in a course at this level.

Time Required

Traditional Schedule			Block	4 x 4 Block
Section 5.1				
1–2 days	Day 1	Overview, sampling with and without replacement	2 days	2 long
	Day 2	Mean and *SD* of a population, summary, exercises		
Section 5.2				
2 days	Day 1	Generating sampling distributions, four-step guide; shape, center, and spread; Activity 5.1	2 days	2 long
	Day 2	Summary, exercises		
Section 5.3				
4–5 days	Day 1	Overview and Activity 5.2; shape, center, and spread from symmetric populations	4 days	2 long, 2 short
	Day 2	Sampling from a skewed population, Central Limit Theorem, properties of sampling distribution of the sample mean		
	Day 3	Finding probabilities for sample means and totals, properties of the sampling distribution of the sum of a sample		
	Day 4	Sample size and population		
	Day 5	Summary, exercises		
Section 5.4				
3–4 days	Day 1	Overview and Activity 5.3	3 days	2 long, 1 short
	Day 2	Sampling distribution for $p = .6$; properties of the sampling distribution of the sample proportion		
	Day 3	Practice using the properties		
	Day 4	Summary, exercises		
Section 5.5				
3 days	Day 1	Overview and Activity 5.4; sampling distribution for two rolls of a regular die and of a tetrahedral die	3 days	2 long, 1 short
	Day 2	Properties of sampling distribution of the sum and difference		
	Day 3	Summary, exercises		
Review				
1 day				

We suggest that you allot more time for this chapter than you may have done with sampling distributions in the past in order to prepare your students for statistical inference. This chapter will probably require about 14 to 17 class periods, not including tests or quizzes. You can move quickly through Section 5.1 and complete just enough of Section 5.2 so that students understand thoroughly what a sampling distribution is, how to simulate it, and how it differs from the distribution of the population. Because the sampling distribution for the standard deviation is not an essential part of the course, that portion of Section 5.2 may be omitted entirely. However, if you have time, you can spend more time in Section 5.2 exploring lesser-known sampling distributions, giving your students a broader and firmer base of understanding. For example, exploring the sampling distribution for the standard deviation does help students understand why we divide by $n - 1$ instead of n in the formula for the standard deviation.

Sections 5.3 and 5.4 should be done in their entirety, because these sections cover the important details of the sampling distributions for the sample mean and the sample proportion. They are as important as any two sections in this book.

Section 5.5 introduces the sampling distributions for the sum and the difference of sample values, and the results will be needed later. Do not get too bogged down at this time. If this section proves difficult for your students, you can come back to it toward the end of the course.

Materials

Section 5.1: A random digit table (See Table D, Random Digits, from the student text, reproduced as a blackline master at the end of Section 5.1.)

Section 5.2: A copy of Display 4.4 (Random Rectangles) and a random digit table (Table D)

Section 5.3: For Activity 5.2, 25 pennies for each student

Section 5.4: For Activity 5.3, a table of random digits, a bag of beads, sampling paddle, or any other mechanical method of taking random samples from a population with $p = .6$

Section 5.5: For Activity 5.4, one die for each student

Suggested Assignments

Classwork			
Section	**Essential**	**Recommended**	**Optional**
5.1	D1–D4 P1, P2		
5.2	Activity 5.1 D5–D9 P3	P4, P5	D10
5.3	D11–D15, D17 P6–P9	Activity 5.2 D16, D18–D20 P10–P12	
5.4	Activity 5.3 D21–D26 P13–P16	D27	
5.5	D30 P17–P19	Activity 5.4 D28, D29, D31	

Homework			
Section	**Essential**	**Recommended**	**Optional**
5.1	E*	E2, E6	E3, E5
5.2	E7, E9	E8, E10, E11	E12–E15
5.3	E16, E20, E22, E26	E18, E21, E24, E25	E17, E19, E23, E27, E28
5.4	E29, E31	E30, E32, E34	E33
5.5	E35, E36, E38–E41	E37	E42, E43
Review	E44–E47, E50, E51, E57	E48, E49, E54, E56, E58	E52, E53, E55

5.1 Sampling from a Population

Objectives

- to learn to use a table of random digits to take a random sample from a specified population
- to learn to take a random sample and compute a summary statistic, such as a mean or a median
- to learn to compute the mean and standard deviation of a population defined by a relative frequency table
- to learn to sample with and without replacement

The main goal for this section is for students to understand the process for sampling from a population that is defined by a relative frequency table.

Important Terms and Concepts

- sampling with replacement
- sampling without replacement
- mean and standard deviation of a population

Lesson Planning

Class Time

One to two days

Materials

A random digit table (See Table D, Random Digits, from the student text, reproduced as a blackline master at the end of this section.)

Suggested Assignments

Classwork		
Essential	Recommended	Optional
D1–D4		
P1, P2		

Homework		
Essential	Recommended	Optional
E1, E4	E2, E6	E3, E5

Lesson Notes: Sampling with Random Digits

Students need to learn how to use a table of random digits to generate random samples. Once they have mastered this technique, teach your students how to generate samples using a graphing calculator or a computer. The instructions below show how to take random samples of any given size using a TI-83 calculator or Minitab. (See page 202 for instructions using Fathom.) These programs randomly select values from a distribution given in relative frequency tables like those in Display 5.1 and Display 5.4.

Using the TI-83 to Randomly Sample from a Relative Frequency Table

The program SAMPLE selects N values at random from a distribution given in a relative frequency table. In the program, PF denotes the probabilities associated with the values of the variable x, and CDF denotes the cumulative probabilities up to and including each value of x in order. Enter the values of x into L1 and the respective proportions or probabilities into L2. The program prompts the user for a sample size, N, and the random sample is stored into L3. (Keystrokes can be found in the calculator guide.)

```
PROGRAM:SAMPLE
ClrHome
Disp "VALUES IN L1"
Disp "PF OR CDF IN L2"
Disp "RESULT IN L3"
DelVar ∟CDF
SetUpEditor L1, L2, L3
ClrList L3
If sum(L2)=1
Then
cumSum(L2)➡∟CDF
Else
L2➡∟CDF
End
Input "SAMPLE SIZE=?",N
Disp "WORKING..."
dim(L1)➡M
For(I,1,N,1)
rand➡X
For(J,1,M,1)
If X≤∟CDF(M-J+1)
Then
L1(M-J+1)➡L3(I)
```

```
End
End
End
DelVar ∟CDF
Pause L3
Stop
```

NOTE: The PAUSE before L3 (in the second-to-last line) displays L3 on the screen and the student can use the right and left arrow keys to scroll through the list. Press ENTER to end the program. ■

Using Minitab to Randomly Sample from a Relative Frequency Table

Enter the values of x into one column, say C1, and the respective proportions or probabilities (as decimals) into another column, C2.

Choose **Discrete** from the Calc | Random Data menu.

In the Discrete Distribution dialog box, enter the sample size into **Generate _____ rows of data**, and enter a column, say C3, into **Store in column(s):**. Enter C1 into **Values in:**, and enter C2 into **Probabilities in:**.

A Note on 0.45 Versus .45. Perhaps you wondered why, for example, 45/100 sometimes is written as 0.45 and sometimes as .45. The distinction is that the leading zero is omitted whenever the value is constrained to be between 0 and 1 inclusive. The probability 45/100 would be written in decimal form as .45 because a probability must be in the interval [0, 1]. However, a standard deviation of the same value would be written as 0.45 because a standard deviation could lie outside the interval [0, 1].

Discussion

D1. The remaining triples are

177 | 324 | 106 | 845 | 248

These represent households with 1, 2, 1, 3, and 2 motor vehicles, respectively.

D2. You could choose any digit to represent the case that smoking is not responsible for lung cancer, and then the remaining nine digits represent the case that smoking is responsible. For example, let the digit 0 represent the case that smoking is not responsible and the digits 1–9 represent the case that smoking is responsible. If your random digit is 3, then this is a case where smoking is responsible for the lung cancer.

Practice

P1. Generate triples of random digits. Assign them as in the following table.

Note: Many other assignments of random numbers are possible.

Number of Children	Proportion of Families	Numbers Assigned
0	.505	001–505
1	.203	506–708
2	.191	709–899
3	.073	900–972
4 or more	.028	973–000

Select three triples representing three families. Do not discard duplicates in this case. For example, the three sets of random digits in the first sample were 488, 309, and 942, so the families in the sample would have 0, 0, and 3 children.

Lesson Notes: Sampling With and Without Replacement

Discussion

D3. You should allow the same three-digit number to be used twice (sample with replacement). Otherwise, it would change the probabilities for subsequent draws. There are many households in the selected category and more than one of them can be in the sample. This situation is different from selecting students from your school for your sample because there, you usually would not use the same student twice (sample without replacement). With the motor vehicle problem each three-digit number is representing thousands of families, whereas each slip of paper is representing only one student.

Lesson Notes: The Mean and Standard Deviation of a Population

Discussion

D4. **a.**

Value, x	Frequency, f	$x \cdot f$
5	12	60
6	23	138
8	15	120
Total	50	318

$$\bar{x} = \frac{\Sigma x \cdot f}{n} = \frac{318}{50} = 6.36$$

Some students will want to divide by 3 because there are three rows, but it is the total frequency that gives the sample size: $12 + 23 + 15 = 50$. An alternative formula is

$$\bar{x} = \frac{\Sigma x \cdot f}{\Sigma f}$$

b.

Value, x	Proportion, $P(x) = f/n$
5	.24
6	.46
8	.30

$$\mu = \Sigma x \cdot P(x)$$
$$= 5(.24) + 6(.46) + 8(.30)$$
$$= 6.36$$

c. $\bar{x} = \dfrac{\Sigma x \cdot f}{n} = \Sigma x \cdot \left(\dfrac{f}{n}\right) = \Sigma x \cdot P(x)$

Practice

P2. See below.
   The mean is 0.916, and the standard deviation is 1.11.

Lesson 5.1, P2

$$\mu = \Sigma x \cdot P(x) = 0(.505) + 1(.203) + 2(.191) + 3(.073) + 4(0.28) = 0.916$$

$$\sigma = \sqrt{\Sigma(x - \mu)^2 \cdot P(x)}$$
$$= \sqrt{\Sigma(x - 0.916)^2 \cdot P(x)}$$
$$= 1.11$$

Exercises

E1. **a.**

x	$P(x)$	$x \cdot P(x)$
0	.45	0
1	.09	0.09
2	0	0
3	.04	0.12
4	.15	0.60
5	.27	1.35
Sum	1	2.16

$$\mu = \Sigma x \cdot P(x) = 2.16$$
$$\sigma = \sqrt{\Sigma(x - \mu)^2 \cdot P(x)} \approx 2.221$$

b. Divide the random digits into groups of two because there are two significant digits in the proportions, as shown at bottom of page.

One way to assign the pairs to values of x is as follows:

x	Proportion	Pairs of Digits
0	.45	01–45
1	.09	46–54
2	0	none
3	.04	55–58
4	.15	59–73
5	.27	74–00

Then the scores in this sample would be 0, 3, 5, and 4.

E2. **a.** Answers will vary depending on the student's choice of center. Here we use the midpoint of the first two age groups, and 35 for the last group.

Age	Proportion
19.5	.442
26	.314
35	.244

$$\mu = \Sigma x \cdot P(x) = 25.323$$
$$\sigma = \sqrt{\Sigma(x - \mu)^2 \cdot P(x)} = 6.163$$

b. Divide the random digits into groups of three because there are three significant digits in each proportion as shown below.

One way to assign the pairs to values of x is as follows:

Age	Percentage	Pairs of Digits
19.5	44.2	001–442
26	31.4	443–756
35	24.4	757–000

The ages of the students selected would then be 19.5, 26, 26, 26, 35, and 35.

E3. Divide the random digits into groups of one, as shown at bottom of page.

Let the digits 1, 2, and 3 represent a parent who occasionally calls. The other digits, 4–9 and 0, represent parents who do not call. Checking the first five digits, we find two "parents" who occasionally call.

E4. Divide the random digits into groups of two as shown below.

Let the pairs of digits 01–12 represent teachers who say email is effective and the other pairs (13–99, 00) represent teachers who do not. Taking a sample of three or checking the first three pairs, we find no "teachers" who say that email is effective.

Lesson 5.1, E1b

30 | 55 | 84 | 59 | 57 | 36 | 91 | 19 | 71 | 99 | 08 | 43 | 2

Lesson 5.1, E2b

305 | 584 | 595 | 736 | 911 | 971 | 990 | 843 | 2

Lesson 5.1, E3

2 | 4 | 7 | 8 | 1 | 9 | 6 | 0 | 4 | 5 | 1 | 5 | 4 | 4 | 9 | 7 | 4 | 5 | 6 | 4

Lesson 5.1, E4

22 | 65 | 93 | 50 | 91 | 36 | 95 | 49 | 21 | 66

E5. You should sample with replacement. A pair of digits, say 25, does not represent just one parent—it represents thousands of parents. To understand how this is so, imagine using pairs of digits to take a random sample of 200 parents. If you discarded each pair of random digits after selecting it, you would not have any pairs left after you selected the first 100 parents. Furthermore, those first 100 parents would reflect the population *exactly,* which would not be the case in a typical random sample of size 100.

E6. The formulas are identical in form except that in the formula for the population standard deviation you use the population mean instead of the sample mean and divide by n, while in the formula for the sample standard deviation you divide by $n - 1$, thus replacing $\frac{f}{(n-1)}$ by $\frac{f}{n}$. Then the relative frequency, $\frac{f}{n}$, is replaced by a symbol for the proportion of times a particular value would occur in the population and written in the form $P(x)$.

In the probability distributions in Chapters 6 and 7, there is no population size but rather a probability that some particular outcome will occur. Thus, this formula for σ will be used exclusively in those chapters.

Lesson 5.1, Lesson Notes

Using Fathom to Randomly Sample from a Relative Frequency Table

In Fathom, you do not put a relative frequency table into a case table. Instead, you create a collection that contains one case and is defined by a formula based on the frequency table. Then you sample from that collection. Here's how you would sample from the frequency table in Display 5.1 on page 268.

a. Drag a new collection from the shelf into the document. Name the collection, if you wish.

b. Double-click the collection to open the inspector. On the Cases panel, click <**new**> and define an attribute called cars.

c. Double-click in the formula cell in the right column. Type this formula.

$$
\text{switch}(\text{random}(\ ))
\begin{cases}
(? < 0.014) & :0 \\
(? < 0.014 + 0.228) & :1 \\
(? < 0.014 + 0.228 + 0.437) & :2 \\
(? < 0.014 + 0.228 + 0.437 + 0.215) & :3 \\
\text{else} & :4
\end{cases}
$$

To get additional choices for the switch function, press the Ins key or Ctrl-Enter (Windows) or Option-Return (Mac). In general, each choice (except the last) is defined by the cumulative sum of the frequencies up to and including that choice; the last choice is always defined by else. Click the **OK** button when finished.

d. Close the inspector and choose **New Cases** from the Data menu. Type 1 in the dialog box and click **OK**. The collection box, which was previously empty, should fill with gold balls.

e. Select **Sample Cases** from the Analyze menu. A new collection will appear called **Sample of....** By default, the sample contains 10 cases sampled with replacement. To change the number of samples, double-click the sample and enter a new number on the Sample panel. Close the inspector when finished.

f. To collect a new sample that overwrites the current sample, select the current sample and choose **Sample More Cases** from the Analyze menu. To collect a new sample that doesn't overwrite the current sample, repeat part e.

After creating a sample, you can display the results in a case table or a graph in the same way that you do for a collection.

Table D Random Digits

Row										
1	10097	32533	76520	13586	34673	54876	80959	09117	39292	74945
2	37542	04805	64894	74296	24805	24037	20636	10402	00822	91665
3	08422	68953	19645	09303	23209	02560	15953	34764	35080	33606
4	99019	02529	09376	70715	38311	31165	88676	74397	04436	27659
5	12807	99970	80157	36147	64032	36653	98951	16877	12171	76833
6	66065	74717	34072	76850	36697	36170	65813	39885	11199	29170
7	31060	10805	45571	82406	35303	42614	86799	07439	23403	09732
8	85269	77602	02051	65692	68665	74818	73053	85247	18623	88579
9	63573	32135	05325	47048	90553	57548	28468	28709	83491	25624
10	73796	45753	03529	64778	35808	34282	60935	20344	35273	88435
11	98520	17767	14905	68607	22109	40558	60970	93433	50500	73998
12	11805	05431	39808	27732	50725	68248	29405	24201	52775	67851
13	83452	99634	06288	98083	13746	70078	18475	40610	68711	77817
14	88685	40200	86507	58401	36766	67951	90364	76493	29609	11062
15	99594	67348	87517	64969	91826	08928	93785	61368	23478	34113
16	65481	17674	17468	50950	58047	76974	73039	57186	40218	16544
17	80124	35635	17727	08015	45318	22374	21115	78253	14385	53763
18	74350	99817	77402	77214	43236	00210	45521	64237	96286	02655
19	69916	26803	66252	29148	36936	87203	76621	13990	94400	56418
20	09893	20505	14225	68514	46427	56788	96297	78822	54382	14598
21	91499	14523	68479	27686	46162	83554	94750	89923	37089	20048
22	80336	94598	26940	36858	70297	34135	53140	33340	42050	82341
23	44104	81949	85157	47954	32979	26575	57600	40881	22222	06413
24	12550	73742	11100	02040	12860	74697	96644	89439	28707	25815
25	63606	49329	16505	34484	40219	52563	43651	77082	07207	31790
26	61196	90446	26457	47774	51924	33729	65394	59593	42582	60527
27	15474	45266	95270	79953	59367	83848	82396	10118	33211	59466
28	94557	28573	67897	54387	54622	44431	91190	42592	92927	45973
29	42481	16213	97344	08721	16868	48767	03071	12059	25701	46670
30	23523	78317	73208	89837	68935	91416	26252	29663	05522	82562
31	04493	52494	75246	33824	45862	51025	61962	79335	65337	12472
32	00549	97654	64051	88159	96119	63896	54692	82391	23287	29529
33	35963	15307	26898	09354	33351	35462	77974	50024	90103	39333
34	59808	08391	45427	26842	83609	49700	13021	24892	78565	20106
35	46058	85236	01390	92286	77281	44077	93910	83647	70617	42941
36	32179	00597	87379	25241	05567	07007	86743	17157	85394	11838
37	69234	61406	20117	45204	15956	60000	18743	92423	97118	96338
38	19565	41430	01758	75379	40419	21585	66674	36806	84962	85207
39	45155	14938	19476	07246	43667	94543	59047	90033	20826	69541
40	94864	31994	36168	10851	34888	81553	01540	35456	05014	51176
41	98086	24826	45240	28404	44999	08896	39094	73407	35441	31880
42	33185	16232	41941	50949	89435	48581	88695	41994	37548	73043
43	80951	00406	96382	70774	20151	23387	25016	25298	94624	61171
44	79752	49140	71961	28296	69861	02591	74852	20539	00387	59579
45	18633	32537	98145	06571	31010	24674	05455	61427	77938	91936
46	74029	43902	77557	32270	97790	17119	52527	58021	80814	51748
47	54178	45611	80993	37143	05335	12969	56127	19255	36040	90324
48	11664	49883	52079	84827	59381	71539	09973	33440	88461	23356
49	48324	77928	31249	64710	02295	36870	32307	57546	15020	09994
50	69074	94138	87637	91976	35584	04401	10518	21615	01848	76938

5.2 Generating Sampling Distributions

Objectives

- to understand what a sampling distribution is
- to learn how to generate a simulated sampling distribution
- to learn about the shapes, centers, and spreads of typical sampling distributions

The goal for students in this section is to understand the process for constructing a simulated sampling distribution.

The sampling distribution for a summary statistic is the distribution of potential values arising from random samples for that statistic. The collection of all the values you get for that summary statistic from actually taking repeated random samples is a simulation of that distribution. Sometimes an exact sampling distribution can be generated by collecting values of the summary statistic taken from *all possible* random samples of a fixed size. For example, in E9, students will construct an exact sampling distribution by listing all possible samples of size 2, calculating the sample mean for each of those samples and then displaying the means in a dot plot. Typically, when we construct a simulated or approximate sampling distribution, we cannot take all possible random samples, so some possible sample means may be missing. It is impossible to overstate how important it is that students understand the concept of a sampling distribution and the differences between *the* (exact) sampling distribution of a particular summary statistic and a simulated sampling distribution.

Important Terms and Concepts

- sampling distribution
- standard error
- rare events and reasonably likely events

Lesson Planning

Class Time

Two days

Materials

A copy of Display 4.4 (Random Rectangles) and a random digit table (Table D)

Suggested Assignments

Lesson Notes: Generating Sampling Distributions

Discussion

D5. *Random sample.* We assumed that each of the ten workers had an equal chance of being one of the three laid off and that the workers were selected by random sampling without replacement. So the model of this chance process consisted of writing the ten ages on identical pieces of paper and drawing three ages at random.

Summary statistic. We took a random sample using the model described and computed the average age of the three workers laid off in that random sample.

Repetition. The previous step was repeated 1000 times.

Distribution. We made a dot plot of the 1000 sample averages. The simulated sampling distribution appears in Display 5.6.

Lesson Notes: Shape, Center, and Spread: Now and Forever

This textbook uses the term *standard error* to mean the standard deviation of a sampling distribution; that is, the standard deviation of the distribution of some summary statistic. Some textbooks, however, limit the use of the term *standard error* to the *estimate* of the standard deviation of a sampling distribution that one computes from a sample. For example, for the sampling distribution of a sample mean, we will call the value $\sigma/\sqrt{n}$ the standard error. Some textbooks limit the use of the term to the value $s/\sqrt{n}$.

Discussion

D6. Make sure that students understand the difference between Display 5.7 and Display 5.8. Display 5.8 shows the population of the areas of all 100 individual rectangles. Display 5.7 shows the mean areas of samples of size 5 taken from that population.

a. The largest rectangles in the population have an area of 18, and there are five such rectangles, as shown in Display 5.8. To get a value of 18 in the sampling distribution for samples of size 5 in Display 5.7, you would have to pick all five of these rectangles of area 18 for your sample. This is not likely to happen in only 200 samples. Similarly, the smallest rectangles in the population have an area of 1, but this time there are 16 of them. Still, it is not very likely to get all 1's in a sample of size 5.

b. If we continued to add more samples to the sampling distribution of Display 5.7 or constructed the exact sampling distribution using all possible $_{100}C_5$ (100 choose 5) samples, then the means would be equal. This fact is not completely obvious, especially with skewed distributions, but it is not difficult to prove. The main concept from this lesson is that random sampling leads to sample means that tend to center at the population mean. As students discovered in the Random Rectangles activity in Chapter 4, this is not the case with judgment samples. In Section 5.3, students will learn that random sampling also leads to a predictable amount of variability in the distribution of sample means.

c. No, comparing the displays shows that the standard deviation of the sampling distribution is smaller than that of the population. The reason for this can be seen in part a. Averages tend to be clustered closer to the center of the distribution than are the original population values.

d. The shape of the simulated sampling distribution of the sample mean is more normal than the distribution of the population but is still slightly skewed to the right.

D7. Because the sampling distribution is approximately normal, we can estimate that the reasonably likely outcomes are those in the interval $7.31 \pm 2(2.39)$ or 2.53 to 12.09 and rare events are means outside this interval.

We can also estimate these values using the histogram. Rare events are those in the upper 2.5% of the distribution and the lower 2.5% of the distribution. Because there are 200 samples, this would be the largest five means and the smallest five means. We will have to approximate because we cannot isolate the five largest and smallest from the histogram: about 12 or larger, or 3 or smaller. So a mean larger than 12 or smaller than 3 from a sample of size 5 would be a rare event, and the other means would be considered reasonably likely.

Lesson Notes: Return of the Random Rectangles

Activity 5.1: The Return of the Random Rectangles

This activity is essential to ensure that students understand the concept of a sampling distribution.

In Activity 5.1 and other problems and exercises in this section, students are introduced to the idea of using the sample maximum to estimate the maximum in the population. Why would anyone ever want to know the maximum value in a population? A real-life example occurred during World War II when the allies attempted to estimate

German war production. They had, for example, a sample from the sequential serial numbers of a specific part on a tank. Assuming that the sample was a random selection from the integers 1, 2, 3, . . . , N, the allies were able to make an estimate of N, the total number of parts produced. Their estimator for a sample of size n is given in E14:

$$N = \frac{n + 1}{n} \cdot sample\ maximum$$

For more on this, see *Exploring Surveys and Information from Samples* by James M. Landwehr, Jim Swift, and Ann E. Watkins (Palo Alto: Dale Seymour, 1987), pages 75–83.

There is a blackline master at the end of this section that gives the summary statistics, boxplots, and histograms for various simulated sampling distributions for the population of rectangles.

1. Students can generate five random numbers between 00 and 99 on a TI-83 by entering randInt(0,99,5). If these numbers are not distinct, students should eliminate the duplicates. For example, say they get 27, 66, 14, 97, and 66. They select another random number to replace the second 66, and get a 93. So their sample consists of rectangles numbered 27, 66, 14, 97, and 93.

2–3. The rectangles that correspond to the random numbers from step 1 have areas 4, 10, 4, 4, and 16. The median is 4.

4. The typical simulated sampling distribution in the following display shows the sample median for 200 random samples of size 5. (These are the same samples that produced the means in Display 5.7.)

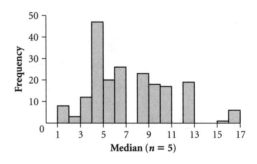

5. The typical simulated sampling distribution from step 4 has a mean of 6.75 and a standard error of 3.43. The mean is a little less than that of the population and the spread is a lot less. It is more mound-shaped than the population, but we still would not call it approximately normal.

6. Because the population median is less than the population mean (6 versus 7.42), the center of the distribution of medians should be below the center of the distribution of means, and it is. (In random sampling, the mean of the sampling distribution of the sample median will be near, but not always at, the population median. In contrast, the mean of the sampling distribution of the sample mean is always at the population mean.) The distribution of medians is more spread out and less mound-shaped than the distribution of means. (This is the general pattern in sampling distributions for these statistics when the population is not highly skewed.)

7. For example, the maximum area in the sample in steps 1 and 2 is 16. A typical simulated sampling distribution of the sample maximum for random samples of five rectangles is shown in this display. Note that the distribution is not symmetric; it is strongly skewed to the left. Here the mean is 13.48 and the standard deviation is 3.70.

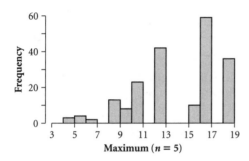

Discussion

D8. **a.** The median of the population of 100 rectangle areas is 6, so it does appear that, for random samples, the center of the sampling distribution of the sample median is close to the population median. In fact, if we took a larger number of samples, the median of the simulated sampling distribution should be even closer to the population median.

b. The maximum in the population is 18. The mean of the distribution of the sample maximum underestimates the population maximum. A small sample is not very likely to contain the maximum value from the population, so the best estimate of the population maximum should be a little larger than the sample maximum. Students will learn how much larger in E14.

Note: A summary statistic is said to be unbiased if the mean of its sampling distribution is equal to the value you would get if you computed the summary statistic using the entire population. For example, the mean area of all 100 rectangles is 7.42. The mean

of the simulated sampling distribution in Display 5.7 is 7.31, very close. If we constructed an exact sampling distribution by taking all possible samples of size 5, the mean of the sampling distribution would be exactly 7.42. The sample mean is an unbiased estimator of the population mean.

The sample maximum is a biased estimator of the population maximum and is biased in the direction of tending to be too small. The sample median is a nearly unbiased estimator of the population median for large samples.

The terms *biased* and *unbiased* do not appear on the AP Statistics syllabus, but you may want to use the terms with your students, especially when discussing D8–D10 and the material about the sampling distribution of the standard deviation. Bias is a property of the method, not of an individual sample.

Note that the idea of a biased estimator is exactly parallel to the idea of bias in a sample survey. The method of taking a sample for a survey is biased if the method produces a summary statistic that tends to be, on average, too large or too small. A summary statistic is a biased estimator of a population parameter if it gives results that are too large or too small on average.

D9. **a.** The sampling distribution is not very mound-shaped, so provisionally we try the formula $6.75 \pm 2(3.43)$ to find the reasonably likely outcomes. This formula gives an interval of -0.11 to 13.61. Rare events would be medians that are outside this interval.

It is better to use the histogram in step 4 of the activity to approximate the reasonably likely outcomes and rare events. Rare events would be the smallest five sample medians and the largest five. The first bar contains more than five medians, so we cannot isolate the smallest five. Sample medians less than 1 (impossible) or more than 16 would be rare events. Medians between 1 and 16 inclusive are reasonably likely.

b. The distribution of the sample maximum is not close to being mound-shaped, so we will use the histogram in step 7 of the activity to approximate the upper 2.5% and lower 2.5% of the 200 sample maximums. Rare events would be the smallest five sample maximums and the largest five. We cannot isolate the largest five. Sample maximums less than 6 would be rare events. Maximums between 6 and 18 inclusive are reasonably likely. You may want to have your students discuss whether or not the middle 95% of values is a good choice for "reasonably likely outcomes" for a skewed distribution.

D10. The *sample mean* will have a sampling distribution whose mean is the population mean, making the sample mean a good estimator of the population mean. It will also have a mound-shaped, somewhat symmetric distribution with a spread that is smaller than the spread for medians from samples of the same size. A smaller spread is better, as the sample mean tends to be closer to the population mean than the sample median is to the population median.

The *sample median* will have a sampling distribution with center close to the population median, making the sample median a good estimator of the population median. This is particularly true for large samples or for situations in which the population distribution is symmetric. Its sampling distribution is less mound-shaped than that of the mean, with a slightly larger spread. The larger spread means that the sample median is likely to be farther from the population median than the sample mean is from the population mean. In summary, the sample mean should be used to estimate the population mean, and the sample median should be used to estimate the population median. The decision to use either the sample mean or the sample median in any specific case depends upon whether the mean or the median is the better choice of parameter for the application at hand. If the population is symmetric, so that its mean and median are the same, then the sample mean is the better choice of estimator because the spread of its sampling distribution is smaller.

Practice

In these Practice problems, students should learn that the sampling distribution of the sample mean tends to be more mound-shaped and less spread out with larger sample sizes. Students should also learn to anticipate what the sampling distributions

of commonly used summary statistics will look like if they are given information about the shape of the population.

P3. **a.** I is B, which is irregular in shape and has a spread nearly as large as the spread of the population. II is C, which is mound-shaped with a very narrow spread. III is A, which is somewhat mound-shaped and has a spread somewhere between the other two. All of these distributions have centers very close to the center of the population.

b. No, a mean of 86 or greater for a class of size 30 did not occur even once in the 100 samples represented in the sampling distribution of Histogram C. Thus, a random sample of 30 students is very unlikely to have a mean score as high as 86. If the class does have a mean score of 86, it cannot reasonably be attributed to chance variation. Perhaps the teacher is very good or the harder-working students had to enroll in this course during the second hour.

P4. **a.** For example, the midrange of the sample of rectangle areas from steps 2–3 of the activity—4, 10, 4, 4, and 16—is $\frac{(4 + 16)}{2}$, or 10.

b. The midrange also has a mound-shaped, nearly symmetric sampling distribution. (Do not be misled by the one short bar; we could change the scale on the *x*-axis to eliminate this.) The center of this distribution is well above the population mean but a little below the population midrange—which is $\frac{(1 + 18)}{2}$, or 9.5. (A larger simulation should produce a center much closer to the population midrange, however.) The spread of this distribution is comparable to that of the mean and appears to be a little less than that of the median. (The spread of the midrange is, in theory, a little larger than the spread of the mean for samples from nearly normal populations.)

c. The midrange of the sample is a good estimator of the midrange of the population of rectangle areas, 9.5. However, this is not a particularly good measure of center for this skewed population, as most of the areas are below 9.5.

In general, the midrange is greatly influenced by outliers—which are not present in this data set—and may produce a very poor estimate in some cases. The mean is influenced by outliers but to a lesser degree. The median is not influenced much by outliers in a sample.

P5. **a.** Histogram A is the lower quartile with its center in the 60's and is approximately mound-shaped. The distribution of a quartile should look much like the distribution of a median, except with a different center.

Histogram B is the maximum, centering in the 90's and highly skewed toward the lower values.

Histogram C is the midrange, centering at around 70 and with a fairly narrow spread, much like what we would expect of a sample mean.

Histogram D is the minimum, centering in the 40's with a large spread and skewed toward the higher values.

b. Histogram D has the largest standard error; Histogram A has the second largest.

Exercises

E7. I – B; II – C; III – A; IV – D

E8. **a.** The distribution is highly skewed toward the larger values. There are two outliers, Alaska and Texas.

b. Students should number the states from 01 to 50 and then use a table of random digits or the TI-83 entry randInt(1,50,5) to select five of them, discarding any duplicates.

Here is a dot plot for one random sample of size five. Although results will vary, it is unlikely that a single sample of size five will include Texas or Alaska, so these values, ranging from 19.9 to 44.6, do appear to capture the essence of where most of the areas lie. The mean of these five values is 30.80.

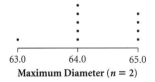

Acres (in millions)

c. The samples will occasionally pick up Texas or Alaska, so the sampling distribution for these small samples is still highly skewed toward the larger values but with a much smaller spread than the population. The mean is still in the low 40's.

d. To get a sample mean between 95 and 105, one of the states must be either Alaska

or Texas. The five states could be, for example, Alaska, Minnesota, Florida, Iowa, and Kentucky. If Texas is chosen, the other four states must all be fairly large, say California, Arizona, Idaho, and Montana.

E9. **a.**

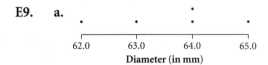

Diameter (in mm)

b. 62 and 63; 62 and 64; 62 and 64; 62 and 65; 63 and 64; 63 and 64; 63 and 65; 64 and 64; 64 and 65; 64 and 65.

c. In the same order as the samples listed in part b, their means are 62.5, 63, 63, 63.5, 63.5, 63.5, 64, 64, 64.5, and 64.5. The exact sampling distribution of the sample mean for samples of size 2 is shown in this dot plot.

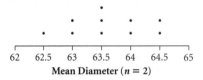

Mean Diameter ($n = 2$)

The sampling distribution has a mean of 63.6 and a standard error of about 0.62. The population has a mean of 63.6 and a standard deviation of about 1.02. The two means are exactly the same and, as usual, the standard error is smaller than the standard deviation of the population.

You (but not your students, yet) may have noticed that the standard error is not equal to $\sigma/\sqrt{n} = 1.02/\sqrt{2} = 0.72$. That is because this formula is true only if there is an infinite population or if sampling with replacement is used, which we did not do in this exercise. Because we are taking a sample of size 2 from a population of only five tennis balls, sampling with or without replacement makes quite a difference in the standard error.

d. The sample maximums for the 10 possible samples are 63, 64, 64, 65, 64, 64, 65, 64, 65, 65. A dot plot is shown here.

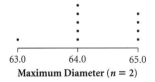

Maximum Diameter ($n = 2$)

e. The sample ranges are 1, 2, 2, 3, 1, 1, 2, 0, 1, and 1. A dot plot is shown here.

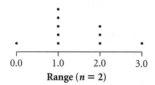

Range (n = 2)

f. The plot for the mean is closer to normal in shape, as is the plot for the range. But it is difficult to judge normality in distributions with so few points.

E10. *Note:* You may want to assign part a and just one of parts b, c, d, or e to each student and then have students share their results before doing part f. Your students may be interested in the results for six trials of the bike with smooth tires, also in centimeters: 341, 348, 349, 355, 373, 391. These data are taken from the textbook *Statistics for Engineering Problem Solving* by Stephen B. Vardeman (Boston: PWS Publishing, 1994), page 349, which contains data from many student projects.

a.

Length of Skid Marks (in cm)

b. The 20 possible samples are listed here.

365, 374, 376;	374, 376, 391;
365, 374, 391;	374, 376, 401;
365, 374, 401;	374, 376, 402;
365, 374, 402;	374, 391, 401;
365, 376, 391;	374, 391, 402;
365, 376, 401;	374, 401, 402;
365, 376, 402;	376, 391, 401;
365, 391, 401;	376, 391, 402;
365, 391, 402;	376, 401, 402;
365, 401, 402;	391, 401, 402

c. The 20 sample means are 371.667, 376.667, 380.000, 380.333, 377.333, 380.667, 381.000, 385.667, 386.000, 389.333, 380.333, 383.667, 384.000, 388.667, 389.000, 392.333,

389.333, 389.667, 393.000, and 398.000. A dot plot appears at bottom of page.

This exact sampling distribution has mean 384.83, which is the same as the population mean. It has a standard error of about 6.30—smaller than that of the standard deviation of the population.

d. The 20 sample medians are 374, 374, 374, 374, 376, 376, 376, 391, 391, 401, 376, 376, 376, 391, 391, 401, 391, 391, 401, and 401. A dot plot is shown here.

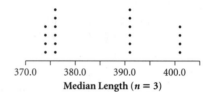

Median Length (n = 3)

The median of this sampling distribution is 383.5. The median of the six measurements is also 383.5. (This does not always occur in distributions that are not symmetric.)

e. The dot plot of the sampling distribution of the sample minimum is shown here. As is typical, it is strongly skewed to the right. The mean of this sampling distribution is 370.65, whereas the minimum in the population of measurements is 365 cm. The sample minimum is not a good estimator of the population minimum; it tends to be too big.

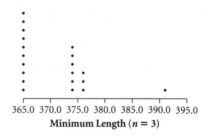

Minimum Length (n = 3)

f. None of these plots, except perhaps the one for the mean, look more normal than the population.

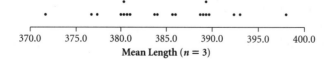

Mean Length (n = 3)

E11. **a.** Because the inspector is selecting only two cartons and the cartons are either all good or all bad, there are only three possible choices for the number of pounds of spoiled fish. The sample of 48 packages will contain 0, 24, or 48 pounds of spoiled fish. We cannot attach a relative frequency to these three values with the information given.

b. The inspector thought he had a sample of size 48, but he only had a sample of size 2. One way he can improve his plan is to have a larger sample size, which means randomly selecting more cartons. Because all fish within a carton are in the same state, sampling any one fish from a carton will tell the whole story for that carton.

A note on dividing by $n - 1$ in the SD formula: E12 and E13 demonstrate why you divide by $n - 1$ in the formula for the sample standard deviation. Even with division by $n - 1$, the sample standard deviation has a sampling distribution that is not quite centered at the population standard deviation. In other words, the sample standard deviation is a biased estimator of the population standard deviation.

However, if you square the standard deviations and talk about variances, the sample variance is an unbiased estimator of the population variance. It is impossible to find a single divisor that would make both the variance and the standard deviation unbiased. But it is possible to find an adjustment to the standard deviation that will make it unbiased.

If students notice that the sample standard deviation still tends to be a bit small, even when dividing by $n - 1$, the following dialogue might help.

Sam: Okay, I can see that when we divide by $n - 1$, the sampling distribution for the sample standard deviation is centered closer to σ than if we divide by n. But it still seems to be a bit smaller than σ.

Pop: I'll bet they hoped you wouldn't notice that.

Sam: You mean it wouldn't be exactly equal to σ even if we took more samples?

Pop: Right. Even if you divide by $n - 1$, the value of s tends to be smaller than σ.

Sam: Then what's the point?

Pop: As you can see from E12, the mean of the sampling distribution of the sample

variance, s^2, is exactly equal to the population variance, σ^2.

Sam: I'm supposed to be impressed by this?

Pop: Well, perhaps not, but it's the best they can do at this stage to explain why you divide by $n - 1$.

E12. **a–e.**

Sample	Mean	Variance, Dividing by $n = 2$	Variance, Dividing by $n - 1 = 1$
2, 2	2	0	0
2, 4	3	1	2
2, 6	4	4	8
4, 2	3	1	2
4, 4	4	0	0
4, 6	5	1	2
6, 2	4	4	8
6, 4	5	1	2
6, 6	6	0	0
Average	4	$1\frac{1}{3}$	$2\frac{2}{3}$

f. The variance of the population {2, 4, 6} is $\sigma^2 = 2\frac{2}{3}$, which is equal to the average of the sample variances when you divide by $n - 1$.

g. Dividing by $n - 1$, because the average of the sample variances is equal to the population variance. Although this phenomenon has been shown for only one example, it is true in all cases.

h. Too small. When you divide by $n - 1$, the sample variance is an unbiased estimator of the population variance. This means that although the sample variance is not always equal to the population variance, the average of the variances of all possible samples is exactly equal to the population variance. If you divide by n, the sample variance tends to be too small, on average. Note that the sample mean, when you divide by n, is an unbiased estimator of the population mean. If you divided by $n - 1$, it would be too big.

E13. Results from the student's samples will vary, but in each case the effect of dividing by 4 rather than by 5 makes the standard deviation larger.

When we divide by $n - 1$, the center of the sampling distribution is much closer to the population standard deviation than when we divide by n. Because we always like the results from our sample to be as close as possible to the population parameter, we choose to divide by $n - 1$.

Note that, even dividing by $n - 1$, the sample standard deviation is a biased estimator of the population standard deviation—it tends to be a bit too small.

These sampling distributions of the sample standard deviation are skewed left. But that isn't typically the case. Because the standard deviation is always positive, there is a wall at 0. For a mound-shaped population, this limit results in a sampling distribution for the standard deviation that is skewed to the right. As the sample size increases, the skew decreases and the sampling distribution becomes more like a normal distribution.

E14. **a.** If the population from which the sample is selected is nearly uniform in shape, we would expect the values from the sample to be somewhat uniformly displayed along a real number line between the smallest value (1 in this case) and the largest value (the unknown N), as shown in the diagram in the student text. In the diagram, with $n = 4$, the sample maximum should occur about $\frac{4}{5}$ of the way from 1 to N. That is

$$sample\ maximum = \frac{4}{5}N$$

Solving for N, we get

$$N = \frac{5}{4} \cdot sample\ maximum$$

This idea generalizes to any sample size, which yields the formula in the student text.
b. The sampling distribution of the adjusted maximum from the same batch of 200 random samples of size 5 is shown in the next display. It appears from this simulation, that the adjusted maximum does a better job of estimating the population maximum. However, the mean of this simulated sampling distribution is still a little less than the

population maximum of 18. This difference is because the distribution of the areas of the rectangles is not uniform. This sampling distribution has mean 16.8, and standard deviation 4.44.

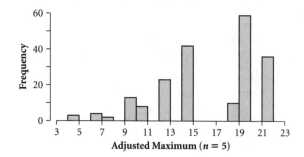

Adjusted Maximum ($n = 5$)

E15. *Note:* Although this exercise is optional, it makes a good small project when students work on the problem and then write up the solution in essay form.

To see that the sampling distribution of the sample median can have a smaller spread than that of means (for samples of the same size), let us go back to the areas of states investigated in E8. The following histogram shows a simulated sampling distribution for the sample median, which can be compared to the simulated sampling distribution of the sample mean in E8. This sampling distribution of the median has mean 33.9 and standard deviation 16.6.

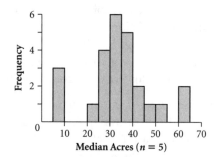

Median Acres ($n = 5$)

The medians are much less affected by the two large states, which is reflected in the much smaller spread for this sampling distribution.

Simulated Sampling Distributions for Rectangles Summary Statistics

	Mean	Median	MidRange	Minimum	Maximum	Adjusted Max	StdN	StdN−1
mean =	7.314	6.745	7.8425	2.205	13.48	16.176	4.5001967	5.0313729
standard dev =	2.386605	3.4320357	2.2155104	1.7857546	3.6997352	4.4396822	1.4608554	1.633286
min =	2.2	1	2.5	1	4	4.8	0.4	0.447214
Q1 =	5.6	4	6.5	1	10	12	3.41162	3.814305
median =	7	6	8.5	1	15	18	4.66476	5.21536
Q3 =	9	9	9.5	3	16	19.2	5.60357	6.26498
max =	14	16	13	10	18	21.6	7.45654	8.33667
IQR =	3.4	5	3	2	6	7.2	2.19195	2.450675

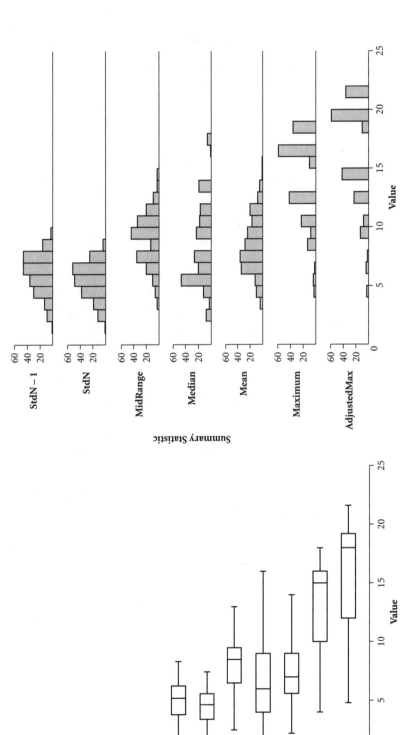

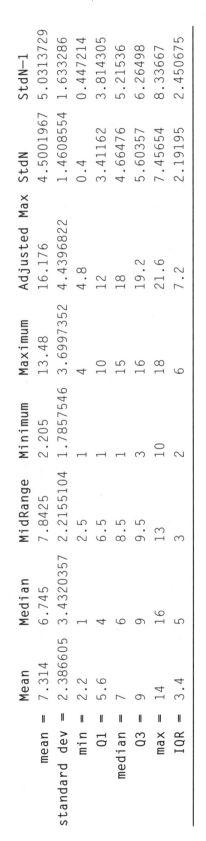

5.3 Sampling Distribution of the Sample Mean

Objectives

- to learn the characteristics of the sampling distribution of the sample mean: shape, mean, and standard error
- to use the sampling distribution to find the probability that a mean from a random sample will fall in a given interval
- to use the sampling distribution to find the probability that the total in a random sample will fall in a given interval
- to know that if the sample size is small relative to the population size, the population size has little effect on the statistical analysis

Much of what students saw in Section 5.2 points to the fact that, for somewhat symmetric populations, the sample mean is the preferred statistic for estimating center. The emphasis on averages in the everyday use of statistics in general is not misplaced, although you do have to be careful about using averages when distributions are highly skewed. Students also saw examples that illustrated the properties of the sampling distribution of the sample mean:

- It is centered at the population mean μ.
- It has a smaller spread when the sample size is larger.
- It has a shape that becomes more normal-like as the sample size gets larger.

In this section, these three facts will be made explicit and extended to the case of the sample total.

Students should now begin to understand why the standard deviation is so important. We use the standard deviation as the basic measure of spread in most problems that involve the relationship between the sample mean and the population mean. It is so useful because the standard error of the sampling distribution of the sample mean is equal to $\sigma/\sqrt{n}$, which students will learn can be estimated by $s/\sqrt{n}$.

Important Terms and Concepts

- sample mean versus sample sum or total
- sampling distribution of the sample mean
- sampling distribution of the sample sum
- Central Limit Theorem
- sample size versus population size

Lesson Planning

Class Time

Four to five days

Materials

For Activity 5.2, 25 pennies for each student

Suggested Assignments

Lesson Notes: Shape, Center, and Spread

The Sampling Distribution of the Sample Median

Students learn that the mean of the sample means is equal to the population mean. Occasionally, a student who understands this concept will then ask about the sampling distribution of the sample median:

- What is the mean of the sample medians?
- What is the median of the sample medians?

In general, the mean of the sampling distribution of the sample median is not equal to the population median. However, the mean of the sampling distribution of the sample median is equal to the population median for symmetric distributions, like the normal. It is also true that for decently large samples you will not be able to detect a difference between the mean of the distribution of sample medians and the population median.

Under fairly general conditions the median of the sampling distribution of sample medians does equal the population median, but this relationship is hard to show and depends on careful definition of the sample median (such as what to do for an even number of values).

The fact that these questions don't have an easily phrased general answer illuminates why the mean is such a useful concept. If students decide to work out some small examples to explore these questions, remind them that their sampling should be done with replacement. In addition, students might wish to explore the question "What is the median of the sample means?"

The Sampling Distribution of the Mean for $n = 1$

Suppose you take a random sample of size 1 from a population and get the value x. When you compute the mean of that sample of size 1, you get the value x itself, of course. Now think of constructing the *exact* sampling distribution for samples of size 1. This process is equivalent to reconstructing the population itself. Thus, the sampling distribution of the sample mean for samples of size 1 is the same as the distribution of the population and has the same shape, mean, and standard deviation. We can check that it has the same standard deviation with the formula for its standard error: $\sigma/\sqrt{n} = \sigma/\sqrt{1} = \sigma$, the standard deviation of the population.

Activity 5.2: Cents and Center

In Activity 5.2, students will discover the properties of the shape, mean, and standard deviation of the sampling distribution of the mean for samples taken from a distribution that is decidedly not normal.

In this activity, students construct a distribution of the population of the ages of a large number of pennies. This distribution will have roughly the shape of a geometric distribution. By sampling from this distribution, students will construct simulated sampling distributions of the mean for samples of size 5, 10, and 25. They will find the sampling distribution's shape, mean, and standard error.

Each student should have 25 pennies or the dates of 25 pennies. The activity is more fun if each student also has 5 nickels, 3 dimes, and a quarter. During the week before the activity, have each student collect the first 25 pennies that he or she receives in change. Students should bring in the pennies and a list of the 25 dates on the pennies. Throughout this activity, be sensitive to the fact that some students may have difficulty reading the dates on the pennies.

The activity is meant for the entire class to do together and works well with a class of any size. If you have a small class, each student should be responsible for several samples; if you have a very large class, you may want to omit some pennies when constructing the histogram for the population.

1. Few students realize that the shape of the distribution of the ages of all pennies will be roughly geometric (see the histogram below for step 2). Many will believe that it should be normal. ("A few pennies are new, a few pennies are old, most are lumped in the middle.")

2. Students love to make the histogram by placing the pennies themselves above a number line on a large table or on the floor of the classroom. Because this can take some time, you might choose to construct the histogram during a break in the class. You could also collect the pennies the class session before and ask for volunteers (with sharp eyes) to come early next time to construct the histogram. Another way to make the histogram is to collect a list of the ages during the class session before, type them into the computer, and bring copies of the histogram to class.

A histogram from one class for 648 pennies is shown at the bottom of the page.

3. Answers will vary. It is best if you have all of the ages entered in a computer or calculator so you can get the exact mean and standard deviation. The mean age for the pennies in the histogram below is 10.4, which is larger than usual. One suspects that a student found some older pennies in the back of a drawer. The mean age tends to be between 7 and 8 years, with a standard deviation of about 8 years.

4. Students like to display the distribution in the following way. Have each student place a nickel above a second number line on the floor or table to represent the mean age of their 5 pennies. So, for example, if the student's sample is 6, 10, 8, 1, 18 with mean 8.6, they'd put their nickel on the number line between 8 and 9 years. It is best if there are about 100 nickels in the sampling distribution, so if your class size is small, have each student compute the means of several samples of size 5.

5. The mean will be the same. Most students will not realize this. A typical answer is to say it will be smaller. Most students will realize that the standard deviation will be smaller.

6. If the mean of the population of penny ages was, say, 7.5 years with a standard deviation of 8 years, then the mean of the sampling distribution should be about 7.5 years with a standard deviation of about $8/\sqrt{5} \approx 3.6$ years.

7. Make a display of the histograms using the dimes and quarters. Students will then be able to visualize that the numbers graphed represent the means of samples, not individual values (ages of the pennies).

8. Students should notice that the shape of the sampling distributions becomes approximately normal as the sample size increases, the mean stays the same, and the standard deviation decreases. Specifically, the mean of the three sampling distributions should be approximately the same as the

Lesson 5.3, Activity 5.2, 2

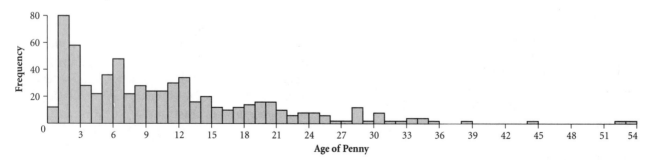

mean of the population of all pennies, $\mu_{\bar{x}} = \mu$. The standard deviation of the sampling distributions should approximately equal the standard deviation of the population divided by the square root of the sample size, $\sigma_{\bar{x}} = \sigma/\sqrt{n}$.

No matter what the sample size, if students had the complete sampling distribution of the mean—that is, if they had computed the mean of all possible samples of size n, sampling with replacement—then the two equations, $\mu_{\bar{x}} = \mu$ and $\sigma_{\bar{x}} = \sigma/\sqrt{n}$, would hold exactly.

Discussion

D11. All three distributions are centered at the population mean of 2.17. The distribution of the population has the largest spread, the distribution for samples of size 4 has the second largest spread, and the distribution for samples of size 10 has the smallest spread. All are approximately normal, but the distributions appear to become more nearly normal as the sample size increases.

Note: Now would be a good time to point out to your students that the population is the same as the distribution of the means of samples of size 1. That's because the mean of a sample of size 1 is equal to one of the values in the population. See "The Sampling Distribution of the Mean for $n = 1$" on page 215 of this section.

D12. With a sample size of 4, it is impossible to get, for example, a mean equal to or larger than 2.3 but less than 2.5. For that to be the mean, the sum of four values selected from {0, 1, 2, 3, 4} would have to be more than 9.2 but less than 10. That is impossible because the sum of integers must be an integer.

Practice

P6. **a.** Take a random sample of size 10 using methods discussed in Section 5.1. Compute the mean of this sample. Do this again and again. Plot these sample means on a dot plot.
b. Take repeated random samples of size 1 using methods discussed in Section 5.1. The resulting distribution, when displayed as a histogram, should look very much like the histogram of Display 5.4.

Lesson Notes: Sampling from a Skewed Population

At about this stage, students may be wondering why we are making such a big deal of sampling distributions. After all, when we do a real survey or experiment, we collect information from only one sample. The reason for studying sampling distributions is to check to see whether the sample we took could reasonably have come from a population with a specified mean and standard deviation. We can construct the sampling distribution for this hypothetical population and check to see whether the sample mean we computed from our sample is a reasonably likely outcome. If it is not reasonably likely, we probably have the wrong population.

Discussion

D13. **a.** The means of the simulated sampling distributions all are equal to the mean of the population (0.916) when rounded to the nearest hundredth. (If students use simulation to duplicate this result, the means will probably not be exactly equal to 0.916. Theoretically, the mean of the sampling distributions should exactly equal the mean of the population; but simulations will be off a little.)
b. No. The mean is equal to 0.92 for all sample sizes.

D14. **a.** Except for the simulated sampling distribution for samples of size 1, the standard errors are all smaller. As the sample size gets bigger, the standard error gets smaller. In a *simulated* sampling distribution for samples of size 1, the standard error should be roughly the same as the standard deviation of the population.
b. Yes, the following scatterplot made from Display 5.20 shows the relationship between n and the standard error. The plot of the standard error against the sample size n shows that the standard error decreases as n increases, but the relationship is not linear.

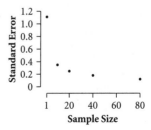

c. If students try various transformations, they will find that the plot of the standard error versus the reciprocal of the square root of n, $1/\sqrt{n}$, is nearly a perfectly straight line, as shown in the following plot.

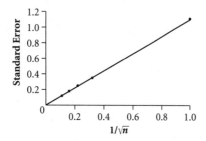

The regression line through these points has slope of 1.11 and an intercept very close to zero. That is,

$$SE \approx 1.11\frac{1}{\sqrt{n}} = \frac{1.11}{\sqrt{n}} = \frac{\sigma}{\sqrt{n}}$$

This slope is the same as the population standard deviation of 1.11. A good rule to relate the standard error to sample size is the following:

> In random sampling, the standard error of the sampling distribution of the sample mean is equal to the population standard deviation divided by the square root of the sample size: $SE = \sigma/\sqrt{n}$.

d. Answers will vary according to the student's rule. The values given by the rule $SE = \sigma/\sqrt{n}$ are approximately the same as those in Displays 5.18 and 5.19.

Sample Size	Standard Errors from the Displays	Theoretical Standard Errors
4	0.47	$\frac{0.945}{\sqrt{4}} = 0.4725$
10	0.30	$\frac{0.945}{\sqrt{10}} \approx 0.30$

D15. **a.** As the sample size increases, the sampling distributions have smaller gaps and become less skewed and more normal in shape. Outliers disappear.

b. Yes. In random sampling, the sampling distribution of the sample mean will tend toward the shape of a normal distribution as the sample size increases. For small samples, the sampling distribution of the mean may

still show some of the characteristics of the shape of the population from which the data came, but this tendency will diminish as the sample size increases.

Discussion

D16. This is a "plain English" version of the rule given in D14. As the sample size increases, the spread of the sampling distribution of the sample mean decreases. Fortunately, this is also common sense: If you want your estimate to be close to the true mean, you take as large a sample as possible.

Practice

P7. The shape will be approximately normal because the population's distribution is approximately normal; the mean will be the mean of the population, or 266, and the standard error will be

$$\frac{\sigma}{\sqrt{n}} = \frac{37}{\sqrt{15}} \approx 9.553$$

Lesson Notes: Finding Probabilities for Sample Means

Once you know the mean and standard error of the sampling distribution, the method given in the student text on pages 290 through 291 can be done in one step using a TI-83 calculator. For example, to do the *Average Number of Children* example, press 2nd [DISTR] 2:normalcdf(and enter normalcdf (−9999999,1.5,0.916,0.2482). The calculator returns approximately .9907.

This calculator function gives the area between any two bounds under a normal curve and is entered in the form normalcdf(*lower bound, upper bound, µ, σ*). Using this function eliminates the need to compute *z*-scores.

Note: In this particular example, we use $\mu_{\bar{x}}$ and $\sigma_{\bar{x}}$.

The question of when students should begin to use this function is the professor's choice in a college course. In an AP Statistics course, if students are not taking the AP exam, there is no reason for them to delay using the function; if students are taking the AP exam, they may be asked how to find probabilities using *z*-scores and should understand how to do all of the steps in the example.

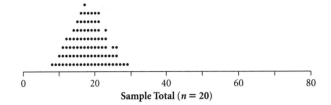

0   20   40   60   80
Sample Total (n = 20)

Discussion

D17. This problem should not be done like the *Average Number of Children* example. The reason is that the sampling distribution is not approximately normal. Display 5.20 shows that the sampling distribution for samples of size 10 still has a skew to the right.

Practice

P8. **a.** The sampling distribution should be approximately normal because this is a very big sample size. With random samples of 1000 families, the potential values of the sample mean are centered at 0.916—the mean number of children per family—and have a standard error of 1.11 divided by the square root of 1000, or about 0.035. This implies that around 95% of the sample means would lie between $0.916 \pm 2(0.035)$ or 0.846 to 0.986. So the distribution of potential values of the sample mean is concentrated very tightly around the expected value of 0.916.

b. The z-score for a mean of 0.9 children is

$$z = \frac{0.9 - 0.916}{\frac{1.11}{\sqrt{1000}}} \approx -0.456$$

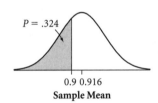

$P = .324$

0.9 0.916
Sample Mean

The probability that the mean is 0.9 or less is about .324.

Lesson Notes: Finding Probabilities for Sample Totals

Discussion

D18. The shapes are exactly the same. The only difference is the scale on the *x*-axis. To convert the dot plots, change the scale on the *x*-axis by multiplying each value by the sample size *n*. For example, for *n* = 20, the dot plot would look like the next plot. Each dot represents 11 points.

Practice

P9. **a.** The sampling distribution of the sample total should be approximately normal because this is a very big sample size. It has mean and standard error

$$\mu_{sum} = n\mu = 1000(0.916) = 916$$
$$\sigma_{sum} = \sqrt{n} \cdot \sigma = \sqrt{1000} \cdot 1.11 \approx 35.10$$

The z-score for 1000 families is then

$$z = \frac{sum - n\mu}{\sqrt{n} \cdot \sigma}$$
$$= \frac{1000 - 916}{35.10}$$
$$\approx 2.393$$

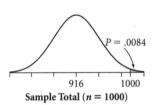

$P = .0084$

916   1000
Sample Total (n = 1000)

The probability of getting at least 1000 children is about .0084. Thus, there is almost no chance the network will get 1000 children.

b. Yes, the probability goes from practically 0 to almost certain. The z-score for 1200 families is

$$z = \frac{sum - n\mu}{\sqrt{n} \cdot \sigma}$$
$$= \frac{1000 - 1099.2}{38.45}$$
$$\approx -2.580$$

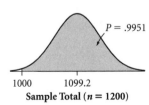

$P = .9951$

1000   1099.2
Sample Total (n = 1200)

The probability of getting at least 1000 children in a random sample of 1200 families is .9951.

P10. You may wish to have each student do only one part of this question. Then have the students compare results and notice that as *n* increases, the range of reasonably likely outcomes for the sample mean decreases.

a. $0.916 \pm 1.96(1.11/\sqrt{25}) = 0.916 \pm 0.435$ or $(0.481, 1.351)$

b. $0.916 \pm 1.96(1.11/\sqrt{100}) = 0.916 \pm 0.21756$ or $(0.698, 1.134)$

c. $0.916 \pm 1.96(1.11/\sqrt{1000}) = 0.916 \pm 0.0688$ or $(0.847, 0.985)$

d. $0.916 \pm 1.96(1.11/\sqrt{4000}) = 0.916 \pm 0.034$ or $(0.882, 0.950)$

Lesson Notes: Sample Size and Population Size

The second dialogue between Pop and Sam hints at a method for adjusting the standard error if the random sample is relatively large compared to the population. The formula for the standard error of the sampling distribution of the mean

$$SE = \frac{\sigma}{\sqrt{n}}$$

is actually a simplified version of a more exact formula:

$$SE = \frac{\sigma}{\sqrt{n}}\sqrt{\frac{N-n}{N-1}}$$

If *N* is large compared to *n*, then the "finite population correction" will be very close to 1 and we can ignore it. For example, let's test the numbers discussed by Pop and Sam in the second dialogue. With a sample of 100 out of a population of 100,000,000, this finite population correction is equal to

$$\sqrt{\frac{N-n}{N-1}} = \sqrt{\frac{100,000,000 - 100}{100,000,000 - 1}} \approx 0.999999505$$

With a sample of 100 out of 5000, the finite population correction is equal to

$$\sqrt{\frac{N-n}{N-1}} = \sqrt{\frac{5000 - 100}{5000 - 1}} \approx 0.9900$$

The size of the population doesn't make much difference once it gets much larger than the sample size.

How Many Repetitions Do You Need in a Simulation?

There is one remaining issue about size that is not discussed in the student text—that is, the effect of the number of repetitions on a simulation. Let's go back to the situation of samples of size 9 from the population of number of children per family (D17). Recall that this population has a mean of 0.916 and a standard deviation of 1.11. The plots below show the simulated sampling distribution of the sample mean for samples of size 9 based on 50, 200, and 1000 repetitions of the process. Summary statistics for the three simulations are provided as well.

Lesson 5.3

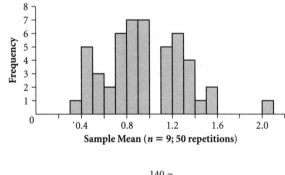

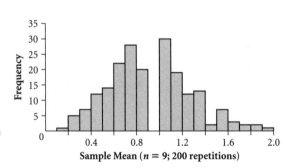

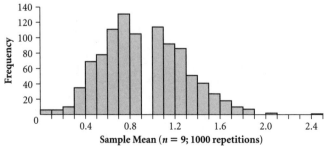

Repetitions	Mean	StdDev
50	0.964	0.342
200	0.911	0.360
1000	0.916	0.365

The main features of the shape do not change with the number of repetitions—the skew toward the larger values is evident in all three histograms. The shape becomes smoother with more repetitions. As the number of repetitions increases, the mean of the simulated sampling distribution gets closer to the theoretical value of 0.916 and the standard error gets closer to 0.37. The important point is that the mean and standard error stabilize after a while, and that is one of the things to look for in deciding on the number of repetitions. For generating simulated sampling distributions for sample means, we suggest using at least 200 repetitions, if time and technology permit.

You should look for the key features of the simulated sampling distribution (shape, center, and spread) to stabilize. This may require that you add a number of repetitions iteratively, adding them in fairly small numbers as you observe what happens to the simulated sampling distribution.

Discussion

D19. For all practical purposes, it would be about the same. However, the standard error is actually a bit larger if $N = 10,000$ than if $N = 1,000$.

If $N = 10,000$, then

$$SE = \frac{\sigma}{\sqrt{n}} \cdot \sqrt{\frac{N-n}{N-1}} = \frac{1.11}{10} \sqrt{\frac{9900}{9999}} = 0.1104$$

If $N = 1000$, then

$$SE = \frac{1.11}{10} \cdot \sqrt{\frac{900}{999}} = 0.1054$$

D20. a. It does not change; for all N, the mean is μ.
b. It decreases by a factor of $1/\sqrt{n}$.
c. The mean will be μ because each sample mean will be equal to μ. The SE will be 0; there is no variation in the sample means.

Practice

P11. a. Assign each household a three-digit number. Select five three-digit numbers at random. Find the five households corresponding to these five numbers. If one or more of the numbers is a repeat, use that household again anyway.

b. Assign each household a three-digit number. Select five three-digit numbers at random. Find the five households corresponding to these five numbers. If one or more of the numbers is a repeat, discard the repeats and get new three-digit numbers. Do not use the same household twice in the sample.

P12. The analysis would not change because the sample size in both cases is a very small fraction of the population size.

Exercises

E16. a. I. Histogram B; $n = 25$
 II. Histogram A; $n = 4$
 III. Histogram C; $n = 2$
b. The theoretical standard error is $2.402/\sqrt{n}$, which turns out to be 1.698, 1.201, and 0.480 for the respective sample sizes of 2, 4, and 25. All of these are fairly close to the observed standard errors.
c. For samples of size 2 and 4, the simulated sampling distributions of the mean reflect the skewness of the population distribution. For samples of size 25, the skewness is essentially eliminated and the simulated sampling distribution looks like a normal distribution.
d. The rule that about 95% of the observations lie within two standard errors of the population mean works well for $n = 25$, and slightly less well for the skewed distributions occurring for $n = 4$ and $n = 2$.

E17. The population is approximately like that in this table. Students' estimates will vary. (Many other assignments for random numbers are possible.)

Value	Percentage	Assignment of Random Numbers
0	26	01–26
1	18	27–44
2	16	45–60
3	10	61–70
4	8	71–78
5	8	79–86
6	6	87–92
7	4	93–96
8	2	97–98
9	2	99–00

To get a sample of size 5, divide the random digits into groups of two and use the assignments given in the third column.

E18. **a.** **I.** Histogram B; $n = 4$
II. Histogram C; $n = 25$
III. Histogram A; $n = 2$

b. The population standard deviation for this distribution is 3.5. This standard deviation divided by the square root of 2, 4, and 25, respectively, yields 2.47, 1.75, and 0.70. These values are quite close to the observed standard deviations of the simulated sampling distributions.

c. Despite the new peak centered at the mean, the simulated sampling distribution for $n = 2$ still reflects much of the pattern of the population, showing the mounds at the extremes. For $n = 4$, a little of the population pattern remains, but by $n = 25$ it disappears and all that is seen is an essentially normal distribution.

d. The rule works well for $n = 25$, but not nearly so well for the smaller sample sizes. As usual, the rule works well for the sampling distribution of the sample mean as long as the sample size is reasonably large.

E19. The population is approximately like that in this table. Students' estimates will vary. (Many other assignments for random numbers are possible.)

Value	Percentage	Assignment of Random Numbers
0	18	01–18
1	14	19–32
2	10	33–42
3	6	43–48
4	2	49–50
5	2	51–52
6	6	53–58
7	10	59–68
8	14	69–82
9	18	83–00

To get a sample of size 5, divide the random digits into groups of two and use the assignments given in the third column.

E20. **a.**

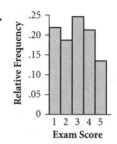

b. A has $n = 25$, B has $n = 1$, and C has $n = 5$. Remind students that repeated sampling with samples of size 1 should produce a distribution that looks very much like the population.

c. If the class can be considered a random sample of the students who took this exam, then an average of 3.6 would be very unusual for a class size of 25. A more reasonable conclusion is that the class size is 5. It is always possible, however, that 25 students in a class would do much better than a random sample of 25 students.

E21. **a.** No. Exactly two accidents happened in about 15% of the days. Two or more accidents happened in about 25% of the days.

b. In Display 5.26, the first plot is the one for eight days, and the second plot is the one for four days.

c. Yes, if the days can be viewed as a random sample of all days. (This would not be true, for example, if the four days were in the middle of an ice storm.) For the four-day averages, two accidents are not very likely. It occurs here about 6 times out of 100.

d. Yes, if the days can be viewed as a random sample of all days. For the eight-day average, an average of two accidents never occurred and, hence, could be deemed very unlikely.

e. The sampling distributions used in parts a–c are based on random samples of four and eight days. A particular period of four (or eight) days may not look like a random sample at all because of the high dependency from day to day. For example, if all days of a sample are taken from the winter season in a region that has ice and snow, the accident rate might be far higher than what is typical for the rest of the year.

E22. Because the scores are normally distributed, we can use the normal approximation with all sample sizes. Point out to students that a larger sample size makes the denominator smaller, which makes the z-score larger and the probability smaller.

a. The z-score is

$$z = \frac{510 - 500}{100} = 0.10$$

which gives a probability of .4602. Alternatively, on a TI-83 the result of normalcdf (510,9999999,500,100) is approximately 0.4602.

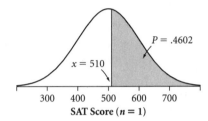

SAT Score ($n = 1$)

b. The z-score is

$$z = \frac{510 - 500}{100/\sqrt{4}} = 0.20$$

which gives a probability of .4207.

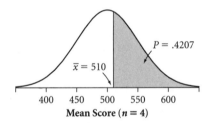

Mean Score ($n = 4$)

c. The z-score is

$$z = \frac{510 - 500}{100/\sqrt{25}} = 0.50$$

which gives a probability of .3085.

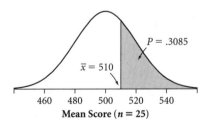

Mean Score ($n = 25$)

d. The probability that one randomly selected score is 510 or greater is about .46. Group the random digits in pairs and assign the digits 01 through 46 to be a score of 510 or greater. The other pairs of digits represent a score less than that. Take four pairs of random digits and see whether all four represent scores of 510 or greater. If so, this repetition is a success. If any of the pairs represents a score less than 510, this would be a failure. Repeat this process many times. The estimate of the probability is the proportion of repetitions that are successes.

Note: The probability can be computed exactly using the Multiplication Rule for Independent Events that students will learn in Chapter 6 on page 366: $(.4602)^4 \approx .045$.

E23. *Note:* E23 contains material that will be covered later on pages 488–489 of the student text. It is optional for now. There are two ways to handle this exercise: Students can work on finding the method themselves, or they can be given the formula below. Whichever way you choose, be sure students understand that the smaller the interval, the larger the sample size must be. They should notice that in order to cut the interval in half, you must quadruple the sample size.

We know that if the sampling distribution is approximately normal, about 95% of all sample means are in the interval $\mu_{\bar{x}} \pm 2(\sigma/\sqrt{n})$. Thus, to be 95% sure that the sample mean is within a value E of the population mean, we must have

$$E \geq 2\frac{\sigma}{\sqrt{n}}$$

$$\sqrt{n} \geq 2\frac{\sigma}{E}$$

$$n \geq \frac{4\sigma^2}{E^2}$$

a. $n \geq \dfrac{4\sigma^2}{E^2} = \dfrac{4(100)^2}{10^2} = 400$

b. $n \geq \dfrac{4\sigma^2}{E^2} = \dfrac{4(100)^2}{5^2} = 1600$

c. $n \geq \dfrac{4\sigma^2}{E^2} = \dfrac{4(100)^2}{1^2} = 40,000$

E24. Because the weights are normally distributed, we can use the normal approximation with all sample sizes.

a. The z-score is

$$z = \frac{0.148 - 0.15}{0.003} = -0.667$$

which gives a probability of .2525.

Alternatively, on a TI-83 the result of **normalcdf**(−9999999,0.148,0.15,0.003) is approximately .2525.

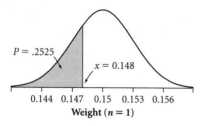

b. The *z*-score is

$$z = \frac{0.148 - 0.15}{0.003/\sqrt{4}} = -1.3333$$

which gives a probability of .0912.

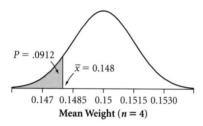

c. The *z*-score is

$$z = \frac{0.148 - 0.15}{0.003/\sqrt{10}} = -2.1082$$

which gives a probability of .0175.

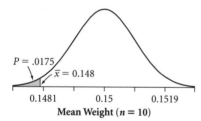

E25. a. The mean of the sampling distribution of the sample mean remains at the population mean μ for all sample sizes. However, as the sample size increases, the standard error of the sampling distribution of the sample mean decreases by a factor of 1 divided by the square root of *n*.

Specifically, $\mu_{\bar{x}} = \mu$ and $\sigma_{\bar{x}} = \sigma/\sqrt{n}$.

b. The mean of the sampling distribution of the sample total increases by a factor of *n*. The standard error of the sampling distribution of the sample mean increases by a factor of the square root of *n*.

Specifically, $\mu_{sum} = n\mu$ and $\sigma_{sum} = \sqrt{n} \cdot \sigma$.

E26. a. For a sample of 10 families to contain at least 30 children, the sample mean would have to be at least 3. From the second plot in Display 5.20 of the student text, we see that this almost never happens.

b. For a sample of 20 families to contain at least 30 children, the sample mean would have to be at least 1.5. From the third plot in Display 5.20, we see that this has a rare chance of happening.

c. For a sample of 40 families to contain at least 30 children, the sample mean would have to be at least 0.75. From the fourth plot in Display 5.20, we see that this happens with a probability of about .8.

d. For a sample of 80 families to contain at least 30 children, the sample mean would have to be at least 0.375. From the last plot in Display 5.20, we see that this is virtually sure to happen.

The *z*-score is

$$\frac{0.75 - 0.916}{\frac{1.11}{\sqrt{40}}} \approx -.9458$$

so the probability is .8279.

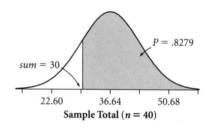

E27. The formula—*mean* ± 2 *SE*—gives an interval that contains approximately the middle 95% of values in a distribution that is approximately normal. For the sample total, this interval would be $n\mu \pm 2\sigma\sqrt{n}$.

a. $25(0.916) \pm 2(1.11)\sqrt{25}$ or (11.8, 34.0)
b. $100(0.916) \pm 2(1.11)\sqrt{100}$ or (69.4, 113.8)
c. $1000(0.916) \pm 2(1.11)\sqrt{1000}$ or (845.8, 986.2)
d. $4000(0.916) \pm 2(1.11)\sqrt{4000}$ or (3523.6, 3804.4)

Students should see from this exercise that the intervals get *wider* as the sample size increases. That is, the sample total tends to be *more* variable as the sample size increases.

E28. *Note:* E28 is difficult and contains optional material.

We will do this problem using the sampling distribution of the sample mean, which has a mean of 0.916 and a standard error $1.11/\sqrt{n}$.

The point that cuts off the lower 0.025 (or 2.5%) on the normal distribution is about 2 standard deviations below the mean. If the total number of children falls below 1000, then the mean number of children per family falls below $1000/n$. Therefore, we must choose the sample size, n, so that the point $1000/n$ lies 2 standard deviations below 0.916, or

$$\frac{1000}{n} \leq 0.916 - 2 \cdot \frac{1.11}{\sqrt{n}}$$

After multiplying both sides by n, we need to solve the equation

$$0 = 0.916n - 2.22\sqrt{n} - 1000$$

This equation is quadratic in form. It can be solved for $\sqrt{n}$ by using the quadratic formula and then squaring the positive solution to get n. Alternatively, the solution can be estimated by plotting the equation on a graphing calculator. Because we only need the nearest integer solution, either method works well. The solution is about $n = 1175$.

5.4 Sampling Distribution of the Sample Proportion

Objectives

- to learn the characteristics of the sampling distribution of the sample proportion: shape, mean, and standard error
- to use the sampling distribution to find the probability that a sample proportion from a random sample will fall in a given interval
- to learn the characteristics of the sampling distribution of the number of successes: shape, mean, and standard error
- to use the sampling distribution for the number of successes to find the probability that the number of successes in a random sample will fall in a given interval
- to use the rule that the sampling distribution will be approximately normal when both np and $np(1 - p)$ are both at least 10

In this section, students essentially will duplicate what they learned in Section 5.3, only this time for proportions. The reason that the two sections are so similar is because proportions are a special kind of mean. For example, suppose you take a sample of 10 drivers and ask whether they used a seat belt the last time they drove a car. You can code each response as a 0 (no) or as a 1 (yes). So you might get 0, 1, 1, 1, 0, 0, 1, 0, 1, 1 in your sample. The sample proportion is 6/10, exactly the same as the sample mean:

$$\bar{x} = \frac{0 + 1 + 1 + 1 + 0 + 0 + 1 + 0 + 1 + 1}{10} = 0.6$$

Consequently, all the formulas in this section are special cases of those that the students learned in Section 5.3.

Important Terms and Concepts

- sampling distribution of a sample proportion
- sampling distribution of the number of successes in a sample
- the sample proportion as a type of mean

Lesson Planning

Class Time

Three to four days

Materials

For Activity 5.3, a table of random digits or a bag of beads, sampling paddle, or any other mechanical method of taking random samples from a population with $p = .6$

Suggested Assignments

Classwork		
Essential	**Recommended**	**Optional**
Activity 5.3	D27	
D21–D26		
P13–P16		

Homework		
Essential	**Recommended**	**Optional**
E29, E31	E30, E32, E34	E33

Lesson Notes: Sampling Distribution for $p = .6$

Statistical Inference

Some of the problems and exercises in this section (for example, D21 and P13) continue to develop the idea of statistical inference.

If a sample proportion falls in the tail of the sampling distribution, something that appears to be very unusual has happened. At this stage, students should understand there are three possible explanations for such a result:

- The sample may not have been selected randomly from the given population, but is special in some way.

- The population percentage given in the problem may be wrong.

- Everything was done properly and the population figure is correct, but the result from the sample is one that would occur very rarely.

Activity 5.3: Buckle Up!

In Activity 5.3, we suggest that you begin taking samples by using a mechanical method, such as drawing from a box of beads of two colors. Fill a box with beads of two different colors, say blue and yellow, such that exactly 60% of the beads are one color (blue) and 40% are the other color (yellow). Then each blue bead will represent a "success" if

selected and each yellow bead will represent a "failure." Have the student pick out 1 bead and record whether it's a success (blue) or failure (yellow), then replace the bead, stir the beads, and then repeat the process 9 more times to get a sample of size 10. The sample proportion will then be as shown here.

$$\hat{p} = \frac{number\ of\ successes}{total\ picked}$$
$$= \frac{number\ of\ blue\ beads\ in\ sample}{10}$$

Some students must actually see the sampling done a few times to catch on to the idea of what is considered a success or failure before they are able to move to tables of random digits on the calculator.

On a TI-83, enter randBin(10,.6,100)→L1 to generate 100 random samples, each of size 10 from a population with 60% successes; count the number of successes in each sample, and store the 100 counts into L1. Then enter L1/10→L1 to divide all of the counts by 10 and convert them to proportions. Now press STAT CALC 1:1-VAR STATS to find the mean and standard error, given by $\bar{x}$ and s_x respectively.

For this activity, you again have to make the difficult decision about how much to use the calculator.

If you are certain that your students understand the process of sampling, have them take a couple of samples by hand, and then let them use the calculator. If your students are still having difficulty setting up a simulation, do not use this command.

If you have your students use a random digit table, then have each student start his or her simulation with a different line of the table. Otherwise, the students will get identical samples.

1. Look at 10 random digits, one by one. Let 1–6 represent a "success" and 7–0 represent a "failure." (Other assignments are possible as long as 60% of the digits represent a success.) To select 10 digits at random from 0 through 9 using a TI-83, enter randInt(0,9,10).

2. For example, if the random digits are 3, 3, 6, 4, 1, 0, 2, 1, 9, and 7, there would be 7 successes and 3 failures.

3–4. A dot plot of the sample proportions from 100 random samples of size 10 appears here.

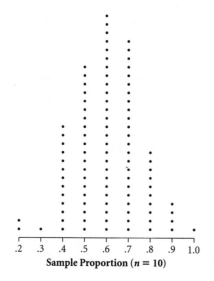

Sample Proportion ($n = 10$)

5. Answers will vary, but the mean should be close to .6 and the standard error close to .155. For the dot plot in step 4, the mean is .6 and the standard error is .152.

6. Sample dot plots appear next. Each dot plot shows 100 repetitions of sample proportions generated with $p = .6$. The sample sizes are 20 and 40, respectively. Each should have a mean close to .6. The one for the sample of size 20 should have a standard error close to .11, and the one for the sample of size 40 should have a standard error close to .08. (The standard error is cut in half with a quadrupling of the sample size.)

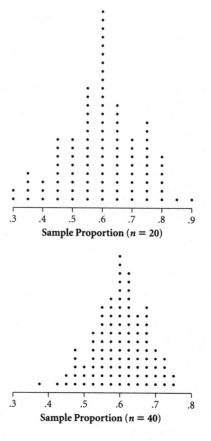

Sample Proportion ($n = 20$)

Sample Proportion ($n = 40$)

Discussion

D21. These answers must be estimated from the histograms in Display 5.27, and as a result the answers may vary slightly.

a. About 60% of 40 or 24 drivers. (Although it has not yet been defined, using the term "expect" in statistics is equivalent to asking for the mean.)

b. This is a borderline call. From the histogram, a sample proportion of .75 is just inside the interval of reasonably likely outcomes.

c. Yes, a sample proportion of .25 or less is very unlikely to occur.

d. Size 10. With larger sample sizes, the proportions tend to cluster closer to .6.

D22. The sampling distribution of the sample proportion for samples of size 10 is mound-shaped with a skew to the left. The center is close to .6, and the spread is large, with reasonably likely sample proportions ranging from about .3 to .9.

The sampling distribution of the sample proportion for samples of size 20 is mound-shaped with only a very slight skew to the left. The center is close to .6, and the spread is smaller, with reasonably likely sample proportions ranging from about .4 to .8.

The sampling distribution of the sample proportion for samples of size 40 is approximately normally distributed with no visible skewness. The center is close to .6, and the spread is small, with reasonably likely sample proportions ranging from about .45 to .75.

D23. a. In Display 5.28 the means of all the sampling distributions are very close to $p = .8$ (as they should be). The standard error decreases as the sample size increases. The shape becomes more approximately normal as the sample size increases.

b. Although the distributions are centered in different places, the characteristics are exactly the same. As the sample size increases, the mean stays the same, the standard error decreases, and the shape becomes more normal-like.

D24. Yes. The rules for sample means hold here. Compare these rules with the statement in D23, part b.

Lesson Notes: Center and Spread for Sample Proportions

Deriving the Formulas

You can derive the formulas for the mean and standard error symbolically using the definitions for the mean and standard error of a probability distribution:

$$\mu = \sum x \cdot P(x)$$
$$= 0(1 - p) + 1(p)$$
$$= p$$

$$\sigma = \sqrt{\sum (x - \mu)^2 \cdot P(x)}$$
$$= \sqrt{(0 - p)^2 \cdot (1 - p) + (1 - p)^2 \cdot p}$$
$$= \sqrt{(p)^2 \cdot (1 - p) + (1 - p)^2 \cdot p}$$
$$= \sqrt{(p)(1 - p)(p + 1 - p)}$$
$$= \sqrt{p(1 - p)}$$

The "np and $n(1 - p)$ at Least 10" Guideline

If the conditions are met that np and $n(1 - p)$ are at least 10, the sampling distribution of $\hat{p}$ is approximately normal. This means that you may approximate probabilities using the z-table. For example, approximately 95% of all values of $\hat{p}$ will be within two standard errors or $2(\sigma/\sqrt{n})$ of p.

Unfortunately, we were not able to give any such simple rule in Section 5.3 for the sampling distribution of the mean. Whether the sampling distribution of the mean is approximately normal is a function of the shape of the original population.

Discussion

D25. For $p = .6$ and sample sizes of 10, 20, and 40, the theoretical means would all be .6. The formula

$$\sigma_{\hat{p}} = \sqrt{\frac{p(1 - p)}{n}} = \sqrt{\frac{.6(1 - .6)}{n}}$$

yields .1549, .1095, and .0775 as the respective theoretical standard errors.

D26. The dot plot for a sample size of 80 definitely looks approximately normal—there is no discernable skew. This agrees with the guideline. For $p = .8$ and $n = 80$, both $np = 64$ and $n(1 - p) = 16$ are 10 or greater.

The dot plots for sample sizes of 10 and 20 definitely look skewed, and $n(1 - p)$ is less than 10 in both cases. For $n = 10$, $n(1 - p) = 2$, and for $n = 20$, $n(1 - p) = 4$.

The situation for $n = 40$ is borderline. The value of $n(1 - p)$ is 8, just a bit less than 10.

Note: In general, the shape of the sampling distribution of a sample proportion tends toward the shape of a normal curve as the sample size increases. However, the sampling distribution tends to be skewed toward the larger values for p less than .5, and skewed toward the smaller values for p greater than .5. The farther p is from .5, the larger the sample size must be to remove skewness.

Some students may be interested to learn that for a fixed sample size, n, the value of $\sigma_{\hat{p}}$ increases as p approaches .5. Thus, $\sigma_{\hat{p}}$ is at its maximum when $p = .5$. To prove this, note that the graph of $y = p(1 - p)$ is a parabola that opens down and has vertex at $p = .5$.

Practice

P13. **a.** This sampling distribution can be considered approximately normal because both $np = 53$ and $n(1 - p) = 47$ are 10 or greater. The sampling distribution has a mean of .53 and a standard error of

$$\sigma_{\hat{p}} = \sqrt{\frac{p(1 - p)}{n}} = \sqrt{\frac{.53(1 - .53)}{100}} \approx .05$$

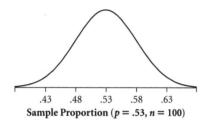

Sample Proportion ($p = .53$, $n = 100$)

b. No. As you can see from the sampling distribution in part a, the probability of getting 9 or fewer women just by chance is almost 0. That there are so few women in the U.S. Senate cannot reasonably be attributed to chance alone, and so we should look for other explanations (for example, that fewer women go into politics, that women are not able to raise as much money for their campaigns, or that voters are reluctant to elect a woman senator).

Lesson Notes: Finding Probabilities for Proportions

Practice

P14. **a.** The sampling distribution is approximately normal because both $np = 121.8$ and $n(1 - p) = 313.2$ are 10 or greater. With $p = .28$ and $n = 435$, the sampling distribution for the sample proportion has a mean of .28 and a standard error of .02. A sample proportion of .51 is more than 10 standard deviations above the mean of the sampling distribution, and therefore it would be very unusual to see such a result. The probability is close to 0.

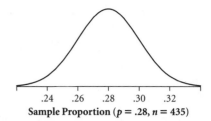

Sample Proportion ($p = .28$, $n = 435$)

b. Yes, as you saw in part a, it is almost impossible for this many representatives to be Republican if they were chosen at random from the general population. Possible reasons include the fact that people do not always vote for their party's candidate. In addition, the population that year identified themselves as 28% Republican, 34% Democrat, and 38% independent, yet there was only one independent in the House. So one possible explanation is that independents tend to vote Republican.

P15. Because the distributions are approximately normal, in each case about 95% of the potential values of the sample proportion will fall within approximately two standard errors of the mean. This interval is

$$p \pm 2\sqrt{\frac{p(1 - p)}{n}} = .6 \pm 2\sqrt{\frac{.6(1 - .6)}{n}}$$

The intervals produced for the various sample sizes are shown here.

a. $n = 40$: $.6 \pm .155$ or $(.445, .755)$

b. $n = 100$: $.6 \pm .098$ or $(.502, .698)$

c. $n = 400$: $.6 \pm .049$ or $(.551, .649)$

Note again that the sample size must be increased fourfold in order to cut the width of the interval in half.

Lesson Notes: Finding Probabilities for the Number of Successes

Students may occasionally use the sample proportion $\hat{p}$ in the formula for the standard error rather than the population proportion p. It is important that they understand that the formula for the standard error of the sampling distribution of p is a function of p. Later, when p is unknown, they will have to estimate p in this formula using $\hat{p}$. But in this chapter, p is always known and so can be used in the formula.

Discussion

D27. As in Section 5.3, to convert formulas from those for the mean to those for the sum, multiply by the sample size n as shown at bottom of the page.

Practice

P16. You can use the normal approximation for both methods because both $np = 320$ and $n(1 - p) = 180$ are 10 or greater.

Using the sample proportion: The mean and standard error of the sampling distribution for the sample proportion are

$$\mu_{\hat{p}} = .64$$

$$\sigma_{\hat{p}} = \sqrt{\frac{.64(1 - .64)}{500}} \approx .02147$$

The z-score for a sample proportion of

$$\frac{316}{500} = .632 \text{ is } z = \frac{.632 - .64}{.02147} \approx -.373$$

The probability of getting a sample proportion of .632 or more who go part time is about .645.

Using the sample total: The mean and standard error of the sampling distribution for the sample total are

$$\mu_{sum} = 500(.64) = 320$$

$$\sigma_{sum} = \sqrt{500(.64)(1 - .64)} \approx 10.733$$

The z-score for 316 successes is, as before,

$$z = \frac{316 - 320}{10.733} \approx -.373$$

The probability of getting 316 or more who go part time is, as with the other method, about .645.

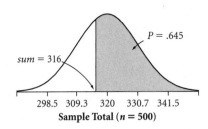
sum = 316 $P = .645$

298.5   309.3   320   330.7   341.5
Sample Total ($n = 500$)

Exercises

E29. The sampling distributions for the sample proportion and the sample total can be considered approximately normal because both $np = 920$ and $n(1 - p) = 80$ are 10 or greater.

a. This distribution is approximately normal with mean and standard error

$$\mu_{\hat{p}} = .92$$

$$\sigma_{\hat{p}} = \sqrt{\frac{.92(1 - .92)}{1000}} \approx .00858$$

The sketch, with scale on the x-axis, is shown in part c.

b. This distribution is approximately normal with mean and standard error

$$\mu_{sum} = 1000(.92) = 920$$

$$\sigma_{sum} = \sqrt{1000(.92)(1 - .92)} \approx 8.58$$

The sketch is shown in part d.

c. $z = \dfrac{.9 - .92}{\sqrt{\dfrac{.92(1 - .92)}{1000}}} \approx -2.33$

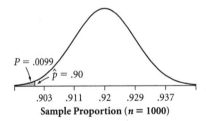
$P = .0099$ $\hat{p} = .90$

.903   .911   .92   .929   .937
Sample Proportion ($n = 1000$)

The probability is about .0099.

$$\mu_{sum} = n\mu_{\hat{p}} = np$$

$$\sigma_{sum} = n\sigma_{\hat{p}} = n\sqrt{\frac{p(1 - p)}{n}} = \sqrt{\frac{n^2 p(1 - p)}{n}} = \sqrt{np(1 - p)}$$

d. $z = \dfrac{925 - 920}{\sqrt{1000(.92)(1 - .92)}} \approx .5828$

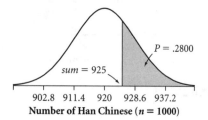

Number of Han Chinese ($n = 1000$)

The probability is about .2800.

e. Rare events would be the totals that are outside the interval $920 \pm 2(8.58)$; that is, larger than 937.16 or smaller than 902.84. Rare events would be the proportions that are outside the interval $.92 \pm 2(.00858)$; that is, larger than .937 or smaller than .903.

E30. For each part of this problem, the sampling distribution for the sample total can be considered approximately normal because both $np = 15{,}640$ and $n(1 - p) = 18{,}360$ are 10 or greater.

a. The sampling distribution is approximately normal with mean and standard error

$$\mu_{sum} = 136(.46) = 62.56$$

$$\sigma_{sum} = \sqrt{136(.46)(1 - .46)} \approx 5.812$$

The sketch is shown in part b.

b. The z-score for 72 is

$$z = \dfrac{72 - 62.56}{5.812} \approx 1.624$$

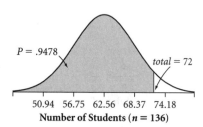

Number of Students ($n = 136$)

The probability of getting 72 or fewer who need remediation is about .9478.

c. This distribution is approximately normal with mean and standard error

$$\mu_{\hat{p}} = .46$$

$$\sigma_{\hat{p}} = \sqrt{\dfrac{.46(1 - .46)}{2075}} \approx .0109$$

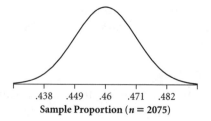

Sample Proportion ($n = 2075$)

d. The z-score for a sample proportion of .63 is

$$z = \dfrac{.63 - .46}{\sqrt{.46(.54)/2075}} \approx 15.5375$$

The probability is very close to 0.

e. The z-score for a sample proportion of .57 is

$$z = \dfrac{.57 - .46}{\sqrt{\dfrac{.46(.54)}{2658}}} \approx 11.38$$

The probability of getting this large of a percentage by chance alone is very close to 0. You should conclude that this group is special in some way. (In fact, many of the students come from urban high schools, and a large percentage do not speak English at home.)

E31. a. .5

b. The sampling distribution can be considered approximately normal because both $np = 25$ and $n(1 - p) = 25$ are 10 or greater. The sampling distribution has mean and standard error

$$\mu_{\hat{p}} = .5$$

$$\sigma_{\hat{p}} = \sqrt{\dfrac{.5(1 - .5)}{50}} \approx .0707$$

The z-score for a sample proportion of .2 is

$$z = \dfrac{.2 - .5}{.0707} \approx -4.2433$$

The probability is .000011.

c. These results are not at all what we would expect from a random sample of 50 people. This group is special in that they are all old enough to have a job. Children are included in computing the 33.1 median age, but they do not hold jobs. Thus, we would expect the median age of job holders to be greater than the median age of all people in the United States, as they are at Westvaco.

E32. Getting 15 or fewer with bad sectors is the same thing as getting 85 or more without. The sampling distribution for the number of disks that have no bad sectors can be considered approximately normal because both $np = 80$ and $n(1 - p) = 20$ are 10 or greater. The sampling distribution has mean and standard error

$$\mu_{sum} = 100(.8) = 80$$

$$\sigma_{sum} = \sqrt{100(.8)(1 - .8)} = 4$$

The z-score for 85 with no bad sectors is

$$z = \frac{85 - 80}{4} = 1.25$$

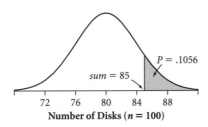

The probability of getting 85 or more with no bad sectors is about .1056.

The assumption that underlies this answer is that the 100 sampled disks are a random sample from a population in which 80% of the disks have no bad sectors.

E33. The first three histograms shown next are simulated sampling distributions for $p = .1$, and the last three are for $p = .98$. The sample sizes for each proportion are 50, 100, and 500.

For $p = .1$, the shape is skewed toward the higher values for $n = 50$ but is approximately normal when $n = 100$ and $n = 500$. For $p = .98$, the shape is highly skewed for $n = 50$ and remains highly skewed for $n = 100$. It becomes approximately normal at $n = 500$. The rule that np and $n(1 - p)$ must both be at least 10 seems to work quite well.

The important message: Situations where the normal model works well as an approximation depend upon both n and p. If p is close to 0 or 1, the sample size must be quite large in order to produce approximately normal sampling distributions for sample proportions.

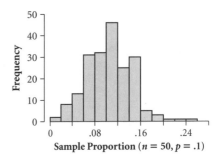

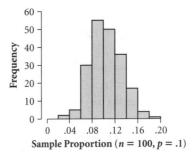

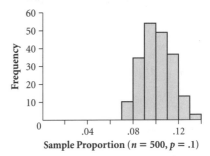

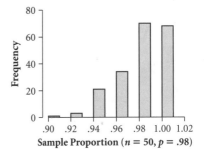

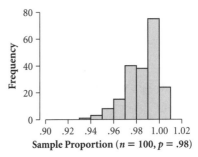

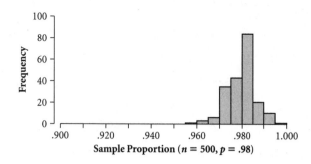

Sample Proportion ($n = 500, p = .98$)

E34. **a.** The means of the sampling distributions definitely depend upon p, as the first three center close to $p = .2$ and the second three center close to $p = .4$. The sampling distributions have centers close to p regardless of the sample size; the centers do not depend upon the sample size.

b. The spreads of the sampling distributions decrease as n increases for both values of p.

The spreads do depend upon the value of p, however. For each sample size, the spread for $p = .4$ has a larger standard error than the one for $p = .2$.

c. For $p = .2$, the shape is quite skewed for $n = 5$ and some slight skewness remains at $n = 25$. For $n = 100$, the shape is basically symmetric. For $p = .4$, the shape shows a slight skewness at $n = 5$ but is fairly symmetric at $n = 25$ and beyond. The farther p is from .5, the more skewness in the distribution of the sample proportion.

d. The rule does not work well for samples of size 5 for either value of p but works well for samples of size 25 or more for both values of p.

5.5 Sampling Distribution of the Sum and Difference

Objectives

- to learn the characteristics of the sampling distribution of the sum of two sample means: shape, mean, and standard error
- to use the sampling distribution to find the probability that the sum of the means of two independent random samples will fall in a given interval
- to learn the characteristics of the sampling distribution of the difference of two sample means: shape, mean, and standard error
- to use the sampling distribution to find the probability that the difference of the means of two independent random samples will fall in a given interval

In this section, students will construct simulated sampling distributions of a sum and a difference, and from them they will learn the formulas for the mean and standard error of these distributions. If two values are selected at random, one from each of two possibly different populations, and then added, the sampling distribution of the sum has mean and standard error

$$\mu_{sum} = \mu_1 + \mu_2$$

$$\sigma^2_{sum} = \sigma^2_1 + \sigma^2_2 \text{ (for independently selected values)}$$

(If the two values are subtracted, the variance is the same as the variance for the sum, but the terms are subtracted in the formula for the mean. This is because a difference can be written as a sum: $a - b = a + (-b)$.)

Students will see in E39 that these formulas generalize to samples of size n taken from n possibly different populations, so the mean and standard error for the sum are

$$\mu_{sum} = \mu_1 + \mu_2 + \cdots + \mu_n$$

$$\sigma^2_{sum} = \sigma^2_1 + \sigma^2_2 + \cdots + \sigma^2_n \text{ (for } n \text{ independently selected values)}$$

The formulas in Section 5.3, $\mu_{sum} = n\mu$ and $\sigma_{sum} = \sqrt{n} \cdot \sigma$, are the special case when all n populations are the same and therefore have the same mean and standard deviation.

Important Terms and Concepts

- sampling distribution of a sum
- sampling distribution of a difference

Class Time

Three days

Materials

For Activity 5.4, one die for each student

Suggested Assignments

Classwork

Essential	Recommended	Optional
D30	Activity 5.4	
P17–P19	D28, D29, D31	

Homework

Essential	Recommended	Optional
E35, E36, E38–E41	E37	E42, E43

Lesson Notes: The Sum and Difference of Two Dice

Activity 5.4: The Sum and Difference of Two Rolls of a Die

This activity is highly recommended, but not essential. For this activity, each student will need a regular die.

1. Answers will vary. Both distributions will look approximately triangular. Many students will understand that the mean of the sum should be $3.5 + 3.5 = 7$, and the mean of the difference will be $3.5 - 3.5 = 0$. The fact that the spreads are equal will be a surprise to almost all students.

2–3. The following dot plot shows the results of 500 simulated sums $x_1 + x_2$ and 500 simulated differences $x_1 - x_2$. The shape of both distributions is triangular, whereas the shape of the population of outcomes is rectangular.

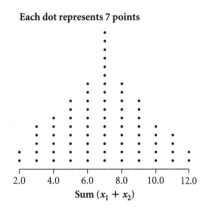

Each dot represents 7 points

Sum ($x_1 + x_2$)

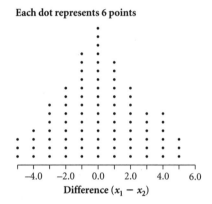

Each dot represents 6 points

Difference ($x_1 - x_2$)

	N	MEAN	MEDIAN	STDEV
X1+X2	500	6.968	7.000	2.297
X1-X2	500	0.062	0.0	2.428

The Minitab procedure that made the first plot is as follows:

a. Choose **Integer** from the Calc I Random Data menu. In the Integer Distribution dialog box, enter 500 into **Generate ___ rows of data**, C1 into **Store in column(s):**, 1 into **Minimum value:**, and 6 into **Maximum value:**. Click OK.

b. Repeat part a except enter C2 into **Store in column(s):**.

c. Choose **Calculator** from the Calc menu. In the Calculator dialog box, enter C3 into **Store result in variable:** and C1 + C2 into **Expression:**. Click OK. (*Note:* In older versions of Minitab, you may need to choose **Mathematical Expressions** from the Calc menu.)

d. Choose **Dotplot** from the Graph I Character Graphs menu. In the Dotplot dialog box, enter C3 into **Variables:**. Click OK.

e. Choose **Display Descriptive Statistics** from the Stat I Basic Statistics menu. In the Display Descriptive Statistics dialog box, enter C3 into **Variables:**. Click OK. (*Note:* In older versions of Minitab, you may need to choose **Descriptive Statistics** from the Stat I Basic Statistics menu.)

If command language is enabled, the Session window output will be

```
MTB > Random 500 C1;
SUBC> Integer 1 6.
MTB > Random 500 C2;
SUBC> Integer 1 6.
MTB > Let C3=C1+C2
MTB > DotPlot C3.
MTB > Describe C3.
```

4. The mean of the simulated sampling distribution of the sum should be close to 7. This is equal to $\mu_1 + \mu_2 = \mu + \mu = 3.5 + 3.5$, where μ is the mean of the distribution of a single roll. The mean of the simulated sampling distribution of the differences should be close to 0. This is equal to $\mu_1 + \mu_2 = \mu - \mu = 3.5 - 3.5$.

5. Both the variance of the simulated sampling distribution of the sum and of the difference should be close to 5.8. These are equal to $\sigma^2 + \sigma^2 = 2.917 + 2.917$, where σ^2 is the variance of the distribution of a single roll.

Note: The standard deviation of the differences is larger than the standard deviation of an individual roll, but the standard deviations do not add. It is the variances that add: The variance of a difference between two independent random variables is the sum of the variances of the component parts.

Discussion

D28. Answers will vary according to the simulation. The results from the simulation above—for 500 rolls—are very close. From the formulas, the mean of the sampling distribution of the sum is 7. The simulated sampling distribution has a mean that is close, 6.968. From the formula, the standard deviation is $\sqrt{2 \cdot 2.917} = \sqrt{5.834} \approx 2.415$, and from the simulation it is 2.297. Similarly, from the formulas, the mean and standard deviation for the sampling distribution of the difference are 0 and 2.415. These are close

to those from the simulated sampling distribution, 0.062 and 2.428.

D29. Consider two variables, each ranging between 0 and 10. Then the sum of two of these values can range from 0 to 20; likewise, the differences can range from -10 to $+10$. Sums and differences tend to have more variability than either of their component parts.

Practice

P17.

Difference	Probability
−5	1/36
−4	2/36
−3	3/36
−2	4/36
−1	5/36
0	6/36
1	5/36
2	4/36
3	3/36
4	2/36
5	1/36

a. Triangular.
b. The mean is 0, and the variance is approximately 5.834.
c. $\mu - \mu = 3.5 - 3.5 = 0$
$\sigma^2 + \sigma^2 = 2.917 + 2.917 \approx 5.834$

Lesson Notes: A Regular Die and a Tetrahedral Die

Practice

P18. a.

Difference	Probability
−3	1/24
−2	2/24
−1	3/24
0	4/24
1	4/24
2	4/24
3	3/24
4	2/24
5	1/24

b. Using the formula
$$\mu = \Sigma x \cdot P(x)$$
we find this distribution has mean $\mu = 1$. (It is also apparent by symmetry that the mean is 1.) The mean of the distribution of the outcomes of the six-sided die is 3.5, and the mean of the distribution of the outcomes of the four-sided die is 2.5. Thus, the mean of the sampling distribution of the difference is equal to $\mu_1 - \mu_2 = 3.5 - 2.5 = 1$.

Using the formula
$$\sigma^2 = \Sigma(x - \mu)^2 \cdot P(x)$$
we find this distribution has variance $\sigma^2 = 4.167$. (Alternatively, because this distribution is the same as that in Display 5.37 except for a shift left of 5, the variance is the same as in that distribution.) The variance of the distribution of the outcomes of the six-sided die is 2.917, and the variance of the distribution of the outcomes of the four-sided die is 1.25. Thus, the variance of the sampling distribution of the difference is indeed equal to $2.917 + 1.25 = 4.167$.

Lesson Notes: Properties of the Sampling Distribution of the Sum and Difference

Discussion

D30. The first set of formulas can be used for two values taken at random and independently from any two distributions. The second set of formulas is both a generalization to the case when there are more than two values, and a restriction to the case where the populations must all be the same. The formulas in each pair are equivalent when $n = 2$ and the two populations from which the values are drawn are the same.

D31. **a.** This one is easy!

Difference	Probability
0	1

b. The mean is $\mu = 0(1) = 0$. The variance is $\sigma^2 = (0 - 0)^2(1) = 0$.

c. Yes: $\mu = 3.5 - 3.5 = 0$.

d. No: $0 \neq 2.917 + 2.917$. The two values are not independent.

Practice

P19. The cap is too loose if $d_c - d_b > 1.1$. From the example on pages 316–317 of the student text, the sampling distribution of the difference is approximately normal and has a mean of 1 and a standard error of 1.562. A difference of 1.1 has a z-score of
$$z = \frac{1.1 - 1}{1.562} \approx 0.064$$

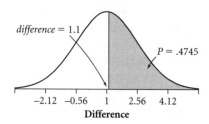

The probability that the cap is too loose is about .4745.

Exercises

E35. **a.** $\mu_{v+m} = \mu_v + \mu_m = 505 + 512 = 1017$
$$\sigma_{v+m} = \sqrt{\sigma_v^2 + \sigma_m^2} = \sqrt{111^2 + 112^2}$$
$$\approx 157.69$$

b. The sampling distribution of the sum will be approximately normal because both distributions are normal. The z-score is
$$z = \frac{800 - 1017}{157.69} \approx -1.376.$$

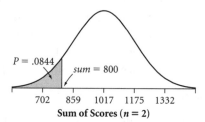

The probability is about .0844.

c. $1017 \pm 2(157.69)$, or between approximately 702 and 1332.

d. We need $v - m \geq 100$. The sampling distribution of the difference will be approximately normal because both distributions are normal. The mean and standard error of the sampling distribution of the difference are
$$\mu_{v-m} = \mu_v - \mu_m = 505 - 512 = -7$$
$$\sigma_{v-m} = \sqrt{\sigma_v^2 + \sigma_m^2} = \sqrt{111^2 + 112^2}$$
$$\approx 157.69$$

The *z*-score for a difference of 100 is

$$z = \frac{100 - (-7)}{157.69} \approx 0.679$$

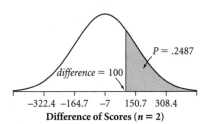

Difference of Scores (*n* = 2)

The probability is .2487.

Note: This does not imply that 24.9% of students have an SAT verbal score of at least 100 points higher than their SAT math score. See part e.

e. The mean of the distribution of the sum will still be 1017. The standard error is unpredictable because the two scores are certainly not independent. Students who score high on the verbal portion also tend to score high on the math portion. The shape is also unpredictable.

E36. a. 39.8 and 21.0; 39.6 and 10.6. (Note that the mean number of games won and lost would be equal if the teams only played each other, but they also play teams from the National League East.)

b. 79.4 and 1.84.

c. The mean number of games won, 39.8, plus the mean number of games lost, 39.6, is equal to the mean number of games played, 79.4. This makes sense and follows the rule that means add. However, the variance of the number of games won, 21.0, plus the variance of the number of games lost, 10.7, is not equal to the variance of the total number of games played, 1.84. This also follows the rule that you cannot expect variances to add unless the values are independent. The number won and the number lost are not at all independent because the more games won, the fewer lost. That makes intuitive sense because some teams won far more games than other teams, so there is a lot of variation in the numbers won and lost. However, each team played about the same total number of games, so there is little variation in the total.

E37. a. 12.8 and 4.56; 8 and 4.

b. 20.8 and 6.96.

c. The sum of the means 12.8 + 8 equals 20.8, as it should. But the sum of the variances 4.56 + 4 is not equal to 6.96, and we do not expect it to be because the morning and afternoon times were not selected independently when we computed 6.96.

E38. No. From Display 5.34 and the discussion on page 313 of the student text

$$\sigma_{sum} = \sqrt{5.834} \approx 2.415$$

whereas

$$\sigma_1 + \sigma_2 = \sqrt{2.917} + \sqrt{2.917} \approx 3.416$$

Note: If variances "add," then the square roots of variances cannot. This would be the same mistake as having $a^2 + b^2 = c^2$ imply that $a + b = c$.

E39. a. These are the formulas for the sum from Section 5.3. They were given again in D30.

b. $3(3.5) = 10.5; 3(2.917) = 8.751$

c. $7(3.5) = 24.5; 7(2.917) = 20.419$

d. The sampling distribution of the sum is approximately normal because we were told in E35 that the distribution of verbal scores is approximately normal. It has mean and variance

$$\mu_{sum} = n\mu = 20(505) = 10,100$$

$$\sigma^2_{sum} = n\sigma^2 = 20(111^2) = 246,420$$

The *z*-score for a total of 10,000 is

$$z = \frac{10,000 - 10,100}{\sqrt{246,420}} \approx -0.201$$

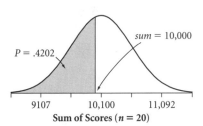

Sum of Scores (*n* = 20)

The probability is about .4202.

E40. The sampling distribution of the sum will be approximately normal with mean and variance

$$\mu_{sum} = n\mu = 50(3.11) = 155.5$$

$$\sigma^2_{sum} = n\sigma^2 = 50(0.43^2) = 9.245$$

Thus, the reasonably likely weights of a roll of 50 pennies are those that fall in the interval $155.5 \pm 2\sqrt{9.245}$, or 149.42 to 161.58 grams.

E41. **a.** Because the distribution of the weights is approximately normal, the sampling distribution of the sum of two (or any number of) weights will be approximately normal as well. The mean and standard error are

$$\mu_{sum} = 75.4 + 75.4 = 150.8$$

$$\sigma_{sum} = \sqrt{7.38^2 + 7.38^2} \approx 10.437$$

b. Using the results from part a, the z-score is -0.556 and the probability is .2892.

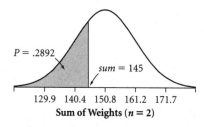
P = .2892
sum = 145

129.9 140.4 150.8 161.2 171.7
Sum of Weights ($n = 2$)

c. From E39, the mean and standard error of the sampling distribution are

$$\mu_{sum} = n\mu = 10(75.4) = 754$$

$$\sigma_{sum} = \sqrt{n\sigma^2} = \sqrt{10(7.38)^2} \approx 23.338$$

The z-score for a total of 750 is

$$z = \frac{750 - 754}{23.338} \approx -0.1714$$

The probability that the total weight is more than 750 kg is .5680.

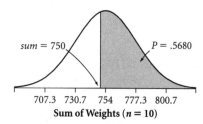
sum = 750
P = .5680

707.3 730.7 754 777.3 800.7
Sum of Weights ($n = 10$)

d. The first ram is more than 5 kg heavier than the second ram if $ram_1 - ram_2 > 5$. The sampling distribution of the difference $ram_1 - ram_2$ has mean $\mu_{1-2} = \mu_1 - \mu_2 = 75.4 - 75.4 = 0$.

The standard error is the same as that in part a, 10.437.

The z-score for a difference of 5 is

$$z = \frac{5 - 0}{10.437} \approx 0.4791$$

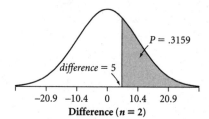
P = .3159
difference = 5

-20.9 -10.4 0 10.4 20.9
Difference ($n = 2$)

The probability that the difference is greater than 5 is about .3159.

E42. **a.** *Note: E42 contains optional material.*
The number of successes can be thought of as the sum of n values taken randomly from a population of 0's and 1's. From Section 5.4, page 304 of the student text, this population of 0's and 1's has mean $\mu = p$ and standard deviation

$$\sigma = \sqrt{p(1 - p)}$$

Then, from E39, the mean of the sampling distribution of the sum of the n values is $n\mu = np$.

Also, from E39, the variance of a sum is $n\sigma^2$ so the standard error of the sampling distribution of the sum of n values is

$$SE = \sqrt{n\sigma^2} = \sqrt{n} \cdot \sigma = \sqrt{n} \cdot \sqrt{p(1 - p)}$$
$$= \sqrt{np(1 - p)}$$

b. From E39, the standard error of the sampling distribution of the sum is $SE_{sum} = \sqrt{n\sigma^2}$.

To get the standard error of the sampling distribution of the mean of the n values, divide by n:

$$SE_{\bar{x}} = \frac{SE_{sum}}{n} = \frac{\sqrt{n\sigma^2}}{n} = \sqrt{\frac{n\sigma^2}{n^2}} = \sqrt{\frac{\sigma^2}{n}} = \frac{\sigma}{\sqrt{n}}$$

E43. Because the roll of a single die has mean 3.5 and standard deviation 1.708, the sampling distribution of the mean of two rolls will have mean 3.5 and standard error

$$\frac{\sigma}{\sqrt{n}} = \frac{1.708}{\sqrt{2}} \approx 1.208$$

Thus, the mean of the sampling distribution of the difference between your average and your partner's average is

$$\mu_{you-partner} = \mu_{you} - \mu_{partner} = 3.5 - 3.5 = 0$$

The standard error is

$$\sigma_{you-partner} = \sqrt{\sigma^2_{you} + \sigma^2_{partner}}$$
$$= \sqrt{1.208^2 + 1.208^2} \approx 1.708$$

The shape will still be basically triangular but rounding out a bit.

Review

Homework	
Essential	E44–E47, E50, E51, E57
Recommended	E48, E49, E54, E56, E58
Optional	E52, E53, E55

Review Exercises

E44. **a.** Assign each of the 32 cities a number from 01 to 32. Generate pairs of random digits. Go through the pairs until you get three distinct pairs between 01 and 32, ignoring all other pairs 33–99 and 00. Do not include the same city twice. Alternatively, to do this more efficiently, you could assign the first city the pairs 01, 02, 03, the second city 04, 05, 06, and so on. Record the API for each of the three cities and compute the mean. Repeat this process many times and construct a dot plot of the sample means. For example, suppose your students have numbered the cities from 01 to 32 and have chosen the sequence of random digits from line 46 of Table D, as shown below.

They would divide the digits into pairs. Ignoring 74, the first city would be 02 (Changchun). Ignoring 94, 39, 02 (as it has been used already), 77, 55, and 73, the second city would be 22 (Shenzhen). Ignoring 70, 97, and 79, the third city would be 01 (Beijing).

b. Because the sample size is less than 10% of the population size, it does not really matter that we sampled without replacement, and so we can use the following formulas for the mean and standard error:

$$\mu_{\bar{x}} = \mu = 140.9$$

$$\sigma_{\bar{x}} = \frac{\sigma}{\sqrt{n}} = \frac{119.4}{\sqrt{3}} \approx 68.94$$

(The formula for the mean holds with or without replacement. Although the formula for the standard error holds exactly when sampling is done with replacement, it is only approximately true when sampling is done without replacement. The larger N is compared to n, the better the approximation.)

c. No. This is a very small sample from a highly skewed population. The sampling distribution of the sample mean will be skewed right.

E45. **a.** Assign each of the 32 cities a number from 01 to 32. Generate pairs of random digits. Go through the pairs until you get three pairs between 01 and 32. Alternatively, to be more efficient, assign the first city the pairs 01, 02, 03, the second city 04, 05, 06, and so on. Check the API for each of the three cities and count the number of cities in your sample for which the API is 100 or less—this is your sample count. Repeat this process and construct a dot plot of the sample counts (or number of cities with good air quality in a sample of size 3).

b. Because 18 out of the 32 cities have "good" air quality, this is the same as sampling from a population with proportion of successes $p = 18/32 = .5625$. Because the sample size is less than 10% of the population size, it does not really matter if we sampled with or without replacement, and so we can use the formulas shown below for the mean and standard error.

Review, E44a

74029   43902   77557   32270   97790   17119   52527   58021

Review, E45b

$$\mu_{sum} = 3p = 3(18/32) = 1.6875$$

$$\sigma_{sum} = \sqrt{np(1 - p)} = \sqrt{3(.5625)(1 - .5625)} \approx .8592$$

c. No, both $np = 3(.5625) = 1.6875$ and $n(1 - p) = 3(1 - .5625) = 1.3125$ are less than 10.

E46. **a.** The shape can be considered approximately normal because both $np = 200(.68) = 136$ and $n(1 - p) = 200(1 - .68) = 64$ are 10 or greater. The mean and standard error are

$$\mu_{\hat{p}} = .68$$

$$\sigma_{\hat{p}} = \sqrt{\frac{.68(1 - .68)}{200}} \approx .0330$$

b. The z-score for $\hat{p} = .75$ is

$$z = \frac{.75 - .68}{.0330} \approx 2.122$$

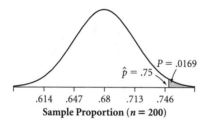

$P = .0169$
$\hat{p} = .75$

.614 .647 .68 .713 .746
Sample Proportion ($n = 200$)

The probability is about .0169.

c. Values less than $.68 - 2(.0330) = .614$, or larger than $.68 + 2(.0330) = .746$.

d. The mean and standard error of the sampling distribution of the sum are

$$\mu_{sum} = 200(.68) = 136$$

$$\sigma_{sum} = \sqrt{200(.68)(1 - .68)} \approx 6.597$$

The z-score for 130 people is

$$z = \frac{130 - 136}{6.597} \approx 0.9095$$

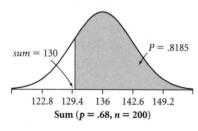

$sum = 130$
$P = .8185$

122.8 129.4 136 142.6 149.2
Sum ($p = .68$, $n = 200$)

The probability is about .8185.

Alternatively, this problem can be done using the mean and standard deviation in part a and with

$$\hat{p} = \frac{130}{200} = .65$$

E47. **a.** The distribution of the sum of the spine widths of 50 randomly selected books should be approximately normal because the population is only slightly skewed right. The mean and standard error of the sampling distribution of the sum are

$$\mu_{sum} = 50(4.7) = 235$$

$$\sigma_{sum} = \sqrt{50}(2.1) = 14.849$$

The books will fit on the shelf if the sum of their widths is less than 240 cm. The z-score for 240 is

$$z = \frac{240 - 235}{14.849} \approx 0.3367$$

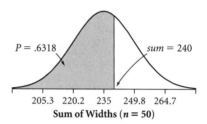

$P = .6318$
$sum = 240$

205.3 220.2 235 249.8 264.7
Sum of Widths ($n = 50$)

The probability is about .6318.

Alternatively, this problem can be done using the sampling distribution of the mean. The spine widths would have to average less than $\frac{240}{50} = 4.8$ cm.

b. No. These are not a random sample of books. If their reputation is deserved, philosophy books may be thicker than the average book, so fewer philosophy books are likely to fit on the shelf.

E48. The sampling distribution of the ages is approximately normal because the population is approximately normal. The mean and standard error of the sampling distribution of the mean age for samples of size 10 is

$$\mu_{\bar{x}} = \mu = 51.5$$

$$\sigma_{\bar{x}} = \frac{\sigma}{\sqrt{n}} = \frac{8.9}{\sqrt{10}} \approx 2.814$$

The z-score for a mean of 53 is

$$z = \frac{53 - 51.5}{2.814} \approx 0.533$$

The *z*-score for a mean of 50 is, by symmetry, -0.533.

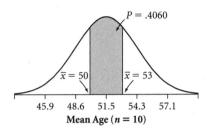

$P = .4060$

$\bar{x} = 50$ $\bar{x} = 53$

45.9   48.6   51.5   54.3   57.1

Mean Age ($n = 10$)

The probability is about $.7030 - .2970 \approx .4060$.

Alternatively, on a TI-83 enter normalcdf $(50,53,51.5,2.814)$ to get approximately .4060.

E49. **a.** There are $(12)(12) = 144$ possible outcomes. Fortunately, we do not have to list them because there are only three ways to get a sum of 3 or less: 1, 1; or 2, 1; or 1, 2. Thus the probability is $3/144$.

b. Each of the outcomes 1, 2, 3, 4, ..., 12 has a $\frac{1}{12}$ chance of occurring. By symmetry, the mean is 6.5. The standard deviation is 3.452.

c. The mean of the sampling distribution of the sum of two rolls of a 12-sided die is

$$\mu_{sum} = 2(6.5) = 13$$

and the standard error is

$$\sigma_{sum} = \sqrt{2 \cdot 3.452^2} = 4.882$$

E50. **a.** The shape is approximately normal because each of the two distributions is approximately normal. The mean and standard error of the sampling distribution of the difference are

$$\mu_{m-w} = \mu_m - \mu_w = 68 - 64 = 4$$

$$\sigma_{m-w} = \sqrt{\sigma_m^2 + \sigma_w^2} = \sqrt{2.7^2 + 2.5^2} \approx 3.680$$

b. The *z*-score for a difference of 2 is

$$z = \frac{2 - 4}{3.680} \approx -0.5435$$

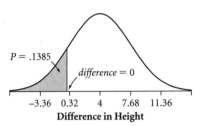

difference = 2 $P = .7066$

−3.36   0.32   4   7.68   11.36

Difference in Height

The probability is .7066.

c. She is taller than he is if the difference is negative (less than 0). The *z*-score for a difference of 0 is

$$z = \frac{0 - 4}{3.680} = -1.087$$

$P = .1385$ *difference* = 0

−3.36   0.32   4   7.68   11.36

Difference in Height

The probability is .1385.

E51. **a.** The best estimate of the number going straight on an average day—under the assumption that one-third go each direction—is

$$113,500(1/3) = 37,833.33$$

The sampling distribution of the sample total should be approximately normal with a mean of 37,833.33 and a standard error

$$\sqrt{113,500(1/3)(2/3)} \approx 158.815$$

b. The range of reasonably likely outcomes includes values within approximately two standard errors of the mean:

$$37,833.33 \pm 2(158.815)$$

In other words, the probability is .95 that between 37,516 and 38,151 vehicles will go straight through on an average day if it is true that a randomly selected vehicle has a $\frac{1}{3}$ chance of going straight through the interchange.

c. It is not a reasonably likely outcome to have an average of 63,800 vehicles go straight through the interchange under the assumption that vehicles are equally likely to go in each of the three directions. This assumption cannot be even approximately true.

E52. **a.** The students must generate five arrival times for Bus 1 paired with five arrival times for Bus 2, where the times are from a uniform distribution over the interval $[0, 10]$. This procedure can be done with a graphing calculator or computer. On the TI-83, enter 10rand and then repeatedly press ENTER. Place the values into two columns of five values each. Then find the absolute value of the difference between these times. We use the absolute difference because there is no restriction on the order in which the buses arrive—we are just looking at the interarrival times. The statistic of interest is the mean of these five differences.

b. Answers will vary. The majority of students should get an average difference between 2.5 and 4. Reasonably likely values for the average difference range between approximately 1.25 and 5.5. No one should get a negative number.

c. The largest mean is about 6.1 minutes. Sets of arrival times will vary. One possible set of pairs, the ones we got in the simulation, is the following:

Bus 1 Arrival Time	Bus 2 Arrival Time	Absolute Difference
8.50189	4.43855	4.06334
7.81519	0.57796	7.23723
7.01766	8.97818	1.96052
0.56625	9.02486	8.45861
8.79205	0.06360	8.72845

d. No. Of the 100 repetitions in the simulation, none of the average differences are 7 or larger. Perhaps the sample was not random. Perhaps there is something in the scheduling that prevents the two buses from arriving close to the same time.

E53. a. *Note:* E53 is similar to E43.

Select two integers at random from 0 through 9 and compute their mean. Repeat this. Subtract the second mean from the first. Students should do this three times.

b. Because the distribution of the results of a single selection from the population {0, 1, 2, 3, 4, 5, 6, 7, 8, 9} has a mean of 4.5 and a standard deviation of 2.87, the sampling distribution of the mean of two selections will have a mean of 4.5 and standard error

$$\frac{\sigma}{\sqrt{n}} = \frac{2.87}{\sqrt{2}} \approx 2.03$$

Then, the mean of the sampling distribution of the difference between the two players' averages is $\mu_{you-opponent} = \mu_{you} - \mu_{opponent} = 4.5 - 4.5 = 0$.

The standard error is

$$\sigma_{you-opponent} = \sqrt{\sigma_{you}^2 + \sigma_{opponent}^2}$$
$$= \sqrt{2.03^2 + 2.03^2}$$
$$\approx 2.87$$

The shape will still be basically triangular, but rounding out slightly.

E54. a. This problem can be done using either the sampling distribution of the mean weight or the sampling distribution of the total weight. We will use the mean weight. The sampling distribution for the mean weight of n people has a mean of 150 and standard error $\sigma_{\bar{x}} = 20/\sqrt{n}$.

If you choose $n = 14$: The mean weight must be less than $\frac{2000}{14} \approx 142.86$. This is 1.34 standard errors below the expected mean weight of 150. Thus, it will be exceeded about 91% of the time. The elevator is almost sure to be overloaded.

If you choose $n = 13$: The mean weight must be less than $\frac{2000}{13} \approx 153.85$. This is 0.694 standard errors above the expected mean weight of 150. Thus, the elevator will be overloaded about 24% of the time.

If you choose $n = 12$: The mean weight must be less than $\frac{2000}{12} \approx 166.67$. This is 2.89 standard errors above the expected mean weight of 150, and the elevator should be overloaded about 0.19% of the time.

It appears that $n = 12$ or less would be a good choice for the maximum occupancy if the consequences could be severe with an overloaded elevator.

This reasoning assumes that the sample of people who get on the elevator are selected randomly from the population. If you expect for some reason that the sample of people who get on the elevator may not be random, then these results will not apply. For example, if there is a weight loss clinic for men on the upper floor and large groups of men tend to leave together after an exercise class, the "sample" of people would not be random and the elevator would be overloaded every time they left.

b. These are almost the same numbers that we got in part a. It's somewhat surprising that their conclusion is this close to ours as their estimates probably were made using different data and different assumptions.

For example, Mitsubishi uses an average weight of 65 kg (about 143 pounds) per person for its elevators. See http://www.otis.com and http://mitsubishi-elevator.com.

E55. **a.** $n = 10$: $.80 \pm 2(.1265)$ or $[.55, 1.05]$ contains $\frac{30 \cdot 7}{33 \cdot 7} = .909$ of the values.

$n = 20$: $.80 \pm 2(.0894)$ or $[.62, .98]$ contains $\frac{41 \cdot 5}{45 \cdot 5} \approx .911$ of the values.

$n = 40$: $80 \pm 2(.0632)$ or $[.67, .93]$ contains $\frac{67 \cdot 3}{72 \cdot 3} \approx .931$ of the values.

$n = 80$: $.80 \pm 2(.0447)$ or $[.71, .89]$ contains $\frac{68 \cdot 3}{72 \cdot 3} \approx .944$ of the values.

Note: The number of values inside these intervals is difficult to count from the graph, but a close approximation is all that is needed.

b. About 95% of the values should lie within approximately 2 standard deviations of the mean for approximately normal distributions. All four of the estimates of the probability of a sample proportion being within two standard deviations of p are less than .95. For the larger sample sizes, the distribution is less skewed and the estimates are closer to .95.

E56 **a.** The results of Kelly's experiment were

```
Long days:    6.625  10.375   9.9     8.8
Short days:  12.500  11.625  18.275  13.225
```

The difference d is $d = \bar{x}_s - \bar{x}_l = 13.90625 - 8.925 = 4.98125$.

b. Four of the values from the eight in part a above should be selected at random without replacement. Then compute the mean of the four selected values and the mean of the other four values. The difference is the value of d. At least 100 values of d should be computed, if possible. Results from a simulation of 200 trials appear next. (If your students do not have access to the technology needed to do such a simulation, you can have them describe how to do it and give them a photocopy of the blackline master of the histogram at the end of this section.)

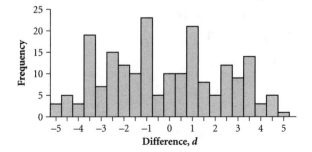

c. No. In 200 trials, a value of d as large as Kelly's (4.98) happened only once. We conclude that her large difference in mean enzyme level was probably not due to chance, but because the length of day does make a difference.

Note that the probability of getting a difference as large as Kelly's can be computed exactly. There are $_8C_4 = 70$ ways to choose 4 hamsters from 8. Kelly got the largest possible difference. So the probability of getting a difference as large or larger than the one Kelly got is $\frac{1}{70}$.

E57. **a.** The shape becomes more approximately normal, the mean stays fixed at the population mean, and the standard error decreases with (or is proportional to) the reciprocal of the square root of n.

b. The shape becomes more approximately normal, the mean increases with (or is proportional to) n, and the standard error increases with (or is proportional to) the square root of n.

E58. Because the distribution from which the samples were selected is highly skewed, the skewness persists in the simulated sampling distribution of the sample mean for samples of size 5 and 10. However, with samples of size 30, most of the skewness disappears and you see a sampling distribution that is nearly normal in shape. The centers of the sampling distributions lie close to the population mean of 5190 passengers. Observe that the standard deviations of the sampling distributions shrink faster, with increasing sample size, than the theory used earlier would predict. For $n = 30$, the observed standard deviation of 705 is much smaller than $5273/\sqrt{30} = 963$. This is because we are taking a sample of size 30 without replacement from a small population, with only 76 values. If one value is removed from the population, the distribution from which the next value is selected changes in a noticeable way. Think of the extreme case: If the sample size is 76, there would be no variation among the possible sample means.

Simulated Sampling Distribution for Kelly's Hamster Experiment

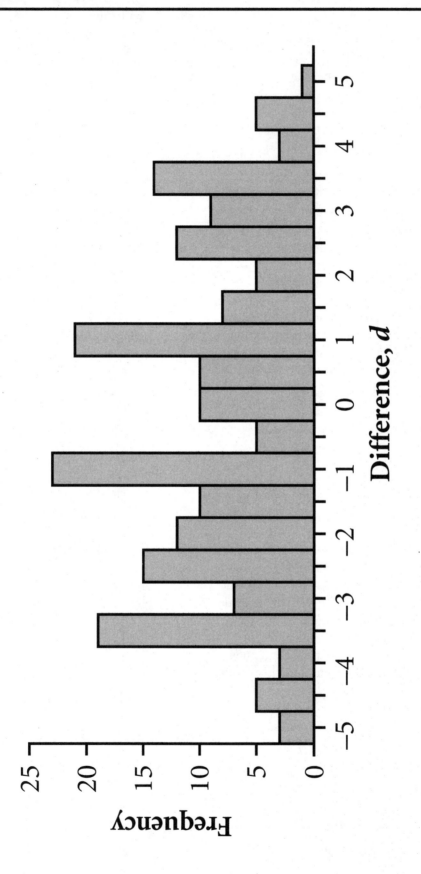

Statistics in Action Instructor's Guide
© 2004 Key Curriculum Press